Project

STAR

Second Edition

The Universe in Your Hands

Harold P. Coyle
Bruce Gregory
William M. Luzader
Philip M. Sadler
Irwin I. Shapiro

Project STAR: *SCIENCE TEACHING THROUGH ITS ASTRONOMICAL ROOTS*

Sponsored by the Harvard-Smithsonian Center for Astrophysics

Original support by the National Science Foundation
with additional support from:
Smithsonian Institution • Apple Computer
Bausch and Lomb Astronomical Telescopes • Celestron International

KENDALL/HUNT PUBLISHING COMPANY
4050 Westmark Drive Dubuque, Iowa 52002

ISBN: 0-7872-6015-0

The material from the first edition was based upon work supported by the National Science Foundation under Grant Nos. MDR-8550297 and MDR-8850424. Any opinions, findings, and conclusions or recommendations expressed in this material are those of the authors and do not necessarily reflect the views of the National Science Foundation.

Printed in the United States of America

10 9 8 7 6 5 4 3 2

In memory of Don Lautman

CONTENTS

NOTE: Colorplates follow p. 258.

PREFACE

You know—and we remember—that being a student is hard work. Writing a textbook is also hard work. Is it worth the effort? Only you can tell. Our purpose is simple: To help you to learn about science. Our philosophy is more complicated: We believe you learn science better by making measurements and observations than by memorizing "facts." Everybody has ideas—models—about how the world works; we believe your teacher should ask you about your models first and then help you to test their accuracy by showing you how to make the relevant measurements and observations. When you prove to yourself that some pre-held view of yours is wrong, you will be better able to learn about models developed by scientists that are in keeping with the way the world does work.

So much for philosophy. What about the book? We tried a new approach, consistent with our philosophy. Each chapter begins with questions to test your pre-held views on the subject treated in the chapter. These questions are followed by activities in which often you build and use simple, but powerful, tools to explore the models discussed in the chapter. The importance of models is stressed, as is the even greater importance of measurements and observations: Predictions from models must be consistent with measurements and observations. The text of each chapter presents a few key parts of models, illustrated with examples, mostly from astronomy. Many questions are sprinkled throughout the book to let you test your understanding of the models and your ability to apply them. Cartoons appear here and there to leaven the learning with humor. We believe that students, like scientists, are not exempt from needing a good laugh now and then.

This book also illustrates the art—definitely not the science—of compromise. What should be included in the course and what should be left out? What models should be used? What methods are too complicated to explain in the text? Resolving these questions required time and patience. Tensions abounded: We must discuss black holes; how can we not discuss the search for extraterrestrial intelligence ("SETI"); we must be true to our principles. In the end, black holes were put in and SETI left out. We added "boxes," many boxes, in the text to provide extra details—on models, on history, and on scientists. How well did we succeed with this book? We value your opinion. Please write and tell us what you liked, and why, and, especially, what you didn't like, and why. We would also appreciate your telling us about any errors, factual or typographical. It would be a miracle if there were none, and we are not great believers in miracles. Armed with your responses, we will make the next edition better for future students.

This book was developed under Project STAR (Science Teaching through its Astronomical Roots); we dedicate it to the memory of Don A. Lautman, whose unflagging enthusiasm and critical mind made this book far better than it would otherwise have been. We are also extremely grateful to the scientists and teachers who contributed unstintingly to the development of this course and to Andrew MacFadyen and, especially, Heather Whipple who worked unbelievably long, and effectively, to make the original text a reality.

Irwin I. Shapiro
60 Garden Street
Cambridge, MA 02138
10 March 2000

A NOTE TO THE STUDENT

This book contains a series of activities. From it, you will not only learn about astronomy, you will also learn many fundamentals of science and scientific inquiry.

In completing these hands-on activities, you will

- make observations of the skies

- build models

- use models to explain observations and make predictions

- find everyday applications for such models

Please keep in mind that, at the beginning of this course, you are not expected to know anything about astronomy or much about science, so do not be afraid to make mistakes. They will help you learn.

Measurement

Astronomy, as do all sciences, relies on careful measurement. Throughout the course, we use the metric system (formally known as the *Système Internationale*, or SI), but we often include the English system equivalent. We use the metric system for two reasons: (1) it is the international standard of science, and (2) many numbers used in astronomy are very large, and large numbers are easy to use in the metric system (because all metric measures increase by factors of 10, and multiplying or dividing by 10s is quite simple).

The approximate conversions between a few metric and English units of distance are

1 centimeter = 0.4 inch	1 inch = 2.5 centimeters
1 meter = 3.3 feet	1 foot = 0.3 meter
1 kilometer = 0.6 mile	1 mile = 1.6 kilometers

The relationships among some metric units are

1 meter (m) = 100 centimeters (cm) = 1,000 millimeters (mm)
1 kilometer (km) = 1000 m = 100,000 cm = 1,000,000 mm

The most common "BIG" and "small" numbers that will be used in this book will be

Scientific Notation		Number with zeros		Number in words	Prefix
10^9	=	1,000,000,000	=	1 billion	giga-
10^6	=	1,000,000	=	1 million	mega-
10^3	=	1,000	=	1 thousand	kilo-
10^{-3}	=	0.001	=	one-thousandth	milli-
10^{-6}	=	0.000001	=	one-millionth	micro-
10^{-9}	=	0.000000001	=	one-billionth	nano-

(EXAMPLES: kilometer = 1,000 meters; megabuck = 1 million bucks)

INTRODUCTION

What is astronomy? It is a subject that deals not only with the Moon, Sun, and stars but also with such topics as extraterrestrial life, black holes, the beginning of time, space stations, and the greenhouse effect. Astronomy also provides practical tools for measuring large distances and predicting the seasons. Some of these tools are important for a variety of professions, from farming through bridge-building to space exploration.

Astronomy is perhaps the oldest science. For thousands of years, humans have tilted their heads upward and wondered about those twinkling points of light. We have learned that they are like our Sun but so far away that we can barely see them. We have walked on the Moon and sent spacecraft to the edge of the solar system. These accomplishments are the result of careful observation, scientific inquiry, and the technical application of scientific discoveries.

Scientists try to increase understanding about the universe and to make predictions about natural events. To do this, scientists build physical and mathematical models that enable them to test their ideas about the nature of the universe. In astronomy, where the field of inquiry is as vast as space itself, model-building is particularly important. It is through model-building that we came to understand accurately the sizes, locations, and motions of the Sun, the Moon, the planets, and the stars.

This book contains activities that will help you develop skills in observing and inquiry. The activities have a physical and/or mathematical model-building component. Most activities begin with questions in which you are asked to make a prediction about a physical concept. It is OK not to know the answers to these questions at the start; the activity will help you find the correct answers. The goal of these prediction questions is to challenge your existing models of nature and help you start thinking about the concepts in the activity. We hope that you will know the answers by the end of the activity; we do not expect you to know them beforehand.

From the perspective of astronomy, this book is composed of two parts. The first part, Chapters 1–8, is focused mostly on the solar system. You will concentrate on observing the sky, both during the daytime and the nighttime. You will learn how to locate objects in the sky and how to determine the sizes and distances from us of the Moon and Sun. You will be introduced to a basic model for light and construct your own telescope. You will also be introduced to the planets and build a scale model of the solar system. In the second part, Chapters 9–15, some of the activities take you beyond the solar system, to the stars, galaxies, and finally to a model of the universe as a whole. You will learn two methods for determining the distance from you to a star and you will use one of these methods to make your own measurement of a star's distance. You will learn about gravity and more about light. In particular, you will learn about the different "kinds" of light and how these forms of light are useful for determining certain properties of stars, such as surface temperature and composition. You will construct a spectrometer, a device used to examine the light emitted or reflected by an object. You will investigate information collected about distant galaxies and what this information tells us about the structure of the universe. You will also be introduced to probability theory and learn how probability can be used to test the accuracy of a theory.

The hands-on activities play a central role in this 1-year course. We hope that you will learn some fundamental principles of science from them and that you will enjoy doing them.

CONTRIBUTORS

Project STAR

Project Staff

Irwin I. Shapiro, Principal Investigator

Philip M. Sadler, Director

Darrel B. Hoff, Associate Director (first edition)

Harold P. Coyle, Publications Manager

Marcus G. Lieberman, Education Evaluator (first edition)

William M. Luzader, Activity Specialist (first edition)

Freeman S. Deutsch, Software Engineer

Andrew I. MacFadyen, Illustrations Editor (first edition)

C. Scott Balderson, Department Administrator

Research Assistants: Jeffrey Dobbins, Timothy Huntington, Greg Sprick, and Gretchen Walker (first edition)

Advisory Panel (first edition)

Kenneth Brecher (Prof. of Physics and Astronomy, Boston University); Richard Tresch-Fienberg (Technical Editor, "Sky & Telescope"); John Galloway (Prof. of Astronomy and Physics, Endicott College, Beverly, MA); Owen Gingerich (Senior Scientist, Smithsonian Astrophysical Observatory, and Prof. of the History of Science and of Astronomy, Harvard University); Bruce Gregory (Associate Director, Harvard-Smithsonian Center for Astrophysics); Alex Griswold (President, Griswold Productions); Marvin Grossman (Education Consultant); Beth Holmberg (Planetary Geologist, Smithsonian Astrophysical Observatory); Don Lautman* (Lecturer, Harvard University); Alan Lightman (Senior Scientist, Smithsonian Astrophysical Observatory, and Prof. of Science and Writing, Massachusetts Institute of Technology); Jana Odette (Film Maker); Samuel Palmer (Senior Engineer, Smithsonian Astrophysical Observatory); Matthew Schneps (Director, Science Media Group, Smithsonian Astrophysical Observatory); Linda Shore (Asst. Prof. of Physics and Education, Boston University); Henry Wadzinski (Space Data Analysis Lab, Boston College); Charles Whitney (Senior Scientist, Smithsonian Astrophysical Observatory, and Prof. Emeritus of Astronomy, Harvard University); Anne G. Young (Asst. Prof. of Physics, Rochester Institute of Technology, Rochester, NY)

Consulting Teachers (first edition)

Robert Amos (North Valley H.S., Grants Pass, OR); Andrew Anzalone (Somerville H.S., Somerville, MA); Richard Ayache (Needham H.S., Needham, MA); Andrea Barton (Wayzata Sr. H.S., Plymouth, MN); Kenneth Beckwith (Whitesboro Sr. H.S., Marcy, NY); Stephen Berr (Colonial Middle School, Norristown, PA); W. Russell Blake (Plymouth-Carver Planetarium, Plymouth, MA); Jack Brokaw (Wausau East H.S., Wausau, WI); Richard Brown (Broad Ripple H.S., Indianapolis, IN); Virginia Flook (Brookline H.S., Brookline, MA); Daniel Francetic (Euclid H.S., Euclid, OH); Linda French (The Park School, Brookline, MA); Walter Gustafson (Brockton H.S., Brockton, MA); Gita Hakerem (Framingham H.S., Framingham, MA); Russell Harding (Norwalk H.S., Norwalk, CT); Jennifer Bond Hickman (Phillips Academy, Andover, MA); Paul Hickman (Belmont H.S., Belmont, MA); Robert Hillenbrand (Mainland Sr. H.S., Daytona Beach, FL); Stephen Jackson (Stoneham Public Schools, Stoneham, MA); Jane Johnson (Phoenix Ctr. for Individual Ed., Phoenix, AZ); Jonathan Keohane (C.E. Jordan H.S., Durham, NC); John Koser (Wayzata Sr. H.S., Plymouth, MN); Jeff Lane (Tri-County Voc./Tech. H.S., Franklin, MA); Jeffrey Lockwood (Sahuaro H.S., Tucson, AZ); Gerald Mallon* (Arcola Intermediate H.S., Norristown, PA); Larry Mascotti (Mayo H. S., Rochester, MN); Fiona McDonnell (Alvirne H.S., Hudson, NH); Bruce Mellin (Brooks School, Andover, MA); Frank Mikan (St. Mary's Hall, San Antonio, TX); Joseph Mongillo (Lyman Hall H.S., Wallingford, CT); Howard Murphy (Moulton-borough Academy, Moultonborough, NH); Hughes Pack (Northfield-Mt. Hermon School, Northfield, MA); Mark Petricone (Watertown H.S., Watertown, MA); Michael Richard (Weymouth H.S., Weymouth, MA); Lawrence Sabbath (Oak Park H.S., Oak Park, MI); Gary Sampson (Wauwatosa West H.S., Wauwatosa, WI); Janet Smith-Robinson (South Carroll H.S., Sykesville, MD); Ann Story (North Augusta H.S., North Augusta, SC); Sharon Stroud (Widefield H.S., Colorado Springs, CO); Polly Vanasse (Nashoba-Brooks School, Concord, MA); Dorothy Walk (Maryville H.S., Maryville, MO); R. Bruce Ward (Belmont H.S., Belmont, MA)

*Deceased

CHAPTER 1

The Daytime Sky

Below is a list of statements concerning the daytime sky. Which do you think might be true?

1. The Sun rises exactly in the east and sets exactly in the west every day.

2. The Sun is directly over your head once a day.

3. The Moon is sometimes visible in the daytime.

A DAY IN THE LIFE OF A SHADOW

The figure below shows a post and its shadow just after sunrise. The shadow points directly toward the west. Make sketches of what you think the shadow will look like, especially its length and direction, at five or more different times of the day. Your last drawing should show the shadow just before sunset.

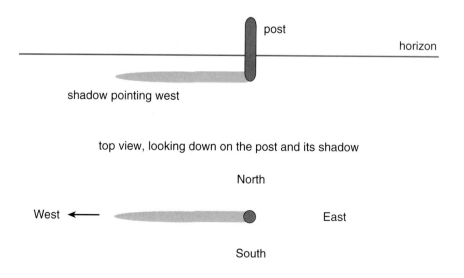

top view, looking down on the post and its shadow

Preview: In this chapter you will (1) learn how to locate objects in the sky, (2) be introduced to the concept of scientific models, (3) observe the apparent daily motion of the Sun across the sky, (4) observe the changes from day to day where the Sun sets, and (5) learn how the Sun's apparent motion changes during the year.

The Sun was shining on the sea,
Shining with all his might:
He did his very best to make
The billows smooth and bright—
And this was odd, because it was
The middle of the night.

You know enough about the sky to think that these first lines of "The Walrus and the Carpenter" from Lewis Carroll's *Through the Looking-Glass* are silly. (A billow, by the way, is a wave.) But people who live in places such as Barrow, Alaska, or Murmansk, in Russia, *do* see the Sun shine on the sea at midnight in June.

So is the poem silly or not? Well, Lewis Carroll meant it to be silly because nighttime is, by definition, the period between sunset and sunrise. Daytime, by contrast, is the period when the Sun is in the sky. At some locations, it is possible for the Sun to shine at midnight, but absolutely crazy for the Sun to shine in the middle of the night.

Yes, that last sentence is a little weird. However, this book is not trying to confuse you. In the places where most people live, midnight does occur in the middle of the night, roughly halfway between sunset and sunrise. But midnight is also a specific clock time, 12:00 A.M., just as noon is a specific time, 12:00 P.M. Some people live where they can sometimes see the Sun at 12:00 A.M. (See Figure 1.1.) At such times and places, "midnight" occurs during daytime, that is, during daylight hours (just as at those same places, people can sometimes experience "noon" in the dark).

FIGURE 1.1
The midnight sun in Antarctica.

NOTE: This book uses "day" to indicate a 24-hour period. The portion of the day when the Sun is visible is called "daytime." "Night" or "nighttime" refers to the part of the day when the Sun is not in the sky. The midpoint between sunrise and sunset is called "noontime," regardless of the clock time.

Something that at first seems weird may only be a phenomenon that is not familiar to you. Although you have already lived more than 5,000 days, you will still encounter some apparently strange ideas as you go through this course. This book contains activities to help you understand these ideas. The activities will give you the opportunity to make your own observations and to use these observations to build models that help you to understand these ideas and to make useful predictions.

NOTE: This book uses "phenomenon" (plural: "phenomena") to indicate an event or experience. As used in this book, "phenomenon" does not mean that something is unusual or rare. The apparent motions of the Sun, Moon, and stars are examples of phenomena. They are not rare. The reading of this book is another example of a phenomenon. (We hope it, too, will not be rare.)

Models

Everyone has some experience with models. Toy animals, dolls, and model airplanes are a few examples of models. But what exactly is a model? And why do people make models?

A model can be a copy of something. A copy can be larger or smaller than the original (but doesn't have to be). For example, a doll is a model of a human. Most dolls simply copy the shape of a human, but some also copy human actions, such as talking and eating.

Models are very important in science. A model can be a physical representation, like a model airplane representing a real airplane; some scientific models are also physical models. But most scientific models are not something that you build out of plastic or wood; most models are descriptions of phenomena, including how the phenomena change when certain conditions are changed. Sometimes these models of change use mathematical or chemical equations. Scientists gather information about a phenomenon, then design a model to help them understand the phenomenon. A good model should allow you to understand what has been observed and also to predict accurately what will be observed under new conditions. A scientific model may be changed, or even abandoned, if the result of a new observation is inconsistent with the model. And the observations themselves must stand up to close inspection. (You don't want to waste time designing a model for a "phenomenon" that turns out to be caused by a faulty instrument.)

Occam's Razor

William of Occam (or Ockham), an English scholar born about 1285, developed a rule to help him select the best model for a phenomenon. William noted that people tended to add features to a model when it was weakened

Dusk and Dawn

There is a period of time after sunset during which the sky dims. This period is sometimes called dusk. The sky also brightens before sunrise. This period is usually called dawn. Both periods are called twilight. (If you are outdoors at dusk or dawn, you are in the "Twilight Zone.")

Because twilight occurs when the Sun cannot be seen in the sky, dusk and dawn will be considered as the beginning and end of nighttime, respectively, instead of as parts of daytime.

by new observations to try to strengthen it, even when a new model could explain all of the observations in a simpler way. William's experiences led him to conclude that if two models explained a phenomenon *equally* well and one model was simpler than the other, then it was reasonable to accept the simpler model as being the better one. William stated his conclusion in a rule that basically says: "Keep your model as simple as possible." This rule is known today as "Occam's razor." The rule is now used in all fields of modern science. (In a recent test of leading brands of razors, "Occam's" was the only one that kept its original sharpness after 700 years of continuous use.)

Features *may* be added to a model on the basis of new observations—Occam's razor does not prohibit additions. The rule is known as Occam's "razor" because it shaves a model of *unnecessary* additions. ("Razor" also indicates that the rule is precise, shaving away only the unneeded portions of a model. If the rule were not so precise, it might have been called "Occam's chainsaw.") The rule does not guarantee that the best model for a phenomenon will be simple; it does mean that the *simplest model that fits all of the observations should be accepted as the best model.* You should use Occam's razor whenever you have to decide which model is the best for some set of phenomena.

Observe First, Model Later

Models are usually based upon observations. Therefore, before you become involved in modeling the sky, you need to make some observations. Your first experiences in observing in this course will involve the daytime sky.

Think about these questions concerning the daytime sky: Will the Sun be directly overhead at noontime today? How many hours of daylight will there be today? What kinds of observations could you make involving the Sun's apparent motion? Activities 1.2 and 1.3 will help you answer the questions just asked. Before you get involved in specific observations, however, Activity 1.1 will familiarize you with some basic observing methods.

What Is the Sun Doing?

You have no doubt heard that the Earth moves around the Sun and that the spinning of the Earth produces night and day. These movements are not, however, what you seem to see in the sky. You see the Sun rising and setting once a day, not the Earth turning.

"Every day the Sun rises in the east and sets in the west." If you ask people what they know about the Sun, they will probably include the preceding sentence as part of their response. If you ask if the Sun always rises exactly in the east and sets exactly in the west, many people will answer, "yes." In Activity 1.3, you will make your own observations of sunsets. ("What's your science homework for tonight?" "I have to watch the Sun set.")

If you observe the apparent motion of the Sun carefully over a period of many days, you will find that the Sun does not do what many people think it does. For example, the Sun does not always rise and set at the same points on the horizon. In the continental United States, the Sun only rises directly east and sets directly west on the first day of spring and the first day of autumn. After the first day of autumn, the Sun rises and sets farther and farther south each day until the first day of winter. After the first day of winter, the Sun rises and sets more and more northward each day, reaching directly east and west on the first day of spring. Then the Sun continues to rise and set farther and farther north until the first day of summer, when it starts moving south again.

Daytime Sky Objects

Did you notice anything else in the sky while you were observing the Sun? Clouds? Birds? Aircraft? A man with a red cape and a big S on his chest? The Moon? Stars? Planets? Have you *ever* seen *any* of these objects in the daytime sky?

You probably have never seen stars or planets in the daytime sky. Why not? Is it because you didn't look hard enough? Is it because they do not exist during the daytime? Or is there some other reason?

You have been outside at sunset; later, when it became dark, you could see some stars. Why did the stars become visible? Were they there before sunset or did they "turn on" after sunset? The ancient Greeks realized that the stars are in the sky during the daytime, but cannot be seen because of the Sun's glare. This discovery may have been made during a total eclipse of the Sun, when the Moon passes directly in front of the Sun, blocking the Sun's light and causing the sky to become dark enough to see stars, even if it is daytime. (For a more complete explanation, see Chapter 7.) In general, planets, too, are not visible in the daytime. Venus, however, is sometimes bright enough to see during the daytime if you know exactly where to look. And some stars have been seen in the daytime. These were "supernovae," exploding stars that appear very bright. Supernovae bright enough to see in the daytime are very rare, however. You will be very lucky if one occurs during your lifetime. (Only certain types of stars can explode. We are fortunate that the Sun does not appear to be one of these types; astronomers do not expect that the Sun will ever explode.)

The Moon was mentioned as passing in front of the Sun during a solar eclipse (see Figure 1.2). Since the Sun is out only in the daytime, the Moon must sometimes be in the daytime sky. Have you ever seen the Moon in the sky when the Sun was up? If the Moon is sometimes in the daytime sky, is it sometimes not in the nighttime sky? Let's move on to the nighttime sky and find out.

SUMMARY

The apparent daily motion of the Sun as well as the position of the Sun at sunrise and sunset vary depending upon where you live and the time of year. Sunrise and sunset times also vary with location and date.

The Sun dominates what you can observe in the daytime sky because it is much, much closer to you than any other star. Celestial objects such as planets and stars are in the daytime sky but are not normally visible. The Moon is sometimes visible in the daytime sky.

A good scientific model should provide the simplest possible explanation for all available observations and predict accurately what will be observed under new conditions.

FIGURE 1.2
A total solar eclipse.

Homework

You have learned that you are at risk of getting a sunburn if the Sun is more than 45° above the horizon. You have also learned that the angular height of the Sun depends upon the time of day. The angular height depends as well upon the time of year and the place on the Earth where you are standing. In this exercise you will be examining graphs of the angular height of the Sun vs. the time of day for three different cities at four different times of the year. Using these graphs, you will make decisions about the length of day and the risk of sunburn, as well as answer that burning question—Why don't people come home from vacationing in Alaska complaining of a sunburn?

1. How many hours of daylight are there in December in Anchorage? in Boston? in Miami? How many hours of daylight are there in June in Anchorage, Boston, and Miami?

2. How many hours of daylight are there in each of these three cities in March and September?

3. Joe is spending his spring vacation visiting his aunt and uncle in Miami. Will he need sunscreen?

4. If you lived in Boston, between what hours would you be at the greatest risk of getting a sunburn in June? in March?

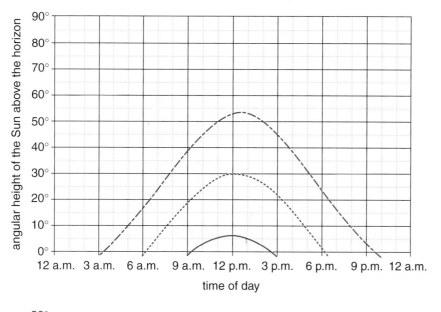

Anchorage, AK

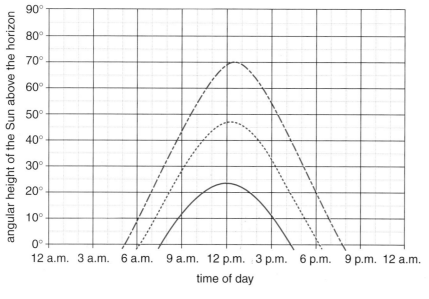

Boston, MA

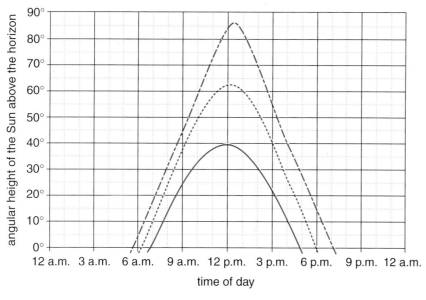

Miami, FL

5. In June, are there more hours of total daylight in Miami, Boston, or Anchorage? Which of these places is going to sell more sunscreen? Which city has the least amount of total daylight? Explain your answer.

6. For which month(s) of the year is it probably safe not to wear sunscreen in Miami?

7. Joe, not having a graph of the angular height of the Sun for Miami handy, calls his aunt to ask her if he'll need sunscreen when he visits her in March. She says he will definitely need it. "The Sun is much stronger here in Miami than it is up in Boston!" she explains. What does she mean by that?

8. Why do few people come home from a vacation in Alaska complaining of sunburn? (Actually, some people do get sunburned in Alaska from sunlight reflected from snow and ice. You should concentrate on answering this question just in terms of the angular height of the Sun.)

9. Standing on Miami Beach at 3:00 P.M. on a day in late June, is your shadow shorter or longer than you? in March? in September? in December?

10. What is wrong with these pictures? Pictures 1 and 2 show two different locations on the Earth at the same time. What astronomical errors can you find in the pictures?

PICTURE 1
The Arctic Circle (66.5° north latitude) in northern Alaska on December 21, looking north at noon.

PICTURE 2
The Tropic of Capricorn (23.5° south latitude) on the island of Tahiti on December 21, looking north at noon.

11. Suppose you measured the Sun's angle above the horizon, using the shadow of a meterstick stuck vertically into the ground. (See diagram on next page.) Suppose you measured this angle at three different times before noon and at three different times after noon on the same date, and then plotted a graph, using the times of day of the measurements on the horizontal axis and the measured angles on the vertical axis.

✳ The Universe in Your Hands

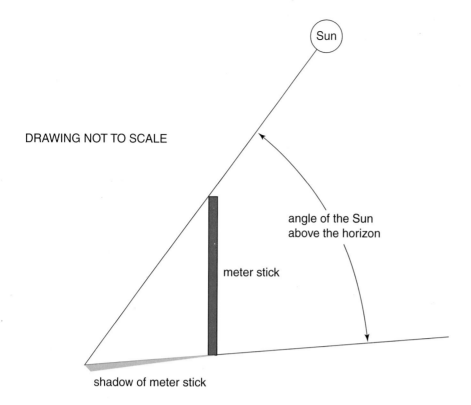

DRAWING NOT TO SCALE

Sun

angle of the Sun
above the horizon

meter stick

shadow of meter stick

a) At what time of day would the Sun be at its greatest angular height
above the horizon?

b) Sketch on the same graph your prediction of what this curve would
look like if you took your data on (1) June 21 and (2) December
21.

SELF-TEST

1. Along which portion of the horizon (east or west) would you see the
rising Sun?

2. Along which portion of the horizon (east or west) would you see the
setting Sun?

3. In what direction would you see the Sun when it was at its greatest
angular height above the horizon?

4. If on one day you observed the Sun at 9:00 a.m., noontime, and 3:00
p.m., at which time would it make the greatest angle with the horizon?

5. Why do you think many people believe the Sun is always directly overhead at noontime?

6. What are the characteristics of a good scientific model?

Ancient Astronomy in the Americas

Records of solar observations by ancient peoples have been found all over the globe. In the Americas, these records range from stone circles called Medicine Wheels in the Northern plains of the United States and Canada to elaborately decorated temples in Mexico and South America. Astronomers and archaeologists have found that some of these structures point to specific places on the horizon where the Sun (as well as the Moon and some bright stars) rises and sets on special days.

If you stand at the outer end of a specific spoke of a Medicine Wheel at sunrise on the summer solstice (June 21), and look down the line of stones out to the horizon, you will see the point on the horizon where the Sun first appears on the longest day of the year. The Maya incorporated similar observation lines in their architecture; many buildings face or form a line with other buildings to point towards a particular sunrise location, such as the days on which the Sun passes directly overhead (the Maya lived in the range of latitudes at which it is possible to see the Sun directly overhead). The Maya developed number systems and writing that their priests used to develop elaborate methods of predicting, calculating, and recording astronomical information. Only those with special training were able to interpret the sky with these complex methods. In comparison, the Sunwatcher-priests of the Hopi and Zuni peoples in the southwestern United States made simple observations based on the location of the Sun with respect to landmarks on the horizon.

Ancient peoples observed the sky with no more technology than you have used to make your observations of the Sun. But while you may look at the sky out of curiosity, many cultures used the movement of the Sun to guide and influence agriculture, government, and religion. In the American Southwest, for example, people used solar observations to tell when to begin planting and harvesting as well as when to hold religious ceremonies. If bad weather or poor harvests followed, the people might blame the Sunwatchers for making inaccurate observations instead of attributing these events to natural causes.

Did the people who built the medicine wheels see the Sun rise in the same place in the east and set in the same place in the west every day? (Remember that they used the wheels to find the place where the Sun first comes up over the horizon on special days of the year.) Does the Sun always rise and set in the same places where you live?

Are there any religious or school holidays that you celebrate that also occur on or near special solar days? Are there any days that celebrate the Sun itself? Why do you have summer vacation?

The Sun, Sunburn, and You

In some respects, sunburning is a matter of astronomy. Your skin tans and burns when exposed to ultraviolet light from the Sun, a form of light you cannot see (see Chapter 11). Even if you could see ultraviolet light, there wouldn't be much to see because ozone, a special form of oxygen, in the upper atmosphere absorbs and scatters most of it (see Chapter 5). Most of

Mayan observatory at Chichen Itza, Yucatan, Mexico.

the ultraviolet light not absorbed by the ozone is absorbed by the lower atmosphere. When the Sun is low in the sky, more of its ultraviolet light is absorbed. As the Sun gets higher above the horizon, less and less of its ultraviolet light is stopped by the atmosphere. To avoid getting sunburn, you need to think about where the Sun is in the sky. When the Sun is much less than halfway between the horizon and directly overhead (that is, when the Sun is at an angular height of less than 45°), you are reasonably safe from sunburn. As the Sun moves higher in the sky, so that more ultraviolet light can come through the atmosphere, your risk of burning increases. If you are outside when the Sun is very high in the sky, you broil.

An easy way to tell how safe you are from burning is to look at your shadow. If your shadow is much longer than you are, the Sun is in the portion of the sky where only a small amount of ultraviolet light gets through. As your shadow shortens to your height or smaller, more of the Sun's ultraviolet light can reach you, and you should be using sunblock, clothing, or the indoors to protect your skin. Hazy clouds don't help; if you can see your shadow at all, the Sun's ultraviolet light can get to you (less so, however, if you are behind glass, which absorbs most of the ultraviolet light coming through it).

Keep track of the length of your shadow for a day. For how many hours was the length of your shadow the same as your height or shorter? During which hours of the day did this occur?

If there were no clouds today, when would your shadow be shortest? On what date and time of day would it be shortest this year? Do you think the air temperature affects how quickly you tan or burn? Do you think you could tan faster in May or in September? Why?

Can you think of any reasons why the part of the sky close to the horizon blocks ultraviolet light better than the sky overhead?

ACTIVITY 1.1   Using a Handy Tool to Locate Objects in the Sky

PURPOSE

To learn how to measure the position of an object in the sky with your hand.

WHAT DO YOU THINK?

P1. *Imagine that you want to describe to some friends the location of an object in the sky. What information would you need to give to your friends so they could locate the object too?*

MATERIALS

    1 hand, with fingers and thumb
    a ceiling or other overhead object
    a sunny day

PROCEDURE

A. One part of the description of an object's position in the sky is how high it is above the horizon. What do "high" and "horizon" mean? The "horizon" is the line along which the sky and land—or sea—appear to meet. However, this "line" is often obscured by hills, trees, or other objects (Figure 1.3). "High" refers to the angle between the line from your eyes to a point on the horizon directly below the object and the line from your eyes to the object; for convenience this angle is called "angular height" in this book. You can estimate an object's angular height using your hand. Remember, an object's angular height is always measured from the point on the horizon directly below it.

FIGURE 1.3

B. Stretch one arm out straight. Make a fist with the hand on your outstretched arm. Close one eye and look at your fist. It appears to be a certain size. The size of your fist can be defined as the angle between the line from your open eye to the top of your fist and the line from this eye to the bottom of your fist. Now slowly move your fist toward your face. (Do *not* move your fist toward anyone else's face. Be sure to stop moving your fist before you hit your nose.) Notice that your fist appears larger as it gets closer to your face. When you use your hand as a measuring tool, it is important that it always appears to be the same size, which means it must always be the same distance from your face. This distance will be the same if you always have your arm fully outstretched (and you have stopped growing!).

C. An angle can be large or small, so what part of your hand should you use for measuring? The best approach is to use different hand shapes for different situations. Convenient hand shapes are those that fit 6 and 9 times between the horizon and the point directly over your head. It may seem odd that the hand shapes selected are 6 and 9 times the distance between the horizon and the point overhead. There is a good reason for using them, however. Angles are measured in degrees defined so that 360 degrees fit in a circle. The point directly overhead is 90 degrees from the horizon since the angle between the horizon and overhead is a quarter of a circle ($1/4 \times 360 = 90$). See Figure 1.4. Therefore, the hand shape that fits between the horizon and overhead 6 times represents 15 degrees ($90°/6 = 15°$). The hand shape that fits between the horizon and overhead 9 times represents 10 degrees ($90°/9 = 10°$). Thus, when your arm is outstretched, 6 and 9 hands correspond to "convenient" numbers of degrees: 15 and 10, respectively.

FIGURE 1.4

D. Start with the hand shape that fits 6 times between the horizon and overhead. Refer to this hand shape as the "big hand," or BH. (One BH = 15°.) Look straight ahead (not up or down) and close one eye. Stretch your arm straight out, with your fist upright and at eye level. See Figure 1.5. Move your fist as if you were making a pile of fists: from position 1, move your arm and fist up to position 2 so the bottom of your fist in position 2 lines up with where the top of the fist was in position 1. Use distant objects or marks on a wall to keep track of your fist from one position to the next. Keep going until your arm is stretched straight up, pointing overhead.

FIGURE 1.5

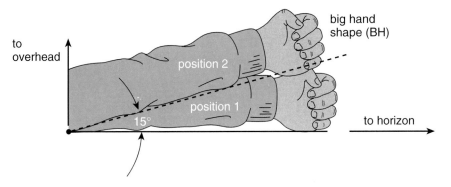

1. *How many fist positions did it take to measure from the horizon to overhead?*

E. If your answer to question 1 was 6, then your fist will work as the BH. If your answer to question 1 was more than 6, your fist is too small: your hand has to be held in a larger shape, such as a fist with your thumb sticking up (the "thumbs-up" sign). If your answer to question 1 was less than 6, your fist is too large: your hand must be a smaller

The Daytime Sky ✳

shape, such as your first three fingers held together. If your fist is too large or too small, experiment to find the hand shape that fits 6 times between the horizon and directly overhead.

2. *Describe or sketch the BH, the hand shape that held at arm's length fits 6 times between the horizon and overhead.*

F. Repeat steps D and E, except now find a hand shape that fits 9 times between the horizon and overhead. Call this shape the little hand shape, or LH. (One LH = 10°.)

3. *Describe or sketch the LH, the hand shape that held at arm's length fits 9 times between the horizon and overhead.*

G. You now have a pair of "instruments" for measuring the angular heights of objects in the sky. Go outside and try out your instruments by measuring the angular height of the Sun. Begin with the BH. Face toward the Sun.

 **CAUTION** **DO NOT STARE AT THE SUN. IT CAN DAMAGE YOUR EYES.**

Stretch your arm out horizontally and shape your hand as in step E. Move your arm up one position at a time until the Sun appears to be covered by your hand.

4. *Record the Sun's angular height above the horizon in BH.*

5. *What is the Sun's angular height in degrees (1 BH = 15°)?*

H. Repeat step G with your hand in the shape recorded in question 3.

6. *Record the Sun's angular height above the horizon in LH.*

7. *What is the Sun's angular height in degrees (1 LH = 10°)?*

I. Check the accuracy of your measurements. The Sun's position in the sky should be nearly the same for questions 5 and 7. If the answers to questions 5 and 7 differ by 5° or more, repeat steps G and H and check your math for questions 5 and 7.

HOMEWORK

J. You have measured one feature of an object's position in the sky, its angular height above the horizon. Notice, however, that you had to face in a certain direction in step G, the direction of the Sun. This direction is the other feature of an object's position in the sky. You could tell someone how high an object is in the sky, but unless that person knew which direction to face, she or he would have a hard time finding the object. The direction can be given as a compass direction, such as southeast. It can also be given as the angular distance along the horizon from a specific starting point to the point on the horizon directly below the object. The starting point is usually north and the angular distance is normally measured in degrees clockwise (to your right) from north to the horizon point directly below the object. The directions *clockwise* and *to your right* are defined from the point of view of someone looking down on the Earth from a position directly over your head. The angular distance can be measured with either of your hand instruments. See the following example.

Instructions:
Look for the object 30° above the horizon.

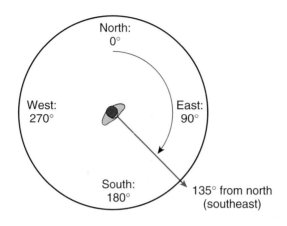

View looking down on the Earth from directly above the observer in the picture.

Better instructions:
Face north and turn 135° clockwise (to your right), then look 30° above the horizon.

8. *Refer to your answer to P1. Did you mention the angular height above the horizon and the direction of the object? Is there any other information that could be important to helping your friend locate the object? (Hint: What if your friend lived far away from you?)*

K. Try using the BH to measure along the horizon in a full circle. Because you are measuring along the horizon, you must hold your hand side-ways. For example, if your hand shape is the thumbs-up shape, hold your hand so your thumb is horizontal (like a hitchhiker "thumbing" a ride).

9. *Calculate how many BH should fit in a full circle.*

10. *Record the number of BH that did fit in a circle.*

If the answer to question 10 is the same as the answer to question 9, or if the answer to question 10 is only one hand more or less than the answer to question 9, your results are as accurate as can be expected from use of this measurement tool. If the answer to question 10 did not pass this accuracy test, repeat step K and check your calculations for question 9.

EXTENSIONS

1. Determine a hand shape that, with your arm fully extended, corresponds to 5°.

Plotting the Apparent Daily Motion of the Sun

PURPOSE

To plot and discuss the Sun's apparent daily movement across the sky.

WHAT DO YOU THINK?

Your teacher will give you a plastic hemisphere. Place the square rim of the hemisphere flat on your desk.

Imagine that the sky is the inside surface of the hemisphere. As an observer, you would be standing at the center of the circle at the base of the hemisphere. This is the spot marked X in Figure 1.6. You will draw the path of the Sun as it would appear from inside the hemisphere.

With the plastic hemisphere in front of you, choose a point on the base at one of the ridges and use a transparency pen to mark it as north and label it "N." Looking down on the dome and going clockwise from north, mark the other three ridges as east (E), south (S), and west (W).

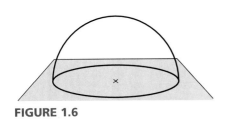

FIGURE 1.6

P1. *a) Predict the following positions for the Sun for today by writing a letter on the dome. Use the letter **r** to show the position of the Sun at sunrise, the letter **n** to indicate its position at noon, and the letter **s** to indicate its position at sunset.*

b) Connect these points on the hemisphere with a curved line that represents how you think the Sun will move across the sky on this day.

P2. *From what direction did the Sun rise this morning?*

P3. *In what direction will the Sun set this evening?*

P4. *Where in the sky is the Sun at noon?*

P5. *How many hours of daylight will there be today?*

You will repeat this activity another day. Meanwhile, store your hemisphere in a safe place to prevent loss, damage, or smudging.

MATERIALS

FIGURE 1.7

Hemisphere Base Diagram (teacher handout)
magnetic compass
cardboard sheet, 20 cm × 20 cm (8 in. × 8 in.)
transparent tape or stapler
plastic hemisphere from the What Do You Think? section of this activity
marking pencil (Use a grease pencil if possible; sunlight may fade felt-tip inks.)

PROCEDURE

A. Tape or staple Figure 1.7 (the "base sheet") to the cardboard sheet. Then tape or staple the base of the hemisphere to the base sheet-card-

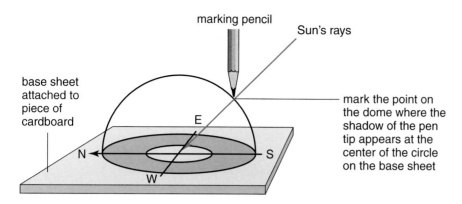

FIGURE 1.8

marking pencil

Sun's rays

base sheet attached to piece of cardboard

E

N

S

W

mark the point on the dome where the shadow of the pen tip appears at the center of the circle on the base sheet

board combination so that the ridge marked N lines up with north on the base sheet and so that the + mark is directly under the center of the hemisphere. See Figure 1.8.

B. Place the hemisphere on a flat, horizontal surface in direct sunlight. With the aid of a magnetic compass, turn the hemisphere so the ridge marked N points north. NOTE: Be careful not to place your hemisphere near iron or steel objects since these metals will attract your compass needle and produce an inaccurate reading. Once the dome is set in place, *do not move it*! (Draw an outline around the cardboard with a piece of chalk just in case the hemisphere is moved accidentally.)

DO NOT STARE AT THE SUN. IT CAN DAMAGE YOUR EYES.

CAUTION

C. Plot the Sun's position in the following way (see Figure 1.8):

1) Carefully move the tip of the grease pencil close to the plastic hemisphere, but do not let the pencil touch the sphere.

2) Move the pencil around until the shadow cast by its tip falls directly on the + mark that is at the center of the base sheet.

3) Touch the pencil tip to the dome and at that point make a dot. The dot's shadow should fall directly on the + mark on the base sheet.

4) Repeat steps C1–C3 every 10 minutes for at least 30 minutes and longer if possible.

5) Connect the plotted points with a line. Draw this line on the inside of the hemisphere. Label the line with the date and time range of C4. *Do not erase this line.*

DISCUSSION QUESTIONS

1. Discuss how the points and line you drew for question P1 compare with the points and line plotted in this activity.

2. From what direction did the Sun rise?

3. Where was the Sun at noon? What was the approximate angular height of the Sun at noon?

4. In what direction did the Sun set?

When you have answered these questions, erase the line you drew for question P1. Keep the line you plotted in step C.

EXTENSIONS

1. Bring the hemisphere and a magnetic compass home on the same day you did this activity. Follow the set-up and plotting procedures described in steps B and C. Plot the Sun's apparent motion across the sky for half an hour before sunset and for half an hour after sunrise the next morning. (You may have to wait a day or more if the sky is overcast at sunset or sunrise.) Label the lines with the dates and time ranges.

2. On a clear weekend day follow steps B and C for the entire day. Plot the points at *1-hour* intervals only.

3. Repeat this plotting of the Sun's apparent daily motion on a clear day one month after the date of your original plot. Repeat this plotting for as many months as possible. Use a different color pen for each month.

4. Refer to an almanac or a calendar to determine the first day of each season. Plot the apparent daily motion of the Sun on the hemisphere for these days. Use a different color pen for each day.

ACTIVITY 1.3

KEEPING A JOURNAL OF THE SUN'S APPARENT MOTION

PURPOSE

To observe sunset from the same location, once a week, for a period of several weeks.

WHAT DO YOU THINK?

P1. *The illustration below shows the Sun setting behind some distant objects. Trace or copy this illustration, and on your copy, draw the Sun where you think it will be at sunset on each of the dates given below.*

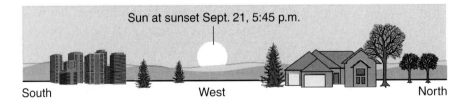

Sun at sunset Sept. 21, 5:45 p.m.

South   West   North

Sept. 21: Sunset time = 5:45   Oct. 21: Sunset time = ?
Nov. 21: Sunset time = ?   Dec. 21: Sunset time = ?

*Write the appropriate date above each Sun you draw and write what you think will be the time of each of these sunsets. (If your area is on **daylight saving time** during the observation, subtract 1 hour from the time so that times will be expressed in local **standard time**.)*

MATERIALS

magnetic compass
watch or other timepiece
pencil (or colored pencils, felt-tip pens)
Chart 1.1 A Sunset Journal
sheet of plain paper, 22 cm × 28 cm (8.5 in. × 11 in.) or larger

PROCEDURE

FIRST DAY: Getting Oriented

A. Find a location convenient to your home or work with as clear a view as possible of the western sky. When facing west, you should be able to look south (to your left) and north (to your right) without any major obstacles blocking your view. (NOTE: If you do not have a compass to determine directions, call the point where the Sun is setting on the first day of observing *west*.)

B. Pick a spot for viewing that you will be able to locate each time you make an observation. Push a stick or stone into the ground, or make a small mark on a paved surface, without damaging the pavement, to help you find the spot. *Make all your observations from this location.*

C. On your sheet of paper, draw the horizon features (see question P1 for an example). Include buildings, trees, power lines, hills, and anything else you can see. (Use objects that are far away; do not use objects that are close to you.) These landmarks will help you locate where the Sun sets on your diagram. Mark where north, south, and west are found along your horizon. Place west in the center of your drawing. Write the location (neighborhood and/or street name) of your observing spot on this chart.

D. As the Sun begins to disappear behind one of the landmarks you have marked, draw the Sun on the chart exactly as it appears in the sky. Write the time to the nearest minute and the date above your drawing of the Sun. Use *Standard Time* (see question P1).

E. On Chart 1.1, keep a log of the weather and anything unusual you observe about the Sun or sky.

F. Make your observations of the sunset *at least once a week*, weather permitting. Your teacher will give you the beginning and ending dates for this activity.

NOTE: The information from this activity will be used in Activity 3.2.

Answer the following questions after completing all your observations.

1. *Did the position of sunset change during the period of your observations? If so, how did it change?*

2. *Did the time of sunset change during the period of your observations?*

3. *Why do you think the sunset position and time changed as they did, if they did change?*

4. *If the Sun did not set at the same time each day, did it set earlier or later each day?*

5. *If the time of sunset changed, do you think the time of sunrise changed? If so, how do you think this change in sunrise might compare to the change in sunset?*

6. *How did the number of hours of daylight change?*

7. *Compare your journal of the sky to your predictions in question P1.*

QUESTIONS TO TEST YOURSELF

1. Does the Sun always set in the same direction?

2. How, if at all, did the Sun's setting position change during your observation period?

3. Does the Sun always set at the same time?

4. How, if at all, did the Sun's setting time change during your observation period?

EXTENSIONS

1. Set up and keep a sunrise journal.

2. Continue the sunset journal through the rest of the school year.

CHAPTER 2

The Nighttime Sky

WHAT DO YOU THINK IS TRUE ABOUT THE NORTH STAR?

Below is a list of statements concerning Polaris, the North Star. Which do you believe are true, and which do you believe are false?

1. Polaris is not the brightest star in the sky.

2. During an evening, Polaris rises in the east and sets in the west just like the Sun does during the daytime.

3. Polaris is always right over your head.

WHAT DO YOUR FRIENDS KNOW ABOUT THE STARS?

Before the next class meeting, interview a friend who is not in this class. Ask the following questions, making sure that you write down his or her responses as completely as possible. Provide your friend with paper so that she or he can make sketches. Bring the answers and drawings to the next class meeting and be prepared to talk about them.

1. About how many stars do you think you can see at night with your naked eye?

2. At night, the stars look like tiny points of light. Are they really as small as they look? How big do you think the stars actually are?

3. Why can't you see the stars in the daytime?

4. What's so special about the North Star?

HOW WOULD YOU RESPOND?

You are out at night with your eight-year-old cousin, who has just learned about the solar system in her science class. She is very curious about the nine planets and she asks you the following questions. How would you respond?

1. Can you see any of the planets at night? If so, which ones can you see and what do they look like? At night, how can you tell whether a spot of light is a planet or a star?

2. What is the difference between a star and a planet, besides appearance?

Preview: In this chapter you will (1) observe the Moon, (2) observe the motions of the stars, and (3) construct a star finder to help you with your nighttime observations.

Chapter 1 began with the first lines from "The Walrus and the Carpenter." The next lines are

> *The Moon was shining sulkily,*
> *Because she thought the Sun*
> *Had got no business to be there*
> *After the day was done—*
> *"It's very rude of him," she said,*
> *"To come and spoil the fun!"*

The poem suggests that the Sun does not belong in the nighttime sky. You learned in Chapter 1 that the Sun is never in the nighttime sky (so the Moon's complaint in the poem is valid) and that the Moon is sometimes in the daytime sky. But is the Moon always in the night sky? Does the Moon's presence in the sky define nighttime the way that the Sun's presence defines daytime? If the Moon is not the key feature of the nighttime sky, are there any other objects that are?

In Activity 1.2, you observed the Sun's apparent daily motion. Although the Sun's motion may not be what you expected, it is quite predictable. In the continental United States, the Sun is never in the sky before 3:30 A.M. or after 9:00 P.M., standard time. The Sun, or the sunlight that filters

FIGURE 2.1
The Moon in the daytime sky over Pike's Peak, Colorado.

✳   The Universe in Your Hands

through the clouds, is the key feature of the daytime sky. Over a month, however, the Moon spends as much time in the daytime sky as it does in the nighttime sky. You may have already seen the Moon in the daytime sky. If not, keep looking; you will eventually see a "daytime" Moon (Figure 2.1). Activity 2.1 may help you locate the Moon in the daytime.

Do you think that you can now construct a model for the Moon's motion? You observed the full Moon on a particular date; on what date do you think the next full Moon will occur? Do you think the Moon will be full on the same date next year? Is moonlight made by the Moon or does it have another source? (If there were no Sun, could you see the Moon?) If you cannot answer those questions yet, don't worry—Chapter 7 includes a detailed investigation of the Moon's motions. Because the Moon is not a permanent feature of the nighttime sky, we will not study its motions now. Let's investigate instead the motions of the nighttime sky's feature attraction: the stars.

The Motions of the Stars

To an observer on the Earth, the sky appears to be a dome with its center directly overhead wherever he or she happens to be standing. If you go out at the same time each night for several nights and carefully note the positions of the stars on this dome, you will discover that the same patterns appear night after night. The stars, unlike the clouds, always seem to have the same positions with respect to each other. The stars seem to be fixed to the dome of the sky. The stars also do not appear to change in brightness from night to night.

If you watch for many hours, or allow a camera to watch, you will find that the dome containing the stars appears to be turning. If you are north of the equator, one fairly bright star, the North Star, seems to be fixed in location, and the other stars seem to turn around it. If you spent all night looking at the sky in the spring or autumn, you would find that the dome of stars makes approximately half a turn between sunset and sunrise. In the winter, the nights are longer and the dome makes more than half a turn. In the summer, the nights are shorter and the dome makes less than half a turn.

If you picked out a bright star that rose in the east and followed that star all night, you would notice that the star moves much like the Sun, travelling across the sky and setting in the west. Stars that rise to the south of east take less time to cross the sky than stars that rise directly east, and therefore remain above the horizon for a shorter period of time before setting to the south of west. When viewed from the Northern Hemisphere, stars that are far enough north never rise or set; they just circle the North Star. However, you lose sight of them when the Sun rises. (For now, we will call these stars "never-setting" stars.)

As the nights go by, you should notice that there is no star that rises at the same time each night. Unless it is a never-setting star, a star rises a little earlier and sets a little earlier than it did the previous night. (Eventually the star rises so early that it will set before sunset, and many months will elapse before it again appears in the evening sky.) If you look in the same direction, say south, each night at the same time, you will see different patterns of stars in different seasons. See Figure 2.2. If you kept up this watch for several

spring

summer

fall

winter

Figure 2.2
Southern horizon with star patterns in spring, summer, fall, and winter as seen from Boston, Massachusetts, at 9:00 P.M.

years, you would discover that the same stars appear at almost exactly the same position at the same time of night on the same date each year.

You don't have to spend months making your own observations to help you visualize the behavior of the stars described above. A simple, two-dimensional (flat) model of the nighttime sky can be used to simulate in a few minutes what you would see in a year. You will make this model, a star finder, in Activity 2.2.

NOTE: Appendix 1 can help you become familiar with the stars and their locations, as well as with some of the mythology of the constellations.

Set your star finder for 9:00 P.M. on January 1. Examine the star patterns visible in the finder's window. Now turn the star wheel so that it shows the sky for 9:00 P.M. on February 1. Continue setting the star finder for 9:00 P.M.

for the first day of each successive month until you return to January 1. Notice how the appearance of the sky changes as some stars disappear below the western horizon while other stars appear above the eastern horizon. Yet after 1 year you are back with the same sky that you started with.

What is going on? Can you explain the changing appearance of the nighttime sky? Recall in Chapter 1 we inferred that stars are in the daytime sky, too, but are not visible because of the Sun's presence. If the stars in the nighttime sky change with the seasons, it is reasonable to assume that the stars in the daytime sky also change. Long ago, humans developed a model to describe the daytime and nighttime skies, a model that explains the motions of the stars and also of the Sun.

NOTE: The words "explain" and "explanation" are encountered frequently, especially in texts and tests. It is important that you know how these words are used before proceeding further in this book. Let's examine a typical situation to investigate the meanings of these words.

A teacher collected a homework assignment and discovered that one student had not handed it in. The teacher asked the student, "Why didn't you give me your homework?" (The teacher could have said, "Explain to me why your homework is missing." This statement has the same meaning as the question that was asked.) The student said, "My dog ate it." The student's answer is an explanation, the reason why the homework was missing. The teacher sought additional information by asking, "How did your dog get the homework? Why did your dog eat your homework?" The student replied with a more detailed explanation: "I left the paper on a table by an open window and a breeze blew the paper off the table. My dog likes the smell and taste of ink, so he ate the paper." The explanation given for the missing homework was now clear to the teacher. But the teacher decided not to accept the student's explanation. The student asked the teacher to explain this decision. It now became the teacher's turn to offer an explanation.

The teacher made the following remarks: "It's a fact that you didn't hand in today's homework. You've offered a model to explain that fact. I do not accept your model because I have a simpler one: you didn't do your homework. That's all—no open window, no breeze, no ink-loving dog. It's ironic that your missing assignment involved Occam's razor, because I've just used the razor. Both models explain your missing homework equally well, but because my model is simpler than yours, Occam's razor indicates that my model is the better one. Of course, if there are additional facts that can be explained more simply by your model, then I may have to abandon my model and accept yours."

The student asked the teacher about "additional facts." The teacher replied, "Well, you need to provide me with evidence that your dog ate your homework. For example, dogs are meat-eaters and don't fully digest plant fiber. Paper is made of plant fiber. If your dog ate your homework, some of the paper should show up by tomorrow morning. Bring the evidence to school tomorrow and I'll have it examined by the local veterinarian. If she confirms that the evidence includes paper identical to the homework sheet, I'll accept your model. In order for my model to explain all of the facts as well as your

Why You Can See Some Stars and Not Others

Different locations on the nighttime side of the Earth can have different views of the sky on the same date. For example, an observer in the United States cannot see all of the stars that an observer in Australia can see, no matter which season it is or what the time of night. And there are stars visible from the United States on every night that an observer in Australia can never see.

If you were to travel north, the northern stars would appear higher and higher in the sky and the stars in the southern sky would appear lower and lower. See Figure 2.3. If you were to travel south, the southern stars would move higher and higher in the sky, while northern stars would move lower and lower. See Figure 2.4.

More than 2,000 years ago people noticed this change in the appearance of the sky as they travelled north or south. The disappearance of some stars below the horizon and the appearance of other stars above the horizon led ancient scholars to conclude that the Earth is shaped like a sphere. If the Earth were flat, the view of the sky would not change in the same way as you traveled.

QUESTION: How would the view of the sky change if you traveled across a flat Earth?

model does, my model would have to include that the evidence was faked and how it was faked, which would make my model more complicated than yours."

Was the teacher's decision fair? Yes. By using Occam's razor to select the better model, the teacher stuck to the facts and kept personal feelings and other irrelevant factors (the teacher was tired, or had a toothache, etc.) out of the decision-making process. The teacher was provided with one fact, the missing homework, and selected the simpler of two models that were both consistent with that fact. If important new facts were explained equally well by both models, but the student's model was simpler and the teacher rejected it, then the teacher's decision would be contrary to Occam's razor.

HEADS UP!

There is one important aspect of Occam's razor that is not emphasized in the above example and that is critical for science: A model must be able to predict accurately the results of experiments not yet done or observations not yet made. Without the capability to make predictions, a model would not help to advance science or to improve our ability to figure out why the world behaves as it does. (*Why do you think a model's predictions are so important?*) Merely stating that "the world is the way it is because it is that way" is certainly a simple model and is certainly consistent with all the facts. But such a model is clearly not useful for making predictions.

HEADS UP!

Use of Occam's razor to defend models for missing homework or other mysterious phenomena is done at the student's own risk. We recommend that the student keep assignments away from dogs, tigers, jet engine intakes, and other hazards.

SUMMARY

Changes in the Moon's shape and position in the sky over several days follow a pattern. The Moon can be seen in the daytime sky just as often as it can be seen in the nighttime sky.

30° North (approximate latitude of Tallahassee, Florida; Houston, Texas)

Northern horizon

Southern horizon

40° North (approximate latitude of Boston, Massachusetts; New York, New York; Chicago, Illinois; San Francisco, California)

Northern horizon

Southern horizon

50° North (approximate latitude of Seattle, Washington; Vancouver, Canada; Winnipeg, Canada)

Northern horizon

Southern horizon

Figure 2.3 View of northern and southern horizons from increasingly northern latitudes at 6:00 P.M. November 1. Notice how the positions of the stars change when viewed from different latitudes. (Can you spot the Big Dipper in the pictures on the left side of the page?)

30° South (approximate latitude of Santiago, Chile; Montevideo, Uruguay; Brisbane, Australia)

Northern horizon

Southern horizon

40° South (approximate latitude of Melbourne, Australia; Piedra de Aquila, Argentina)

Northern horizon

Southern horizon

50° South (approximate latitude of Santa Cruz, Argentina; Falkland Islands)

Northern horizon

Southern horizon

Figure 2.4 View of northern and southern horizons from increasingly southern latitudes at 6:00 P.M. November 1.

"Nighttime" means "on the unlighted side of the planet," the side of the Earth facing away from the Sun.

The apparent daily motion of the stars is predictable and follows seasonal patterns; each day, stars rise and set a little earlier. This shift leads to an annual cycle so that stars appear in the same place in the sky at the same time a year later. It is possible to orient yourself to the nighttime sky using the North Star.

Picture 1 A few hours after sunset   **Picture 2** 6 hours later

1. What is wrong with these pictures? In picture 1, you and a friend are looking toward the western horizon somewhere in the Northern Hemisphere. The Sun set a few hours ago. Picture 2 is a sketch of the sky 6 hours later. There are several errors in these pictures. Try to find them.

2. Early on a clear night, locate the Big Dipper and the North Star. On a sheet of plain paper draw these stars as they appear in the sky. Label the time next to each object. Draw in your apparent horizon and label the north point of the horizon. See the sample drawing below. Go out 1 hour after your first observation and on the same paper, draw the Big Dipper and the North Star as they appear then and write the time next to each. Repeat this procedure once more, 1 hour after the previous observation.

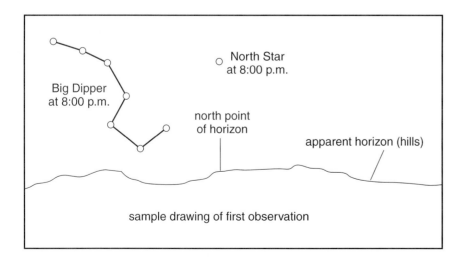

North Star
at 8:00 p.m.

Big Dipper
at 8:00 p.m.

north point
of horizon

apparent horizon (hills)

sample drawing of first observation

The Nighttime Sky ✳   **29**

a) How did the Big Dipper appear to move in the sky during the 2-hour period? How did the North Star's position change with respect to the Big Dipper's?

b) Why did the Big Dipper and the North Star appear to move as they did?

SELF-TEST

1. On your first Moon observation (Activity 2.1), did you see the Moon closest to north, east, south, or west?

2. Refer to Activity 2.1; on your final observation, did you see the Moon closest to north, east, south, or west?

3. During the 2-week period of your Moon observations, did the Moon's apparent shape stay the same or did it get fuller or less full each day?

4. During your observations of the Moon, how did its position in the sky relative to that of the Sun change?

5. Why are different stars seen in the nighttime sky at different times of the year?

Astronomer

You may discover from this course, or just from looking over the chapter titles in this book, that astronomy involves a lot more than looking at stars through telescopes. Similarly, the work of astronomers today extends into many different areas of science and even philosophy to try to answer questions about the light coming from the stars and the chemical elements that make up the stars. Astronomers also help to build telescopes, satellites, and spacecraft; study how stars and galaxies form; imagine how the universe began; and even look into the possibility of life on other planets. No one description could tell you something about all astronomers. Instead, here is one astronomer and what she does.

When Dr. Sallie Baliunas (bal-OO-nas) was growing up, she was interested in being a ballet dancer, an astronaut, and an aeronautical engineer (someone who designs aircraft and spacecraft), though not all at the same time. (The title of doctor—Dr.—doesn't always mean a medical doctor; it may be earned by study and research in a specialized topic in graduate school after college.) In high school she enjoyed painting and sculpture as well as physics. She almost decided to follow up on her childhood goal to become an aeronautical engineer, but she continued with physics instead, and eventually ended up in astrophysics—the physics of the cosmos. She likes science because it gives her the opportunity to be creative in trying to figure out how the universe (or at least a part of it!) might work.

Her studies now focus on the Sun and other stars that are about the same size and temperature as the Sun, and the newly discovered planets orbiting those stars. One way she studies them involves detecting "star spots," spots on other stars like the sunspots you may have heard about on the Sun. She also looks at these Sunlike stars to predict how the Sun might change and how its changes might affect the Earth. (These changes are very small and very slow, so you don't have to worry about the Sun changing drastically before you wake up tomorrow.) Furthermore, she can use what she learns about these stars to help her examine how other kinds of stars function. To investigate such changes, Dr. Baliunas has to first plan observations of stars. She uses a computer and library research to design the best observations for her purposes; then she transmits her instructions to the computer that directs the telescope.

Many of the telescopes used in today's astronomical research are huge; computers are used to point the telescopes to the desired part of the sky. Most telescopes used for research are placed on top of mountains, and all are located as far as possible from towns and cities to avoid the lights used in buildings and on streets that make it harder to observe the stars. Astronomers from all over the world go to observatories all over the world to do their research; since there are far more astronomers than research telescopes, considerable sharing occurs. Part of planning an experiment includes applying for access to a telescope and the computers that guide it, and ensuring that the telescope will be able to collect the information you need about the light it receives. Today, astronomers mostly obtain this information with electronic devices whose images can be stored in computers in the form of numbers that can be analyzed, also with computers. No longer

Dr. Sallie Baliunas standing near the 150-cm (60-in.) reflecting telescope (see Chapter 6) at Mount Wilson Observatory in California. The very large object behind her is the base of the telescope.

is astronomical research done by astronomers looking through a telescope with their own eyes or taking an ordinary photograph through the telescope. Modern electronic equipment does far better than human eyes can.

Once Dr. Baliunas has her data, she analyzes and then interprets the results. Other tasks that might occupy her time include considering new experiments and research programs, writing astronomy articles for science and popular publications, repairing equipment, and talking with other astronomers about her work and theirs. She also presents the results of her work at conferences where professional and sometimes also amateur astronomers meet to learn about new information and developments in astronomy. Being an astronomer has given her the opportunity to travel

and meet people all over the Earth, as well as to strive to understand things beyond it.

Tycho Brahe: The Man with the Golden Nose

Tycho Brahe (TEE-ko BRA-hee) (1546–1601) was a Danish astronomer who spent his life observing the sky and making measurements of the relative positions of the Sun, Moon, planets, and stars using only his eyes and some basic instruments. The first telescopes were built after he died, so he never had one. Nevertheless, the accuracy of his measurements was unsurpassed by his contemporaries or predecessors. He had a strong (and strange!) temper. As a young man he lost part of his nose in a sword duel, reportedly over who was a better mathematician, and replaced it with a gold one. When he finished school, he organized a center for astronomical studies that became popular with the political and scientific leaders of the time. More people wanted to study astronomy once they saw others enjoying it, so Tycho's observatory was a very busy place.

Before Tycho, many astronomers did not worry about making accurate measurements; they thought that the sky records made by the ancient Greeks 1,000–2,000 years earlier would always be adequate. When Tycho started watching the sky, he soon found differences between what he saw and what the Greeks and their followers had predicted. He invented and improved instruments for measuring the positions of objects in the sky. These instruments allowed him to make very precise measurements, and his careful work over 20 years provided data that other scientists interpreted to give our modern view of planetary motions. In several letters to Johannes Kepler, his assistant for 10 months, Tycho commented on his strong belief in making observations first and then thinking about why the events happened the way they did, instead of imagining a theory and then looking for facts to "prove" it. After Tycho's death, Kepler used Tycho's data to figure out a better model for the orbits of the planets.

The picture on the preceding page is actually a picture of a picture. The large arc (called a quadrant) going up to the right was made of brass and was used to measure the angle of an object above the horizon through a special sighting hole in the wall (see the upper left corner of the picture). Rather than have a blank wall behind the quadrant, Tycho had a mural painted there showing himself, his observatory, and many of the instruments he and his assistants used to find and measure the positions of the Sun, Moon, planets, and stars. (Tycho is the man in the mural pointing up to the hole in the wall.)

ACTIVITY 2.1   KEEPING A JOURNAL OF THE MOON'S MOTION

PURPOSE

To record observations you make, from the same location over a period of about two weeks, of the Moon's appearance and location in the sky.

WHAT DO YOU THINK?

P1. *The illustration below shows the Moon's shape and position in the sky for the date and time shown.*

Trace or copy the illustration below, and on your copy draw the Moon's shape and location at 8:00 P.M. on **August 23** *and* **August 27** *(put the date above each of your drawings). Note that the observations are made at the same time of day. If you think the Moon would not be visible, explain why.*

East   South   West

MATERIALS

      pencil (or colored pencils, felt-tip pens)
      watch
      Chart 2.1
      sheet of plain paper, 22 cm x 28 cm (8.5 in. × 11 in.) or larger
      magnetic compass

PROCEDURE

FIRST DAY: Getting Oriented

A. Choose a specific time to make your observations. Depending on the phase of the Moon, this choice might have to be late afternoon, early evening, or in the morning.

B. Find a location convenient to your home or work with as clear a view as possible of the southern sky. When facing south, you should be able to look east (to your left) and west (to your right) without any major obstacles blocking your view. (NOTE: If you do not have a compass to determine directions, orient yourself by calling the direction of the setting Sun *west*.)

C. Pick a spot for viewing that you will be able to find each time you make an observation. Push a stick or stone into the ground, or make a small mark on a paved surface, without damaging the pavement, to help you find the spot. *Make all your observations from this location.*

D. On your sheet of paper, draw the horizon features (see question P1 for an example). Include buildings, trees, power lines, hills, and anything else that falls into your field of view. (Use objects that are far away; do not use objects that are close to you.) These landmarks will help you locate the position of the Moon on your drawing. Mark east, south, and west along your horizon, placing south in the center of your drawing. Write the location (neighborhood and/or street name) of your observation spot on this chart.

E. Draw the shape of the Moon on your observation sheet, and place it where it appears in the sky. If there are any bright stars or planets visible nearby, include them in your drawing. Write the date and time next to the drawing of the Moon.

F. On Chart 2.1, record the weather conditions and anything unusual you observe about the Moon or the sky. Pay special attention to the Moon's apparent shape and color.

G. Make all your observations of the Moon at the *same time* (you must be no more than *15 minutes* early or late) from the *same location* for as many nights as possible. (Make at least four observations.)

NOTE: The information from this activity will be used in Activity 7.2.

Answer the following questions after completing all your observations.

1. *How did the appearance of the Moon change?*

2. *How did the position of the Moon change?*

3. *As seen in the sky, was the Moon getting farther from or closer to the Sun, or did it seem to stay in the same position with respect to the Sun?*

4. *Over the period of your observations, did you see more or less of the "lit-up" part of the Moon as it changed its position with respect to the Sun?*

5. *Why do you think the Moon's position on the sky changed as it did?*

6. *Why do you think the Moon's apparent shape changed as it did?*

7. *Was the Moon setting earlier, later, or at the same time from one night to the next?*

8. *Was the difference between the time of sunset and moonset getting longer, shorter, or staying the same from one night to the next?*

9. *Was the angle between the Sun and the Moon increasing, decreasing, or staying the same during your observation period?*

10. *From your observations, estimate the time it would take for the Moon to return to the same place in the sky it was on the night you started keeping a journal.*

11. *Compare your journal of the sky with your predictions from question P1.*

QUESTIONS TO TEST YOURSELF

1. Is the Moon in the same place in the sky at the same time every night?

2. How does the position of the Moon in the sky change from one night to the next?

3. How does the appearance of the Moon change from one night to the next?

EXTENSIONS

1. Keep observing the sky from the same location until the Moon returns to the same place in the sky or until it appears the same shape as it did when you began your journal. Note the date. How many days did it take the Moon to complete this cycle?

2. Keep a Moon journal for the morning sky if your original journal was for the evening sky (or vice versa).

ACTIVITY 2.2   BUILDING AND USING A STAR FINDER

PART A BUILDING A STAR FINDER

PURPOSE

To build a device that can be used to locate stars and constellations.

MATERIALS

1 star finder envelope sheet   1 pair of scissors
1 star map sheet   1 sharp pencil
glue   1 ruler

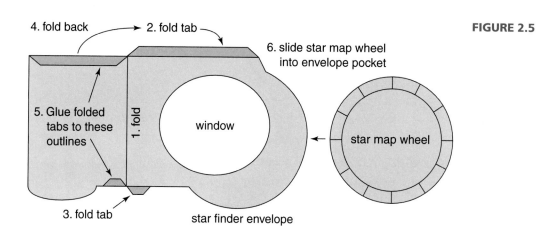

FIGURE 2.5

PROCEDURE

A. Cut out the star map along the outer edge of the calendar ring. Be sure to cut smoothly along the curve; if the edge of the map is not cut properly, the star finder will be hard to use.

B. Cut out the star finder envelope, discarding the shaded areas, including the "window" section of the envelope. Be careful *not* to cut off the tabs; these are needed to assemble the star finder.

C. Fold the envelope along the line indicated (see Figure 2.5). Then fold the two tabs. To make better folds, crease the fold lines with a sharp pencil, using a ruler as a guide.

D. Glue the tabs in place, indicated by the outlines on the envelope.

E. Slip the star map wheel into the envelope so that the printed side of the map faces out of the envelope's window. The map wheel should fit snugly inside the envelope.

PART B USING A STAR FINDER

PURPOSE

To learn how to use the star finder assembled in Part A.

MATERIALS

1 star finder
1 watch or other timepiece
1 clear nighttime sky

PREOBSERVING PRACTICE

A. The portion of the star map inside the window displays the stars visible in the sky for the date and time selected. This star map is a model of the sky. The stars are represented by star symbols on the map. The brighter a star appears to be compared to other stars, the larger is the star symbol that represents it on the map. Stars in the center of the window correspond to the stars overhead. Stars near the edge of the window are stars that are near the horizon. Stars on the map near *north* on the envelope are visible in the northern sky. Stars on the map near *east* on the envelope are visible in the eastern sky. Stars in the southern and western skies can be located near *south* and *west*, respectively, on the envelope.

B. To simulate the movement of the stars across the sky, turn the star wheel in a counterclockwise direction. Note that when you do this, stars move into the window near *east* on the envelope; these stars are rising. At the same time, other stars move out of the window near *west* on the envelope. These stars are setting.

FOR PRACTICE: Adjust the star wheel until Orion is just inside the window near *east* on the envelope. This represents Orion rising above the east point on the horizon. Turn the wheel counterclockwise until Orion is above *south* on the envelope. Note that Orion is about halfway between the *south* edge of the envelope (the southern horizon) and the center of the window (overhead). Orion's location in the sky would therefore be about 45° above the south point on the horizon. Continue turning the wheel counterclockwise until Orion reaches the edge of the window near *west*. This position represents Orion setting.

C. To "set" the star finder, turn the star map wheel until the desired date on the calendar ring lines up with the arrow on the envelope for the time selected. If you are on daylight saving time, subtract 1 hour from the time selected and use that as the time.

D. Set the star finder for 7:00 P.M. on February 1.

1. *Name two constellations that would be visible overhead.*

2. *Name the constellation that has just risen above the east point on the horizon.*

3. *Name the constellation that is setting at the west point on the horizon.*

4. *Describe Orion's position in the sky using its compass direction and approximate angular height.*

5. *Describe the position of the Big Dipper in the sky using its compass direction and approximate angular height.*

6. *At about what time will Orion set on February 1?*

7. *At about what time will Virgo rise on February 1?*

8. *Can the Great Square of Pegasus be seen on February 1? If yes, describe where it can be seen in the sky and give the time(s) visible. If no, explain why not.*

9. *Can Sagittarius be seen on February 1? If yes, describe where it can be seen in the sky and give the time(s) visible. If no, explain why not.*

OBSERVING PROCEDURE

A. Turn the star map wheel until today's date on the calendar ring of the wheel lines up with the arrow on the envelope for your observing time. If it is daylight saving time, subtract 1 hour and use that as the observing time.

B. The stars visible inside the window are the stars visible in the sky (if it is clear!) at the time and date selected. The size of the star on the map is related to the star's apparent brightness: the brighter the star appears relative to other stars, the larger its star symbol is on the map. Concentrate on locating the stars that appear brightest in your sky. The stars that appear brightest for each season are discussed in Appendix 1.

C. Face north. Hold the star finder in front of you so that *north* on the envelope is at the bottom. The stars on the map near *north* on the envelope are in the northern sky, which you are facing. The stars in the

FIGURE 2.6

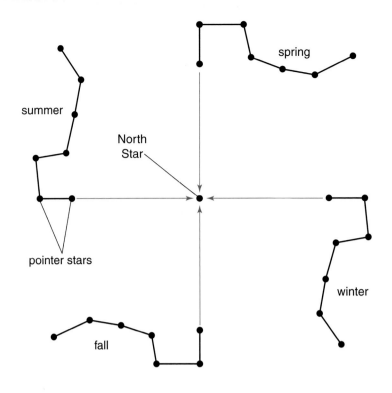

summer

North Star

spring

pointer stars

winter

fall

Approximate northern horizon, without trees, hills, or other obstructions.

center of the window are overhead. Stars around the edge of the window are near the horizon and may be difficult to locate. Look for the Big Dipper, which is part of Ursa Major (the big bear) on the map. Figure 2.6 shows the Big Dipper's general position in the evening sky for each season. For more information, read the section titled "Getting Oriented" in Appendix 1.

D. Face south and hold the star finder so that *south* on the envelope is at the bottom. Look at the stars on the map near *south* on the envelope. These stars are in the southern sky, which you are facing.

E. Repeat step D for the stars in the eastern and western sky.

If you repeat steps A–E on a regular basis, say once a week, you will become familiar with the appearance of the night sky. If you use Appendix 1 in conjuction with your observing, you may find that the night sky is like a storybook filled with interesting pictures.

CHAPTER 3

The Celestial Sphere: A Model of the Sky

WHAT DOES YOUR FAMILY KNOW ABOUT THE CONSTELLATIONS?

Before the next class meeting, interview a member of your family. Ask your family member the following questions and write down the responses as completely as possible. Provide your family member with paper to make sketches. *If possible, also provide a world map.* Bring the answers to the next class session and be prepared to talk about them.

1. Say you are in Chicago at night. You look up and see the Big Dipper almost directly over your head. Do you think that people living in Santiago, Chile, will be able to see the Big Dipper sometime that night? If so, will the Big Dipper ever be over their heads? What about people living in Fairbanks, Alaska? What about people living in Cairo, Egypt?

2. Let's go back to you in Chicago, with the Big Dipper almost directly over your head. Will the Big Dipper stay in the same place all night? If not, where will it go?

3. Are stars in the sky during the daytime? Explain why or why not.

WHAT DO YOUR FRIENDS KNOW ABOUT THE SEASONS?

Before the next class meeting, interview a friend who is not in this class. Ask your friend the following questions, making sure that you write down the responses as completely as possible. Provide your friend with paper to make sketches. Bring the answers and drawings to the next class meeting and be prepared to talk about them.

1. In the Northern Hemisphere, the weather is usually warmer during July than it is during January. In the Southern Hemisphere, the weather is usually warmer in January than it is during July. Why do you think this is so?

2. It is June 21. Where in the sky is the Sun at noontime in your hometown?

3. During which month in your town are the days the longest—June, July, or August? During which month are the days the shortest—December, January, or February?

4. What do you think causes the number of hours of daylight to change during different times of the year?

Preview: In this chapter you will (1) learn about a model of the sky called the celestial sphere, (2) build a celestial sphere, and (3) use the celestial sphere to explore the reasons for the seasons.

The Celestial Sphere

The facts about the apparent motions of the Sun and stars described in Chapters 1 and 2 were discovered by people who lived several thousand years ago. They developed a model that fits these facts. In this model the stars are fixed on the inside of a sphere surrounding the Earth. This sphere is sometimes called the celestial sphere (CS). In this model, the CS rotates slightly faster than once a day, causing the stars to rise almost 4 minutes earlier each day, as both ancient and modern people observe (see Figure 3.1). You might think that because the stars rise at a different time each night that there would be no connection between the time of year and the stars visible in the evening sky, as discussed in Chapter 2. However, the slight change in rising time from day to day adds up to a full day after 1 year; if you turn back a watch a little less than 4 minutes each day, after 1 year the watch will read the same time as when you started—you will have turned it back a full 24 hours. Thus the change in the rising time of the stars follows a pattern exactly 1 year long. Since it does not matter on which day you start keeping track of the stars (or the watch), what you see in the sky (or read on the watch) will be the same 1 year later.

Figure 3.1
Path of a star with rising and setting times on several dates.

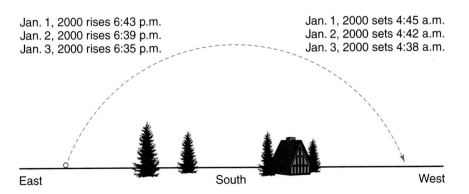

Jan. 1, 2000 rises 6:43 p.m.
Jan. 2, 2000 rises 6:39 p.m.
Jan. 3, 2000 rises 6:35 p.m.

Jan. 1, 2000 sets 4:45 a.m.
Jan. 2, 2000 sets 4:42 a.m.
Jan. 3, 2000 sets 4:38 a.m.

East   South   West

✳   The Universe in Your Hands

In this (old) model, the Sun is located on the CS and, like the stars, is carried around the Earth once a day by the CS. However, the Sun, unlike the stars, is not fixed in place on the CS. Instead, the Sun moves along a path that carries it once around the CS each year. As the Sun moves around the CS, it passes in front of different stars. See Figure 3.2.

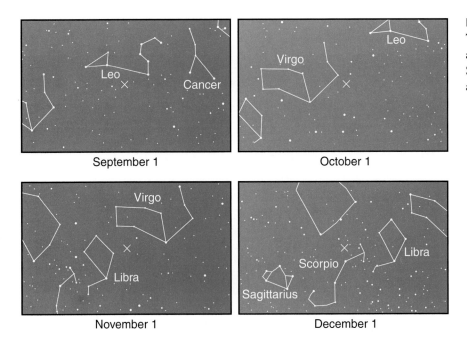

September 1

October 1

November 1

December 1

Figure 3.2
The "X" marks the position of the Sun against the background stars on about September 1, October 1, November 1, and December 1.

NOTE: By 3,500 years ago, people had made observations that indicated that the CS made about 360 complete turns in the time it took the Sun to travel once around the CS. In other words, an early estimate of the length of a year was 360 days. As observing methods and instruments improved, the length of the year was refined to 365 days, then to 365.25 days (365 days 6 hours). Around 150 B.C.E., the Greek scientist Hipparchus calculated the number of days in the year to within 6 minutes of the true value, which is just a fraction of a second more than 365 days 5 hours 48 minutes 45 seconds.

Because you cannot see the Sun and stars together in the daytime sky, you cannot directly observe and check this claimed motion of the Sun along the CS. However, the CS provides you with a model with which you can make predictions that you can check concerning the position of the Sun on the CS.

As you may recall from doing Activity 1.2, the Sun is due south at noontime as seen by an observer in the continental United States. Twelve hours later, after the CS has made one-half of a complete turn, the portion of the CS that is opposite the Sun will be visible in the southern sky (see Figure 3.3). If the Sun did *not* move on the CS, the same portion of the CS would always be exactly opposite the Sun. That would mean that you would always see the same stars 12 hours after noontime, regardless of the date. (You do not need to wait 12 hours; some portion of the CS is always in the

Figure 3.3

The Sun is on the side of the CS facing away from you. The portion of the CS facing you is that part of the sky that is opposite from the Sun. Try modeling this with your CS.

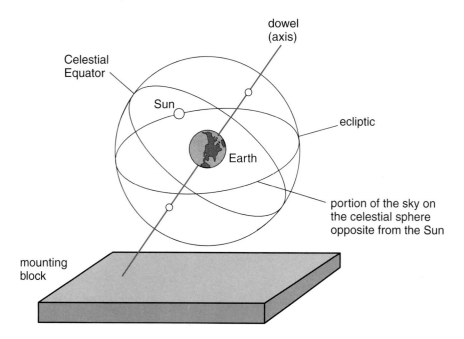

southern sky, regardless of the time. If the Sun's position on the CS were fixed, the same portion of the CS would always be due south the same number of hours after noontime.) But you already know that different stars are visible in the evening sky at different times of the year (refer to Activity 2.2).

Observations of the sky made long ago during total solar eclipses, when stars can be seen in the daytime sky, provided evidence consistent with the model of the Sun's motion on the CS. Different stars appeared to be near the Sun during eclipses seen at different times of the year. (These observations were not made by one person, because a total solar eclipse is visible from a specific location on the Earth only once in about 300 years. Rather, the results of observations made by many people over many years from different locations were combined to plot the Sun's apparent motion on the CS.) In modern times, the Sun's position against the background of the stars has been observed by astronauts orbiting the Earth; above the Earth's atmosphere, which interferes with your view of the stars during the daytime, the sky away from the direction of the Sun is always dark and you can see the stars that appear near the Sun. If you lived on the Moon, which has no atmosphere, you would always be able to see the stars in the daytime sky.

The stars that pass directly overhead at the Earth's equator are said to lie on the celestial equator. The points that are directly overhead at the Earth's poles are said to lie at the celestial poles; the North Star, for example, is very close to the north celestial pole. The Sun's path around the CS does not follow the celestial equator. Because the Sun's path on the CS is not on the celestial equator, the Sun does not pass directly overhead at the Earth's equator every day. You can study the Sun's path along the CS in more detail with the model of the CS that you built in Activity 3.1.

Why a Model of the Sky?

You may have found it hard to picture the behavior of the Sun and stars. You also may have found it difficult to use a flat sheet of paper in Activities 1.3 and 2.1 to illustrate what you saw when you looked at the sky. The CS is a more useful model of the sky because it represents the sky as a dome, the way you see it, although it, too, has limitations (see below).

In Activity 3.1 you built a physical model of the CS to help you study the motions of the sky. (See Figure 3.4.) This plastic replica of the CS has limitations. You look at the replica from the outside, but you look at the real sky from the inside. This shift in viewpoint may take you a little while to get used to. The following exercise may help you understand better the differences between "outside" and "inside" viewpoints. Imagine a baseball game in which you are a player in the outfield and the batter has hit the ball in your direction. To someone "outside" of the action, for example, a person watching the game from the stands, the scene would look like Figure 3.5. Your "inside" view of the action would look like the scene in Figure 3.6. Both scenes involve the same objects and action, but look different from one another. As a player, you are interested in the "inside" view. Sometimes, however, an "outside" viewer may see motions that are not apparent to the "inside" viewer.

The ideal physical model of the sky is one that puts you inside the dome of the sky. One model of this kind is called a planetarium (Figure 3.7). If you have a planetarium available, you will find it very helpful in seeing how the relationships you can observe using your plastic CS appear in the real sky.

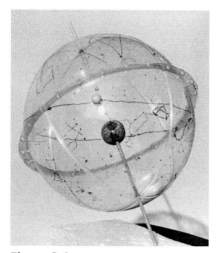

Figure 3.4
A celestial sphere.

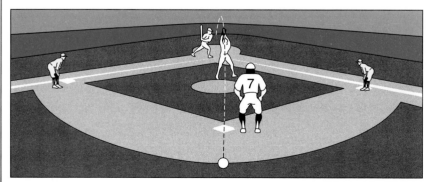

Figure 3.5

Figure 3.6

On the Field and in the Stands

When a baseball is hit to the outfield, this is what a fan sitting behind first base sees.

This is what the center fielder sees.

The game looks different from the point of view of each of the players and from the point of view of the fans seated in different parts of the stadium. In this book you will look first at the apparent motions of celestial objects from the viewpoint of a "player" on the Earth. Later you will look at the same objects from the viewpoint of a "fan" on the Sun.

Although it doesn't look like a computer, the model of the CS is a kind of computer—the only kind of computer that people had for many thousands of years. With it you can quickly "calculate" what the sky would look like at any time of the day, night, or year at any place on the Earth.

The model of the CS is a very good computer for the apparent motions of the Sun, Moon, and stars. The CS is less useful for "calculating" the motions of the planets. The apparent motions of the Sun, Moon, and stars are relatively simple, but the apparent motions of the planets are more complicated. You will have a chance later to practice using your model of the CS as a computer to explore the simplest motions.

Modeling the Sun's Motions

The plastic model of the sky built in Activity 3.1 is not like a doll or a model car, because there is no real object corresponding to the "celestial sphere." Instead the celestial sphere is a representation of the sky. Your plastic CS is

useful because it lets you figure out how the sky would appear at different times from any location on the Earth. The CS can also help you understand some of the reasons that summer is hotter than winter, but the CS doesn't answer such questions as Why does the Sun move across the sky each day? Why does the Sun move north and south in the sky each year? Your model of the CS is useful for figuring out the Sun's apparent motions, but it does not tell you much about what *causes* these motions. (There can be a big difference between describing an event and explaining its cause with a simple physical model. You can easily use a model airplane to describe the motion of a real aircraft through the air. But how well does a model airplane explain what causes a real airplane to fly?)

One possible answer to the questions above involves the Sun moving once around the Earth each day, just as it seems to, and the Sun also moving once each year around a path traced through the background of the stars. Indeed, people thought this description was correct for more than 2,000 years. But there is another possibility.

When people travel by train or subway, they notice that it is sometimes difficult to tell at a station whether their train is moving or, instead, the train next to them is moving in the opposite direction and they are standing still. If you are flying in an airplane you have little sense of how fast you are moving (if you do not look out the window, you often cannot tell you are moving at all). Suppose you drop a spoon while eating on an airplane. The spoon falls directly beneath the point where you released it, just as if you were parked on the ground rather than flying more than 850 km per hour (500 mi per hour).

These experiences suggest that if you are on a platform that is moving sufficiently smoothly, it is difficult to tell whether you are in motion. You also cannot tell if an object is moving or whether you are moving and the object only appears to be moving. You can use this Principle of Relative Motion to raise the question whether the apparent motion of the Sun and stars across the sky might be due to a spinning Earth rather than a spinning CS.

The daily motion of the Sun and stars across the sky can be explained by either the Earth or the CS spinning. But how can you explain the Sun's apparent motion against the background of the stars that was described at the end of Chapter 2? Suppose the Earth moves around the Sun. Would this motion explain why different stars appear after sunset at different times of

The Celestial Sphere Is a Model

At one time people thought that the celestial sphere was an accurate picture of what they saw in the sky. When people found that the stars were not all at the same distance from us (you will get a chance to measure some of these distances for yourself), they realized the CS could not be an accurate picture. Still, the CS is a very useful model. The celestial sphere is a good, but not perfect representation of what you see when you look into the sky, and so you can continue to use the CS although you now know that it is not a very accurate copy of the way the sky "really is."

Galileo

Galileo (1564–1642) lived more than 300 years ago. There were no airplanes in Galileo's day, but he argued that a stone dropped from the top of the mast of a sailing ship falls to the base of the mast, whether the ship is tied up in the harbor or traveling under full sail. If you cannot tell whether a ship that you are on is moving by watching something dropped from its mast, Galileo reasoned that you cannot tell whether the Earth is moving by watching something you drop.

Does the Earth Spin?

Is there any way to tell if the Earth is spinning without looking at the CS? If a car is on a very smooth straight road and the radio is playing loudly, it is hard to tell if the car is moving without looking outside. If the car goes around a curve, however, you can tell it is moving, even without looking outside, by the force that seems to push you toward the outside of the curve. Similar effects occur on a spinning Earth, but they are not obvious.

Imagine you take a pendulum to the North or South Pole. Imagine further that the pendulum can swing freely in any direction. If you started the pendulum swinging, the endpoints of each swing would trace out a circle during the course of the day as the Earth rotates. This device is called a Foucault pendulum after the French physicist Jean Foucault (Foo-KOH) (1819–1868) who first demonstrated this effect. The motion of the pendulum is easiest to visualize at the North or South Pole. Foucault did not go to either pole, since the demonstration works just as well in France (but is much harder to understand!).

---

the year? Would it explain why the Sun appears to move against the background of the stars?

You can answer the last question most easily. If you stand in the middle of the classroom and watch another student walk around you, you will see the other student against the background of all four walls of the room. What did the other student see? The other student saw you against the background of all four walls of the room. (See Figure 3.8.) In other words, the change in the position of the Sun against the background of stars can be explained just as readily by the Sun moving around a motionless Earth as by the Earth moving around a motionless Sun.

If the other student slowly spins while moving around you (spinning rapidly is a good way to get dizzy and miss the point of the exercise), the student will see different walls while facing away from you at different points on the journey, just the way you see different stars at different times of the year. So the model that the Earth spins and travels around the Sun once each year explains the same appearance of the sky as the model in which the CS spins and the Sun makes one trip around the CS each year.

So far, you have two models: in one the CS spins once each day and the Sun goes around the CS once each year; in the other the Earth spins once each day and travels around the Sun once each year. On what basis do you choose one model over the other? This is the question that people faced when first Aristarchus (Ar-i-STAR-kus) and then Copernicus (Ko-PER-ni-kus) proposed the second model. You will come back to this question when you learn something about the motions of the planets in Chapter 9. For now, you will see how you can use Copernicus's model to understand why there are seasons. The first model, in which the Earth is motionless, can also explain the seasons. However, because the explanation for the seasons was not the key factor in choosing one model over the other, we will deal only with the explanation for the seasons provided by the model that is in use today.

Aristarchus and Copernicus

Somewhat more than 2,000 years ago, the Greek astronomer Aristarchus of Samos suggested that the Sun does not go around the Earth, but rather that the Earth goes around the Sun. Aristarchus's model was ignored for almost 1,800 years, until the Polish astronomer Nicholas Copernicus (1473–1543) revived it in the 1500s. Apparently Copernicus was the first person to use this model also to explain the motions of the planets.

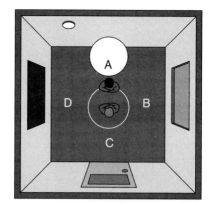

Figure 3.8
The apparent motion of two students against the background of a classroom (shown in the upper diagram as a view seen from above the classroom) as one student circles the other.

What Causes the Seasons?

Why is the summer hotter than the winter? If you ask people this question, many will answer, "because the Earth is closer to the Sun in the summer." This answer seems to make sense, because if you are closer to a fire you definitely feel warmer. Unfortunately, in the case of the Earth and Sun this explanation cannot be correct. While you are on summer vacation in early July, Australian students are on winter break. (See Figure 3.9.) Both American and Australian students have New Year's Day off, but while you might spend the day snow skiing, the students "down under" will be at the beach celebrating the start of summer vacation. If the distance between the Earth and the Sun determined the seasons, then you and your Aussie counterparts should enjoy summer vacation at the same time, when the Earth is closest to the Sun. However, since winter and summer occur at the same time on the Earth, the Earth-Sun distance cannot be responsible for the seasons.

Figure 3.9
A student facing south at noontime in Massachusetts (left) and in Australia (right) near June 21.

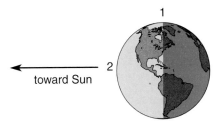

Figure 3.10
In a scale model of the Earth and the Sun with the Earth as shown (about 2.5 cm in diameter), the Sun would be about 290 m away to the left and would be about 2.7 m in diameter. At this scale, the difference between the distance to the Sun from point 1 on the Earth and the distance to the Sun from point 2 is 1.25 cm. Do you think that this difference in distance to the Sun could make a big difference in the temperatures at points 1 and 2?

Why isn't the Earth-Sun distance responsible for the seasons? There is one basic reason: The Earth's path around the Sun is almost circular (see Activity 3.2). Although the distance between the Earth and the Sun does vary, the change in distance is very small compared to the maximum Earth-Sun distance. Imagine that the Earth and the Sun were shrunk so that the greatest distance between them was 10 m (33 ft). The minimum Earth-Sun distance would then be 9.7 m (32 ft), only 30 cm (12 in.) shorter than the maximum distance. If you were standing 10 m from a fire and felt "wintery" cold, would you feel "summery" warm if you moved 30 cm closer? No. And neither would the Earth. Since the slight variation from a perfect circle of the Earth's path around the Sun does not cause the seasons, then the much, much smaller difference in the Earth-Sun distances of two points on the side of the Earth facing the Sun (see Figure 3.10) cannot cause the seasons either. So the question still remains: What causes the seasons?

If you are north or south of the Tropics, you can easily observe that the Sun is higher in the sky in the summer than it is in the winter and that the daylight periods are longer in the summer than they are in the winter. Those two observations help to explain why the summer is warmer than is the winter. First, when the Sun is most nearly overhead (when the angle between the horizon and the Sun is vertical or nearly so), the ground gets hottest; at sunrise and sunset, the angle from the horizon to the Sun is small and the ground does not get so hot. *(Why is it usually hotter at sunset than at sunrise?)* Second, when the daylight periods are longer there is more time for the Sun to warm the ground each day (see Figure 3.11). The second factor can be shown from other facts to be less important than the first.

QUESTION: Why do you think the angle of the Sun above the horizon might be more important than the amount of daylight? (Hint: What happens in the spring and summer near the North Pole?)

The angle of the Sun above the horizon at noontime is critical because that angle determines how much light (and, more relevant here, how much

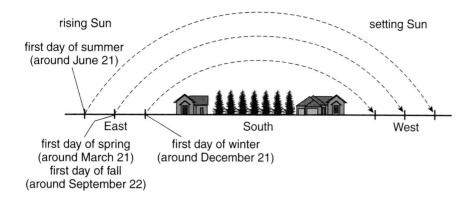

energy) is received from the Sun by a given patch of ground on the Earth. A given area will receive more light from the Sun the more nearly overhead the Sun is in the sky (Figure 3.12). The more sunlight that this patch receives, the hotter it gets. Also, the longer the Sun is above the horizon on a given day the longer it has to heat up the ground, although this factor is not nearly so important as the angle of the Sun above the horizon at noontime.

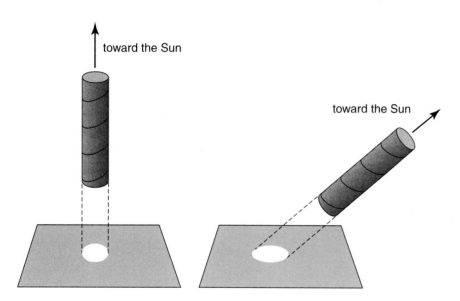

Figure 3.12
The paper towel tube is pointed directly at the Sun in both drawings. The same amount of sunlight enters the tube in both situations. In the right-hand drawing, the Sun is at an angle above the horizon of less than 90°, causing the sunlight to strike the ground in such a way so as to shine on a larger area than in the left-hand drawing, in which the Sun is overhead. Thus, in the right-hand drawing, the sunlight is spread out over a larger area, and therefore each unit of area receives less sunlight than in the situation shown in the left-hand drawing.

Why do the angle of the Sun above the horizon at noontime and the duration of daylight change throughout the year in a regular way? If you plot the path of the Sun against the stars, as seen from the playing field on the Earth, you will find that the Sun travels as far as 23.5° north of the celestial equator (see Figure 3.13)—when it is summer in the Northern Hemisphere and winter in the Southern Hemisphere—and as far as 23.5° south of the celestial equator—when it is winter in the Northern Hemisphere and summer in the Southern Hemisphere.

Since in Copernicus's model, the Sun isn't moving but the Earth is, this apparent behavior of the Sun must be produced by the Earth's motion. But what could the Earth be doing from the viewpoint of someone in the "stands" located on the Sun? One possibility is that the Earth is slowly wobbling as it spins, making the Sun appear to travel first above and then below

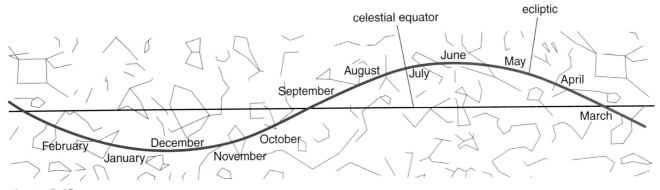

Figure 3.13
The path of the Sun against the background of the stars during the course of a year.

the celestial equator (see Figure 3.13). However, this wobble would also make the stars appear to move north and south as the Sun does, but the stars do not behave this way. Because this proposed behavior of the Earth does not predict what is actually observed, it is clearly wrong. Which model of the Earth's behavior predicts accurately the motions of both the Sun and the stars? It is a model that involves a moving Earth whose axis of spin is "tilted." But what does it mean to say that the spin axis of the Earth is tilted? You can think of the Earth as spinning around a line that passes through its North and South Poles. This line is often called the Earth's axis of rotation or axis of spin or just "axis," for short. If you watch for many years, you will find that the Earth's axis remains pointed in almost exactly the same direction in space. (How do you know? Hint: What do you know about the North Star?) Because the angle from the plane of the Earth's path around the Sun to the Earth's axis is not 90°, the Earth's axis is said to be "tilted." The angle from the plane of the Earth's path to the axis is about 66.5°, which is 23.5° from being at a right angle (90°) to the plane of the Earth's path (90° − 66.5° = 23.5°); the Earth's axis is therefore described as being tilted at an angle of 23.5°. Refer to Figure 3.14.

Figure 3.14
The plane of the Earth's orbit with the Earth's axis tipped 23.5° with respect to the perpendicular to this plane.

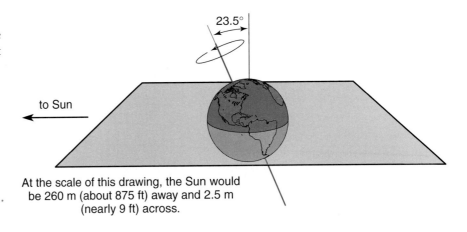

At the scale of this drawing, the Sun would be 260 m (about 875 ft) away and 2.5 m (nearly 9 ft) across.

It is not a coincidence that the "tilt angle" of the Earth's axis is the same as the maximum angle that the Sun can be from the celestial equator. Because the celestial equator is parallel to the Earth's equator, the celestial equator must be tilted with respect to the plane of the Earth's path around the Sun. Thus the path of the Sun on the CS does not follow the celestial equator, but instead follows the path (called the ecliptic) that you traced on your model of the CS in Activity 3.1.

Your model of the CS allows you to follow the changes in the path of the Sun across the sky from one time of the year to another and from one location on the Earth to another; Activity 3.3 provides you with the opportunity to do so. You can use the Copernican model to account for these observations, if you use the additional assumptions that (1) the Earth rotates about an axis whose direction is "fixed" in space; and (2) this axis is tilted with respect to a line at right angles (perpendicular) to the plane containing the Earth's path around the Sun.

QUESTION: The Earth's path around the Sun lies nearly on a circle (see Activity 3.2) with the Sun nearly at the center of the circle. What difference(s) would there be in the seasons if the Earth's axis were perpendicular to (aimed exactly 90° from) the plane containing the Earth's orbit? (See Figure 3.15.) Would the amount of daylight change from day to day? Explain why or why not.

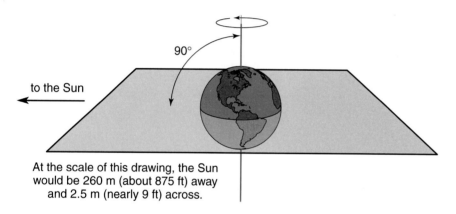

90°

to the Sun

At the scale of this drawing, the Sun would be 260 m (about 875 ft) away and 2.5 m (nearly 9 ft) across.

Figure 3.15
The Sun and the Earth for the *imaginary* case in which the Earth's axis is oriented 90° from the plane of the Earth's orbit.

QUESTION: Suppose the spin axis of the Earth pointed directly at the Sun on the first day of summer (Figure 3.16). Suppose further that, with respect to the stars, the direction of the Earth's spin axis remained fixed. Would the North Pole then always point at the Sun? How many hours of daylight would there then be at different times of the year at different places on the Earth, if the Earth continued to make one complete turn on its axis every 24 hours? What would happen to the seasons?

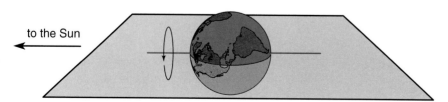

to the Sun

At the scale of this drawing, the Sun would be 260 m (about 875 ft) away and 2.5 m (nearly 9 ft) across.

Figure 3.16
The Earth's orbit for the *imaginary* case in which the Earth's spin axis pointed directly at the Sun on June 21.

Complications

The tilt of the Earth's axis of rotation is the main factor that determines the different yearly variations of temperature at different places on the Earth. But other factors also play roles in determining the temperature in particular places. For example, the oceans affect the temperature of coastal regions, because water warms and cools more slowly than does land; as the seasons progress from, say, spring to winter, the ocean will first warm more slowly than the land and then cool more slowly than the land.

You can observe the difference between land and water heating and cooling at a beach at a lake or at an ocean on a single day. For example, on a summer day, the unshaded sand on the beach will feel warmer than the water. Go wading at night (unless you've seen the movie Jaws) and you will notice that the water feels warmer than the sand. During the day, the sand's temperature may reach 35°C (95°F) with a water temperature of perhaps 25°C (77°F). At night, the water will still be about 25°C, but the sand may be only 20°C, around 70°F.

Changing wind patterns, particularly the "jet streams," north and south of the equator, also have a significant effect on seasonal temperatures, bringing air that is either cooler or warmer than average to these regions. Wind patterns in general affect the temperature, sometimes rather dramatically at unpredictable times around the globe, especially in the temperate regions, where most of the continental United States is located. What causes the wind patterns is a harder question to answer.

Thousands of years ago, large portions of the Earth were covered with ice. Before that time there was far less ice in the arctic and antarctic regions of the globe than now. Some people believe that increasing releases of carbon dioxide produced by burning coal, oil, and wood will lead to a heating of the entire Earth (the so-called "greenhouse" effect), making it more tropical in nature. Such global changes are very complex, but even much smaller changes, such as the year-to-year variations in average temperature and total precipitation are not easy to either understand or predict!

SUMMARY

The positions on the horizon of sunrise and sunset shift with the seasons, and the Sun does not necessarily pass overhead at noontime. The angular height of the Sun at noontime depends on the observer's latitude and on the date.

The North Star is approximately directly in line with the axis of rotation of the apparent dome of the sky; this fact can be observed visually or photographically. You can model the sky by using a device called the celestial sphere, which has an equator and poles. The celestial sphere allows you to model the changing seasons and daily motions you observe in the sky, including changes in the angular height of the Sun at noontime, and the differences throughout the year in the length of daylight.

The seasons are mainly caused by the spin axis of the Earth not being perpendicular to the plane of the Earth's orbit around the Sun. The Earth's spin axis is tilted 23.5° from this perpendicular. Because the Earth's axis is observed to be fixed in space, the Sun's apparent motion across the sky changes over the course of the year. It is the change in the angular height of the Sun at noontime that has the greatest effect on the seasons. The length of the daylight period is a secondary factor. The changing distance of the Earth from the Sun during a year, that is, the shape of the Earth's orbit, which is nearly circular, has no noticeable effect on the seasons.

HOMEWORK

1. Solar houses depend on the Sun for heat. In the winter, sunlight must get into the house to heat it. In the summer, sunlight should be kept out to keep the house cool. The fact that the Sun is at different angular heights in the summer and winter allows us to construct an eve or awning that will shut out the summer light, but let in the winter light. (Of course, the angular height of the Sun varies over the course of each day as the Sun rises and sets. This exercise focuses on the greatest angular height of the Sun on the 21st day of each of the months shown.)

   The drawing of the house at right shows light coming from the Sun at noontime for June, March and September, and December. Design an awning over the window or off the roof that will block most of the summer light and some of the March and September light from entering the house at noontime. The awning should allow as much winter light into the house as possible.

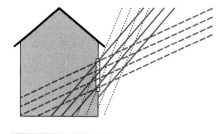

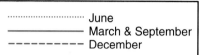

2. Imagine you are at the North Pole of the Earth. The imaginary hemisphere above the North Pole represents the entire sky above you. Using your hemisphere from Activity 1.2, sketch what you think is the path of the Sun on the following dates:

   a) June 21   c) December 21

   b) September 22   d) March 21

3. A camera is pointed at the North Star and the shutter remains open for several hours.

   a) Use the sketch at right of six stars' positions to show the appearance of the resulting photo. What do the traces in the photo have in common?

   b) If you measured the length of a trail in such a photo to be 30°, what was the duration of the time exposure?

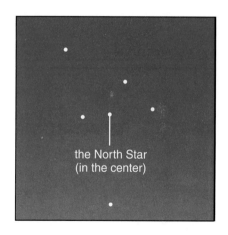

the North Star
(in the center)

4. A star lies at a position on the celestial sphere that is 25° north of the celestial equator. An observer at 40° north latitude watches the star for an evening.

   a) Where, north or south with respect to the west point on the observer's horizon, does the star set?

   b) What is the angle of the star above the horizon when it is directly south of the observer?

5. Where is the position of the Sun on the ecliptic (north or south) with respect to the position of the celestial equator in the evening sky during

   a) summer?   b) winter?

SELF-TEST

1. How many days each year does the Sun rise exactly in the east and set exactly in the west?

2. Describe the difference between the sunrise and sunset points in March, June, September, and December. Explain why the sunrise point changes.

3. If you observed a particular star 24 hours after you had seen it the day before, would its position with respect to a landmark on the horizon be the same as, slightly more toward the east, or slightly more toward the west than where you saw it the day before? Would the length of time between two consecutive risings of a star be longer or shorter than 24 hours? Why?

4. Since the Northern Hemisphere of the Earth experiences summer when the Southern Hemisphere experiences winter, it is unreasonable to assume that the distance from the Sun affects the seasons, since both the summer and winter areas are virtually the same distance from the Sun. What is the primary reason for the seasons?

5. What is the difference in the angular height of the Sun at noontime on June 21 and its angular height at noontime on December 21? Explain your answer.

6. Why does the Sun's position relative to the celestial equator change?

Scientific Notation

This book often uses "scientific notation." Scientific notation allows you to more easily understand the size of a number and to work with it conveniently. It is nothing but a shorthand for writing numbers. The number 1,000 can be written as $10 \times 10 \times 10$, or, in scientific notation, as 10^3. The 3 is called the exponent of 10. (The number 10^3 can also be read as 10 to the third power, or just 10 to the third.) Look at another number: 1,054,632,211. It is not easy to tell how big this number is. One way is to count the number of digits, starting at the decimal point of the number and moving to the left until only one digit, the last digit on the left, has not been counted. The resulting number is 9. In scientific notation this number is therefore expressed in the following way: 1.054632211×10^9. Now you can understand the size of this number more easily—it is approximately 1×10^9 or about one billion.

Another advantage of scientific notation is that it allows you to replace multiplication and division with addition and subtraction. For example, how many times larger is 100,000,000,000 than 10,000,000? You could find the answer by dividing 100,000,000,000 by 10,000,000. This process can be a bit tedious, but using scientific notation, it is easier. $100,000,000,000. = 10^{11}$ and $10,000,000. = 10^7$. You can divide the first number by the second number by subtracting the exponents: $11 - 7 = 4$. The first number is 10^4 (10,000) times larger than the second. Note that the exponent for each number is equal to the number of digits (in this case all of them are zeroes) between the decimal point and the first digit. In a similar fashion, you can obtain the result of multiplying two numbers by adding their exponents. To multiply 100,000,000 by 100,000, first convert the numbers into scientific notation: $100,000,000. = 10^8$ and $100,000. = 10^5$. Now add the exponents: $8 + 5 = 13$. The answer is thus 10^{13}, or 10,000,000,000,000.

Scientific notation provides a convenient way of comparing the sizes of very small as well as very large numbers. For very small numbers, the rule for changing them to scientific notation is slightly different. To change a number less than one to scientific notation, you count the number of zeroes after the decimal point and before the first nonzero digit and then add one. Consider 0.0000003. Here there are six zeroes between the decimal point and the first nonzero digit, so you add one to the six and write this small number as 3 x 10^{-7}. The exponent is –7 and you say, "ten to the exponent minus seven" or, more simply, "ten to the minus seven." Suppose the number were 0.000203. How would you write it in scientific notation? First, count the number of zeroes between the decimal point and the first nonzero digit. The answer is 3. So you add one to the three, and write this number in scientific notation as 2.03 x 10^{-4}. Remember this rule for changing numbers is just a shorthand; no new mathematics is involved. Practice with a number of examples of multiplication and division with very small and very large numbers to convince yourself that the rule always "works." What about addition and subtraction? Does scientific notation make these easier? Why or why not?

EXAMPLE 1: Using scientific notation, multiply 20,000,000 by 30,000. First, convert the numbers into scientific notation. 20,000,000 = 2×10^7 and 30,000 = 3×10^4. Next, multiply the two numbers by adding their exponents. In this case, 7 + 4 = 11. You must also multiply 2 times 3: 2×3 = 6. (These numbers are not exponents and are therefore multiplied in the usual way, not added.) The answer is 6×10^{11}.

EXAMPLE 2: Using scientific notation, divide 4,500,000,000. by 0.0005. Converting the numbers to scientific notation, 4,500,000,000. = 4.5×10^9 and 0.0005 = 5×10^{-4}. To divide numbers in scientific notation subtract the exponents: 9 – (–4) = 9 + 4 = 13. You must also divide 4.5 by 5: 4.5/5 = 0.9. The answer is 0.9×10^{13}, which can also be written as 9×10^{12}. Changing 0.9 to 9 involves multiplying by 10. If you multiply one part of a number by 10, you must divide the other part by 10 so as not to change the value of the original number. Dividing the other part by 10 is the same as subtracting one from the exponent, changing it from 13 to 12. To check that the number has not changed, note: $0.9 \times 10^{13} = 9 \times 10^{12} = 9,000,000,000,000$.

QUESTION 1: Divide 2,560,000 by 0.0032. (The answer is 8×10^8.)

QUESTION 2: Divide 350,000,000 by 80,000. (The answer is 4.375×10^3.)

ACTIVITY 3.1 BUILDING A CELESTIAL SPHERE

PURPOSE

To construct a celestial sphere to model the apparent motions of the Sun and stars in the sky.

MATERIALS

1 ruler
6 paper clips
1 thumbtack
1 foam block
1 protractor (the larger the better)
transparent tape
1 wooden dowel, 30 cm (12 in.) long
1 pair of scissors
1 star chart sheet (northern and southern stars)
2 plastic hemispheres
1 2.5-cm (1-in.) ball (or small Earth globe, if available)
1 plastic drinking straw
colored marking pens (transparency pens work best)
1 map pin, yellow-headed
1 sheet construction paper, 30 cm × 45 cm (12 in. × 18 in.)

PROCEDURE

A. Cut out the two star charts with the scissors. Cut along the *outside lines* only. When it is cut out, each star chart should look like a flower with eight black petals.

B. Place the chart of the southern sky inside one of the plastic hemispheres with the printed side facing up. *Carefully* align the chart so the ends of the *ecliptic* (the line that crosses each of the chart's "petals") touch the base of the hemisphere at *two opposite ridges*. Secure the chart by placing the other hemisphere over the star chart and pushing it against the first hemisphere (see Figure 3.17A). Make sure that the ridges of both hemispheres match.

C. Have your teacher check this "hemisphere/star chart sandwich" before you continue to the next step.

D. Tape the edges of the two hemispheres together.

E. Mark the stars on the *inside* of the *inner* hemisphere with the marking pen (Figure 3.17B). Also, draw the lines that mark the ecliptic and some brighter constellations. (You may wish to use different color pens for the ecliptic and the constellation lines.) The greater a star's apparent brightness, the bigger is the symbol used to represent it.

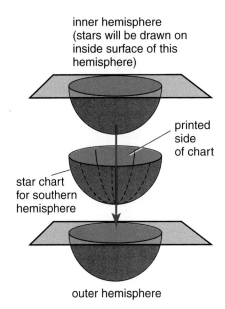

inner hemisphere
(stars will be drawn on
inside surface of this
hemisphere)

printed
side
of chart

star chart
for southern
hemisphere

outer hemisphere

Figure 3.17A

Figure 3.17B

F. When you have marked all the stars, separate the hemispheres and remove the star chart. Repeat steps B–E with the northern star chart and the unmarked hemisphere (the "outer" hemisphere in Figure 3.17A). Confirm that the ecliptic lines touch the base at opposite ridges. Use the hemisphere you have already marked to secure the chart in place.

G. Have your teacher check this "sandwich."

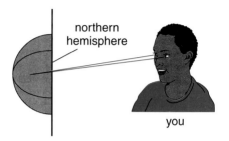

northern hemisphere

you

Figure 3.18

H. Look into the opening of the northern hemisphere (see Figure 3.18).

1. *What star is found in the center of the northern hemisphere?*

2. *What pattern of stars can be used to help you locate this star?*

The constellations with lines on the northern hemisphere are Leo, Gemini, Taurus, Pegasus, Cassiopeia, Cygnus with the Summer/Fall Triangle, the Big Dipper (an easily recognized pattern, not a true constellation), and the northern half of Orion. The lined constellations on the southern hemisphere are Scorpius, Sagittarius, Canis Major, the Southern Cross, the southern half of Orion, and the stars Alpha and Beta Centauri. See Appendix 1 for the pronunciation of constellation names.

Figure 3.19

straw

straw

I. Slide the Earth globe to the center of the wooden dowel. Cut the drinking straw into two pieces, each 7.5 cm (3 in.) long. Slide these two pieces of straw over each end of the dowel (see Figure 3.19).

J. With the thumbtack, make a small hole through the center of both hemispheres (where the ridges cross). Slide the two star hemispheres onto the dowel with the southern hemisphere of the small Earth globe facing into the southern bowl of stars and the northern Earth globe facing into the northern bowl of stars. See Figure 3.20.

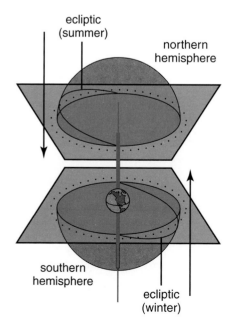

ecliptic (summer)

northern hemisphere

southern hemisphere

ecliptic (winter)

Figure 3.20

K. Rotate the hemispheres until *the points where the ecliptic touches the equator match on both hemispheres.* The ecliptic should completely encircle the sphere and should pass both above and below the equator as shown in Figure 3.21.

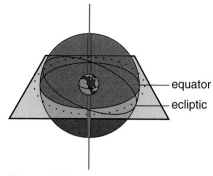

equator
ecliptic

Figure 3.21

L. Tape the edges of your two spheres together. Trim the rim of the plastic sphere leaving the plastic bumps. Make sure that the hemispheres are still aligned as in step K; if not, realign and tape the trimmed spheres together again. See Figure 3.22.

Figure 3.22

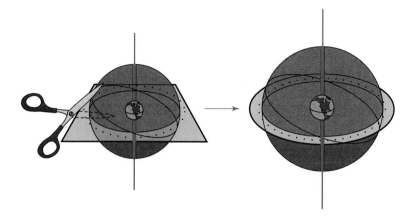

M. The clear plastic sphere should rotate freely on the dowel; the Earth globe should be at the center of the sphere with North America facing up; and the northern hemisphere should be on the upper half of the sphere.

N. Hold the protractor upright with its flat edge on the foam block. Line up the dowel with the line on the protractor indicating the angle of your latitude. Push the dowel into the foam block at this angle. Be careful to place the celestial sphere in the block so that the Earth globe is over the block; this will help keep the celestial sphere from tipping over. See Figure 3.23.

O. Measure the height of the center of the Earth globe above the tabletop. Cut two strips of construction paper, each with a width equal to the height of the Earth globe above the table. Tape the pieces together to make a strip of paper 80 cm to 90 cm (about 35 in.) long. *Cut these strips evenly!*

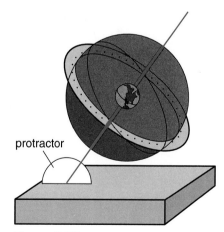

protractor

Figure 3.23

P. Refer to Figure 3.24. Connect the ends of the long strip together with paper clips to form a loop. The top edge of the construction paper loop represents the *horizon*, the imaginary circle one sees where the sky "touches" the Earth. The celestial sphere should be able to sit inside of the paper loop. Make any necessary adjustments of the paper clips to tighten the horizon around the sphere. The top edge of the loop, which represents the horizon, should be at the same height above the table as the center of the Earth globe.

Figure 3.24

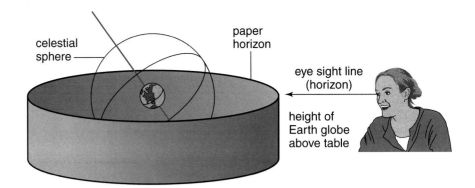

Q. On the upper, outside edge of the paper collar, at the point directly beneath where the dowel sticks out from the upper part of the sphere, place an "N" for north. On the paper horizon opposite N, place an S for south. Looking down on the horizon, go clockwise halfway from N to S; mark this point E for east. Opposite E, place a W for west.

R. Save the yellow pin, paper horizon, and celestial sphere for later activities. The celestial sphere will be used in this and a later activity to help you describe, explain, and predict the motions of the Sun and the stars in the sky. You will now identify certain reference points and lines on your celestial sphere, with the help of the following figures.

Refer to Figure 3.25. There are imaginary points such as the **north** and **south celestial poles** (**NCP** and **SCP**) and an imaginary line such as the celestial equator positioned on this sphere. The Earth is located at the sphere's center. Currently, the north celestial pole is very close to a star called Polaris (see Chapter 2).

Refer to Figure 3.26. The **ecliptic** is the apparent annual path of the Sun on the celestial sphere. Notice that the ecliptic is tilted relative to the celestial equator. The Sun passes the highest point on the ecliptic on the summer solstice, and the lowest point on the winter solstice. The Sun passes midway between the solstices on the vernal (spring) and autumnal (fall) equinoxes. As the Sun appears to move across the sky, it passes through a band of constellations known as the **zodiac**.

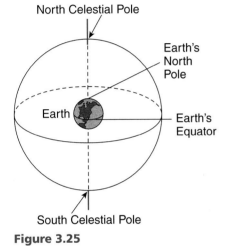

Figure 3.25

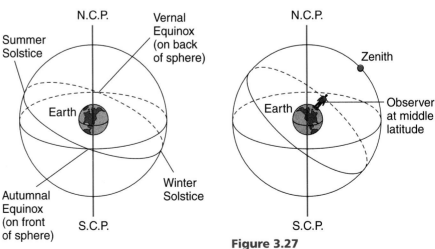

Figure 3.26

Figure 3.27

Refer to Figure 3.27. The point directly over the head of the observer is called the **zenith**. The **horizon** is located 90° in every direction away from the observer's zenith. If the observer were standing on a flat desert plain or in a boat on a calm sea, the horizon would be the circle where the sky "meets" the land or water.

Figures 3.25, 3.26, and 3.27 are related to the celestial sphere that you have just built. The dowel that passes through the globe is the vertical line in Figures 3.25, 3.26, and 3.27. The point where the dowel comes out of the northern hemisphere is the **north celestial pole**; the point where the dowel goes into the southern hemisphere is the **south celestial pole**. The **celestial equator** is where the two hemispheres are fastened. The **horizon** is the top edge of the paper collar. The **ecliptic** is the circle made by the arcs drawn on the inside of each hemisphere.

ACTIVITY 3.2   MODELING THE SUN'S APPARENT MOTION

PURPOSE

To use the celestial sphere to model the apparent motions of the Sun and stars in the sky.

PART A   MODELING THE SUN'S APPARENT DAILY MOTION

MATERIALS

      celestial sphere with accessories from Activity 3.1
      plastic hemisphere with observations from Activity 1.2

PROCEDURE

A. On the ecliptic, locate the date that you made the observation in Activity 1.2. Stick the pin into your celestial sphere at this date.

B. Place the horizon collar around the celestial sphere. Be sure the collar's north point is properly aligned with the sphere's dowel ("axis"). Rotate the sphere and collar together until "south" on the collar faces you.

C. Look at the sphere along a horizontal line level with the top of the collar and the Earth globe. Turn the sphere on its axis until the Sun marker is level with the top of the right side of the collar. This is the sunrise position for the date from Activity 1.2.

D. Slowly rotate the sphere from east to west (clockwise, as viewed from above the north celestial pole) and watch the motion of the pin. When the pin is again level with the top of the collar, it is at the *sunset* position.

The celestial sphere is a model of the sky. Turning the sphere on its axis represents the Earth turning on its axis. One complete rotation of the sphere, therefore, corresponds to 24 hours. There are 24 bumps on the otherwise flat surface at the sphere's equator, each indicating 1 hour of time.

1. *Turn the sphere to move the Sun marker from sunrise to sunset. Count the bumps that pass the western horizon. The result is the number of hours of daylight for the day in Activity 1.2.*

   a) *About how many hours of daylight were there in that day?*

   b) *What fraction of a 24-hour day is represented by the turn you gave the sphere?*

   c) *From an astronomy web site, newspaper, or your teacher, obtain the daylight period at your location for the date you did Activity 1.2. How did that time compare with the sphere time?*

2. *Compare the path of the Sun as demonstrated with your celestial sphere to the path you plotted on the hemisphere in Activity 1.2.*

3. *Set the celestial sphere for 2 hours after sunset for the date you did Activity 1.2.*

   a) *Name a constellation visible on that date in the southern sky.*

   b) *Name a constellation near the zenith.*

   c) *Describe the position of the Big Dipper in the sky.*

   d) *Name a constellation that is just rising. Specify the direction from which it is rising.*

   e) *Name a constellation that is below the horizon and cannot be seen at this time.*

EXTENSIONS

1. On the hemisphere from Activity 1.2, plot the apparent daily motion of the Sun on several days throughout the school year and use the celestial sphere to explain these apparent motions of the Sun.

PART B MODELING THE SUN'S APPARENT MOTION ON THE CELESTIAL SPHERE

MATERIALS

    celestial sphere with accessories
    journal from Activity 1.3
    tape
    protractor

PROCEDURE

Figure 3.28 shows a side view of the celestial sphere at the summer solstice as seen from a latitude of 42° north. Using Figure 3.28 as a sample, position your celestial sphere and horizon collar to correspond with your home latitude.

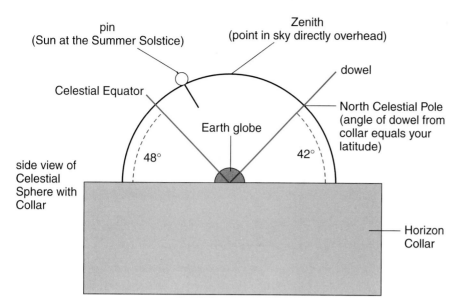

Figure 3.28

pin
(Sun at the Summer Solstice)

Zenith
(point in sky directly overhead)

dowel

Celestial Equator

North Celestial Pole
(angle of dowel from
collar equals your
latitude)

Earth globe

side view of
Celestial
Sphere with
Collar

48°

42°

Horizon
Collar

A. Adjust the dowel in the foam block so the celestial sphere is set for your latitude. If your teacher approves, tape the foam block to the top of the table for stability.

B. When drawing, always observe the celestial sphere with your eyes at the level of the Earth globe and the top edge of the paper horizon. Place north to your right. To answer questions 1–24 , refer to the following instructions and Figure 3.28. Draw copies of Figure 3.29 and use the copies for the drawings described below.

1) Draw the dowel. Indicate the north celestial pole (NCP) and the horizon.

2) Starting from the right-hand side of the collar in the figure (as in Figure 3.28), measure the angle between the NCP and the northern horizon. This angle is equal to your latitude. Place the protractor on the diagram with the vertex of this angle at the center of the Earth globe.

3) Draw the celestial equator. This line forms a 90° angle with the NCP.

4) Measure the angle between the celestial equator and the paper collar horizon. Label this angle on the diagram.

5) Draw the position of the Sun above the horizon at noontime on June 21. Label this position as the summer solstice.

C. Position the Sun marker on the ecliptic line of the celestial sphere at the point of the summer solstice, June 21. Be sure the compass points of the horizon's collar are lined up properly with the sphere. Viewing horizontally at the same height as the top of the collar, set the Sun marker even with the top edge of the east side of the horizon collar. This position corresponds to sunrise. Turn the sphere clockwise (as viewed from overhead) until the Sun is level with the horizon on the

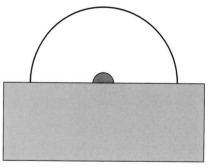

Figure 3.29

The Celestial Sphere: A Model of the Sky ✳

other side of the collar. This movement represents the apparent motion of the Sun from sunrise to sunset on June 21.

1. *What was the general direction of sunrise?*

2. *What was the general direction of sunset?*

3. *Turn the sphere to move the Sun marker from sunrise to sunset. Count the number of bumps that pass the western horizon. This number represents the hours of daylight. How many hours of daylight are there on June 21?*

4. *Figure 3.29 represents a side view of your celestial sphere. On your copy of the figure, draw and label the approximate position of the celestial equator, NCP, and the Sun's position above the horizon at noontime on June 21. (Noontime occurs when the Sun is halfway between its rising and setting positions or when the Sun is at its highest point in the sky for that day.)*

5. *What pattern of stars will be close to zenith just after sunset?*

6. *What pattern is close to the zenith at 1 a.m.?*

D. Place the Sun on the ecliptic at the autumnal equinox, September 22. Set the Sun marker even with the top edge of the east side of the horizon collar when viewed horizontally. Turn the sphere clockwise until the Sun is level with the horizon on the other side of the collar. This movement represents the apparent motion of the Sun from sunrise to sunset on September 22.

7. *What was the general direction of sunrise?*

8. *What was the general direction of sunset?*

9. *How many hours of daylight are there on September 22?*

10. *On another copy of Figure 3.29, draw and label the position of the celestial equator, the NCP, and the Sun at noontime on September 22. Label the Sun's position as the autumnal equinox.*

11. *What constellations are visible close to the southern horizon just after sunset?*

12. *Describe the location of Cygnus in the sky just after sunset.*

E. Place the Sun on the ecliptic at the winter solstice, December 21. Set the Sun marker even with the top edge of the east side of the horizon collar when viewed horizontally. Turn the sphere clockwise until the Sun is level with the horizon on the other side of the collar. This movement represents the apparent motion of the Sun from sunrise to sunset on December 21.

13. *What was the general direction of sunrise?*

14. *What was the general direction of sunset?*

15. *How many hours of daylight are there on December 21?*

16. *On another copy of Figure 3.29, draw and label the position of the celestial equator, the NCP, and the Sun at noontime on December 21. Label the Sun's position as the winter solstice.*

17. *What constellations will be rising from the east just after sunset?*

18. *What constellation will just be setting in the northwest about midnight?*

F. Place the Sun on the ecliptic at the vernal equinox, March 21. Set the Sun marker even with the top edge of the east side of the horizon collar when viewed horizontally. Turn the sphere clockwise, until the Sun is level with the horizon on the other side of the collar. This movement represents the apparent motion of the Sun from sunrise to sunset on March 21.

19. *What was the general direction of the sunrise?*

20. *What was the general direction of the sunset?*

21. *How many hours of daylight are there on March 21?*

22. *On another copy of Figure 3.29, draw and label the position of the celestial equator, the NCP, and the Sun at noontime on March 21. Label the Sun's position as the vernal equinox.*

23. *Describe the location of Orion in the sky just after sunset.*

24. *What constellation is high in the southern sky at 9:00 p.m.?*

DISCUSSION QUESTIONS

1. a) Does the Sun always rise exactly from the east?

   b) List the direction of sunrise at the beginning of each season: summer, winter, autumn, and spring.

2. a) Does the Sun always set exactly in the west?

   b) List the direction of sunset at the beginning of each season: summer, winter, autumn, and spring.

3. Compare the results from this activity with the data you collected in the sunset journal (Activity 1.3).

   a) Were your observations consistent with the data from your celestial sphere model?

   b) Describe how the direction of sunset changed from the beginning of autumn to the beginning of winter.

   c) Use your celestial sphere to predict how your sunset journal would look for the next 3 months. Draw your predictions.

4. How did the number of daylight hours change from the

   a) summer solstice to the autumnal equinox?

   b) autumnal equinox to the winter solstice?

   c) winter solstice to the spring equinox?

   d) vernal equinox to the summer solstice?

5. What is the difference between the number of hours of daylight for the day with the longest period of daylight and the number for the day with the shortest period of daylight?

6. Describe the changes in the noontime position of the Sun from

    a) summer solstice to autumnal equinox?

    b) autumnal equinox to winter solstice?

    c) winter solstice to vernal equinox?

    d) vernal equinox to summer solstice?

7. Was the Sun ever directly overhead at noontime for your location? If so, on what date(s)?

8. Describe the location in the sky of the constellation Orion at *sunset* for the beginning of each season: summer, winter, autumn, and spring.

QUESTIONS TO TEST YOURSELF

1. If the Sun sets in the northwest as viewed from the continental United States, what season is it?

2. If the Sun sets in the northwest, from what direction did it rise on that day?

3. On a diagram similar to Figure 3.29, draw the celestial equator and the NCP for your location on the Earth. Mark and label the positions for the Sun's noontime locations for both of the equinoxes and the solstices.

    a) Put an "X" at the position of the Sun at noontime on November 23.

    b) How many hours of daylight are there on November 23?

    c) Where in the sky would the constellation Sagittarius be found at sunset on November 23?

4. On or about which day of the year would the constellation of Cygnus be rising at sunset?

5. Describe the motion of the Big Dipper and Cassiopeia in the sky during a 24-hour period.

EXTENSIONS

1. Research and write about how open-air athletic stadiums are designed to account for the changing position of the daytime Sun for various seasons of the year.

2. Research and write about passive solar houses and buildings.

3. Research and write about how various technologies can and are being used to harness solar energy.

ACTIVITY 3.3   MODELING THE REASONS FOR THE SEASONS

PURPOSE

To plot the distance from the Earth to the Sun and examine the reasons for
the seasons.

WHAT DO YOU THINK?

Figure 3.30 shows two pictures of the Sun taken 6 months apart with the
same camera, at the same time of day, from the same location.

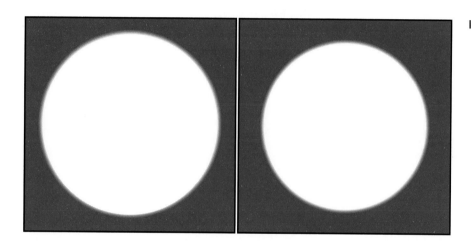

Figure 3.30

P1. *Are the images of the Sun the same size?*

P2. *If they are not the same size, how could you explain the difference?*

P3. *In which month of the year do you think each picture was taken?*

P4. *In which month or months of the year is your weather the warmest?*

MATERIALS

1 metric ruler	calculator
Chart 3.1	pencil
Graph 3.1 or 3.2 (metric or	felt-tip pen
English version, depending	
on teacher's instructions)	

PROCEDURE

A. Look at Chart 3.1 (adapted from photographs of the Sun published by
R.A.R. Tricker in *Paths of the Planets*). Each rectangle is a section taken
through the middle of the Sun from a larger picture. See Figure 3.31.

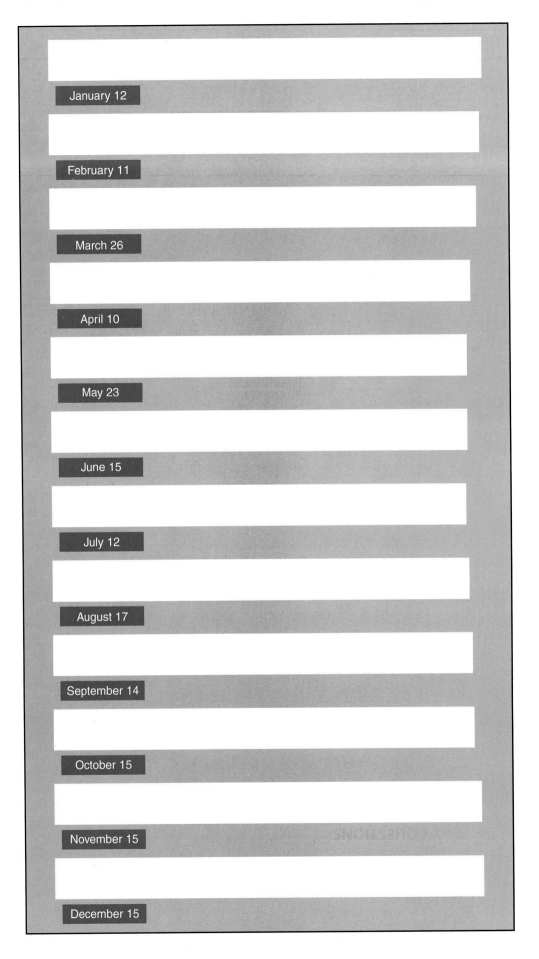

Chart 3.1

✳ The Universe in Your Hands

B. Measure the length of each rectangle to the nearest tenth of a centimeter and record your measurements. Make sure you keep track of which length goes with which date!

C. For the specific date of each strip, calculate the distance to the Sun by *dividing* the conversion factor (provided by your teacher) by the length of each strip.

D. Record the distance to the Sun corresponding to each measured diameter. Again, keep track of which distance goes with which diameter.

E. Plot the distance of the Earth from the Sun for each date on Graph 3.1 (or Graph 3.2 if you use miles). Because the dates of the strips are not at the beginning of each month, you will have to estimate the position of the Earth for each date on the graph.

F. Connect the points on the graph with a smooth curve. Use a pencil first, then trace over this penciled curve with a felt-tip marker.

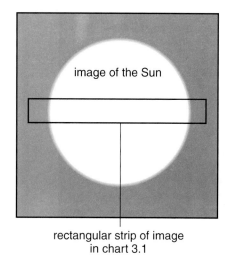

rectangular strip of image
in chart 3.1

Figure 3.31

DISCUSSION QUESTIONS

1. What does this curve tell you about the Earth's orbit?

2. In what month is the Earth farthest from the Sun?

3. In what month is the Earth closest to the Sun?

4. Compare the answers from the two previous questions to your predictions regarding Figure 3.30.

   From your measurements, calculations (step C), and Graph 3.1 or 3.2, answer the following questions:

5. Describe what your graph shows.

6. What conclusions can you draw from the observation that the Sun has a different apparent size in the summer than in the winter?

7. Do the months of your warmest weather include the month when the Earth is closest to the Sun?

Distances, Sizes, and Angles

HOW BIG IS IT?

Some common objects are listed below in the left-hand column. Imagine holding each of these objects at arm's length and comparing its apparent size to the apparent size of each of the celestial objects listed in the right-hand column. Which of the objects held at arm's length would most closely match in apparent size with each of the celestial objects? (There will not be a match for every object in the left-hand column.)

an aspirin	the Moon
a nickel	the Sun
a quarter	the Big Dipper
a tennis ball	Orion
a Frisbee	

Before the next class meeting, go outside in both the daytime and the nighttime (but not alone) with the five objects listed above and compare their apparent sizes when held at arm's length to the apparent size of each celestial object that you can locate. Were you surprised? If so, by what?

Do *not* look directly at the Sun.

CAUTION

LOOKING AT THE FULL MOON

Get a calendar or almanac and find the date of the next full Moon.

If it is clear on that evening, go outside shortly after sunset and look for the Moon. You should see it rising.

How much of your hand, held out at arm's length, do you think will just barely cover the Moon? **Now try it.** *What did you find out?*

Wait 3 or 4 hours. Go back outside (again, not alone) and find the Moon.

Now how much of your hand do you think will just barely cover the Moon? Try it. What did you discover? Were you surprised?

Preview: You will learn how to describe the apparent size of an object using two methods: (1) size/distance ratio, and (2) angular size. You will also learn how your ability to see distant objects is related to their size/distance ratios and angular sizes.

How Big?

"How big does the Moon appear to be?" Because you have observed the Moon on a regular basis (Activity 2.1), this might seem to be a simple question to answer. But is it? When asked this question, some people say that the Moon looks as big as a basketball. What does this answer tell you about the size of the Moon? Not much, since there is no indication of how far away from you the basketball has to be for the Moon to appear to be the same size as the ball. And therein lies the problem addressed in this chapter: How to describe the apparent size of an object, that is, how big an object appears to be.

NOTE: An object's "apparent" size is not the same as its actual size. If a building is 100 m (330 ft) tall, then its height is 100 m; no matter how far away you are from the building, the building's height is 100 m. If you looked at the building while standing within arm's reach of it, the building would be the only object that you could see—it would "fill" your field of view. (Your field of view is the entire scene visible to you without moving your head or your eyes.) But if you looked at the building from a distance of 5 km (3 mi), you would see other objects, not just the building—the building would occupy a smaller part of your field of view. The building's "apparent" size would thus be smaller. However, the building's actual size would be unchanged.

The term "size" itself is vague; it can refer to the height, width, or length of an object. Size can also be an object's area, volume, or weight; it can even refer to the number of items in a group, for example, the number of students in your science class. Whenever "size" is used in this chapter in reference to a single object, it refers to the object's height, width, or length. For celestial objects, such as the Moon and Sun, size always refers to the object's diameter.

In using the apparent size of a basketball to describe the apparent size of the Moon, a difficulty is encountered in addition to the need to know the distance to the basketball. To use a comparison between the apparent sizes of the Moon and a basketball to find the apparent size of the Moon, you must know the diameter of the basketball as well as its distance from you. Although many people have either played with a basketball or seen one, not everyone knows its size, and most find it hard to imagine how "big" the ball would appear to be at a certain distance away. These difficulties suggest that some method other than a vague comparison of objects ("The Moon looks as big as a basketball") is necessary to describe the apparent size of the Moon.

Size/Distance Ratios

In Activity 4.1, you described the apparent size of an object (your little finger) using a ratio: the size of the object (the width of your little finger) divided by the distance from the observer to the object (the distance from your eye to your little finger, with arm outstretched). This ratio, called a size/distance ratio, is a useful way of describing how big an object appears to be. For most people, the size/distance ratio for the little finger is about 1/50. A size/distance ratio of 1/50 means that the little finger, with arm outstretched, is at a distance from the eye of 50 finger widths. Activity 4.1 also demonstrated that any object that has the same apparent size as your little finger also has the same size/distance ratio as your finger, so you can use your finger as a tool to measure the apparent sizes of other objects. For example, if a distant building appeared as high as the width of your little finger when your arm was outstretched, you would know that the building was at a distance from you of 50 times its height. If you knew the building's height, you could then calculate the distance to the building. If, instead, you knew the distance from you to the building, you could then calculate the building's height.

NOTE: Whenever "size/distance ratio" is used in this book in reference to a single object, the distance is the distance from the observer to the object and the size is the object's height, width, or length. Whenever "size/distance ratio" is used for two objects close to each other, "size" refers to the distance between them.

EXAMPLE 1: A boat is returning to port from a whale-watch cruise. A passenger on the boat is looking at the city skyline and observes that the tallest building in the city appears to be the same size as her little finger when she stretches her arm. Thumbing through a city guide, the passenger learns that the building is 180 m (590 ft) tall. How far is the boat from the building? (Assume the size/distance ratio for the passenger's finger is 1/50.)

Since the building's size/distance ratio matches that of the passenger's finger, the building is at a distance from the passenger of 50 times its height. The distance is therefore: 50×180 m $= 9,000$ m (9 km or about 5.5 mi).

EXAMPLE 2: Suppose the passenger on the whale-watch boat observed the 180-m tall building when it appeared one-half as high as the width of her little finger. Would the distance to the building be greater or less than when the building appeared as tall as the width of her finger?

Since the size/distance ratio (1/50) for the passenger's finger would not change (if she keeps her arm outstretched when observing), nor would the height of the building, then the distance between the boat and the building has to be greater than the distance when the building and finger appeared to be the same size. If the building appears to be one-half the size of the finger, then the building's size/distance ratio must be smaller than that of the finger. Why? Note that in the ratio, size is divided by distance. If

Table 4.1: Angular sizes and size/distance ratios	
angular size	**size/distance**
0.1°	1/573
0.2°	1/287
0.3°	1/191
0.4°	1/144
0.5°	1/115
0.6°	1/95
0.7°	1/82
0.8°	1/72
0.9°	1/64
1.0°	1/57
2.0°	1/29
3.0°	1/19
4.0°	1/14
5.0°	1/12
6.0°	1/10
7.0°	1/8
8.0°	1/7
9.0°	1/6
10.0°	1/5

the distance increases, but the size does not change, then the ratio must decrease. If the building appears to be one-half the width of the finger, then the distance to the building must not only be greater than in Example 1, the distance must be twice as great. Thus the size/distance ratio is halved to 1/100. The distance to the building is therefore: 100 × 180 m = 18,000 m (18 km or about 11 mi).

EXAMPLE 3: Suppose the passenger observed that the 180-m tall building appeared to be three finger widths tall. What would be the distance between the boat and the building? Try this one yourself. Hint: What is the building's size/distance ratio? *The distance is 3,000 m (3 km or about 2 mi).*

Angular Size

In Activity 1.1, you determined what shape to make your hand so that when your arm was outstretched, your hand could be used to measure an angle of 10°. This hand shape's apparent size can be described by the angle it represents: Your hand shape at arm's length has an angular size of 10°. Notice that you did not need either the distance from your eye to your hand or the size of your hand to determine the hand's angular size. However, an object's angular size and its size/distance ratio are related, as is discussed in the next section. Table 4.1 lists some angular sizes and the related size/distance ratios. Figure 4.1 illustrates that different sized objects placed at different distances can all have the same angular size.

The fact that an object's apparent size can be stated in terms of an angle is very useful to astronomers. The distance and size of an object outside of our solar system cannot be measured directly; such objects are too far away to be reached by spacecraft or radar signals. (The use of radar signals to measure the distances to objects within the solar system is discussed in Chapter 8.) If an object's distance or size cannot be measured, the object's size/distance ratio cannot be calculated. However, an object's angular size can be measured without knowing either the object's distance or its size. If you know the angular size of an object, you can use Table 4.1 to find its size/distance ratio, and if you know the distance to an object and its size,

Figure 4.1
Objects of different sizes placed at different distances can have the same angular size.

Is the Moon "Bigger" at Moonrise?

Many people who have seen the Moon rise, especially a full Moon, think that the Moon appears larger then than it does a few hours later. If the Moon did have a noticeably larger angular size when it rose, it would mean that the Moon was significantly closer to the observer at moonrise. Is this possible?

In Figure 4.2, an observer on the Earth at position 1 sees the Moon rise; the distance from the observer to the Moon is X. About 6 hours later, due to the Earth's rotation, the observer is at position 2; the distance from the observer to the Moon is now Y. Notice that the distance Y is shorter than the distance X. The difference between distances X and Y is nearly equal to the radius of the Earth, about 6,400 km (4,000 mi). Thus, the Moon is actually farther away from the observer at moonrise than it is 6 hours later. The Moon must therefore have a smaller angular size at moonrise than it does a few hours later. Why, then, does the Moon appear to be so large when it rises?

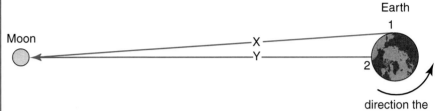

Figure 4.2
Relative positions of the Moon and an observer on the Earth at two different times, 6 hours apart. (This figure is not to scale and does not show the motion of the Moon in its orbit.)

Why indeed! Various models have been offered to explain this phenomenon, but none has been accepted by all scientists. One model is given below, but why the Moon appears to be bigger when it's rising is not well understood.

Model: At or shortly after moonrise, the Moon is near the horizon and is then visible near familiar objects (houses, trees, etc.). Your brain compares the Moon to the familiar objects and "sees" the Moon as being "big." In this model, your brain "sees" the Moon as being "big" because it does not have any direct experience involving the Moon's size and it therefore does not "know" the size of the Moon. (For example, you have never held the Moon or stood next to it.)

But your brain does have direct experience with houses and trees, and therefore "knows" how big they are. When you see the Moon with an angular size similar to, or larger than, the angular size of a house or tree, your brain "sees" the Moon as a "big" object. (It's as if your brain said, "Wow! The Moon's as big as a house!")

Exercise: You can directly measure the Moon's angular size by comparing it to some object held at arm's length. Make one measurement at moonrise and another one a few hours later; the angular size should not change noticeably. You may want to compare your results with those obtained by your classmates and discuss the results with your teacher.

you can use the table to find the object's angular size. You compared the size/distance ratios and angular sizes of different objects in Activity 4.3.

QUESTION: If you know the angular size of an object as well as its size, can you calculate the object's distance from you?

The Moon has an angular size of about 0.5°, as does the Sun. The fact that the Moon and the Sun have nearly the same angular size is just a coincidence—one that makes possible rare and spectacular total eclipses of the Sun. See Figure 4.3. That the Sun and Moon each has an angular size of 0.5° is another way of saying that they both have a size/distance ratio of 1/110. Any object at a distance from you equal to 110 times its diameter would appear to be the same angular size as the Sun or the Moon. Solar and lunar eclipses are discussed in more detail in Chapter 7.

Figure 4.3
A total solar eclipse.

Telescopes: Beyond the Limit

Another topic that can be discussed using size/distance ratios is your capability to see two objects as separate objects, rather than as one (blurred) object. For this discussion, we consider "size" to be the separation (distance apart) of the two objects and assume that the separation of the objects is much larger than the size of either object. Figure 4.4 illustrates this situation. Whether or not you can see two objects as separate objects or see them as one depends upon a characteristic of your eyes called the resolution limit. You determined the resolution limit for your eyes in Activity 4.2; there it was called the smallest size/distance ratio, because the resolution limit is the size/distance ratio for two objects that are barely detectable by you as two separate objects. At any greater distance, the two objects would appear as one. For a person with normal eyesight (or corrected to normal), the size/distance ratio for two such objects is about 1/3,300. Thus, for example, two small disks, 1 cm (0.4 in.) apart, should be just detectable as two objects

Figure 4.4
Two objects are shown separated by a distance ("size") represented by a dark bar. The distance from the observer to the objects is indicated by the arrows. Notice that the objects are separated by a distance much greater than their diameters (sizes).

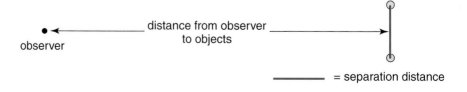

at a distance of 3,300 cm (33 m, or slightly more than 100 ft). The disks must have light shining on them, or be emitting their own light—see Chapter 5—to be visible to you. And they should not be "camouflaged"; for example, if the disks were yellow, they should not be in front of something that is also yellow.

Your ability to detect the shape of a distant object is also related to the resolution limit of your eyes. This limit is therefore especially important in astronomy. How is the detection of the shape of a single object similar to the detection of two neighboring objects as distinct? A single object can be thought of as being composed of smaller objects. For example, you can think of the full Moon as having a left side and a right side. The left and right sides of the Moon are separated by a distance approximately equal to the Moon's diameter. You already know that you can see the full Moon as a distinct shape. Why? Because the size/distance ratio for the two "objects," the left and right sides of the Moon, is greater than your resolution limit. In fact, the size/distance ratio for the left and right sides of the Moon is about 1/110. Since the separation of the two "objects" is approximately equal to the Moon's diameter, the size/distance ratio for the Moon itself can be used. In this way, the size/distance ratio for any object can be compared to your resolution limit to determine if the object, when visible, can be seen as a distinct shape by your unaided eyes.

All of the planets have size/distance ratios that are less than 1/3,300 as seen from the Earth, so they appear as points of light to the unaided eye, not as objects with distinct shapes. (Venus, the planet that approaches the Earth most closely, has a size/distance ratio of almost 1/3,300 at its nearest approach, so some people can detect a disk, or crescent-shaped, appearance for Venus with just their eyes. See Figure 4.5.) Because the planets are not generally detectable as distinct shapes to the unaided eye, features on planets are not detectable either: Any feature associated with a planet will have a size/distance ratio smaller than the planet and is therefore far smaller than the resolution limit of your eyes. Thus, trying to detect features on a planet is similar to trying to read the letters on a distant sign. If the sign is so far

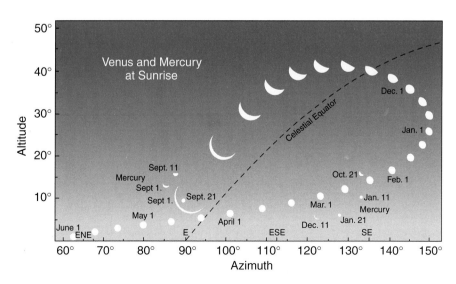

Figure 4.5
The positions and telescopic appearances of Mercury and Venus in the morning sky for September 1991 through June 1992. Venus appears as a crescent when it is nearest to the Earth; some people can then detect Venus's crescent shape with only their eyes.

away from you that you cannot tell what shape it is, you would also be unable to read the letters on the sign.

Telescopes are used to see the planets and the features on their surfaces or, in some cases, in their atmospheres. A telescope makes an object appear closer to you than it really is, effectively increasing the object's size/distance ratio so that it exceeds the resolution limit of your eyes. The ability of a telescope to "bring" an object closer is referred to as the telescope's magnifying power, or just "power." The more powerful a telescope is, the greater the size/distance ratios of the objects viewed or photographed through it, and the better the object can be seen.

Since 1959, space probes have traveled past the Moon, all of the planets (except Pluto), Comet Halley (rhymes with "valley"), and some asteroids. Cameras carried by these probes helped bring our eyes closer to these objects. In addition, humans have landed on the Moon, and automated probes with cameras have landed on Mars and Venus. However, for objects outside our solar system, such as stars and galaxies, telescopes are the only way to see them in any detail. You will explore telescopes more in Chapter 6 when you build and use your own.

SUMMARY

The apparent size of an object can be described by the ratio of its size to its distance from you. This ratio is called a size/distance ratio. The farther a given object is from you, the smaller is its size/distance ratio.

The apparent size of an object can also be described as an angle—its angular size. The size/distance ratio and angular size of an object are related: the smaller the object's size/distance ratio, the smaller is its angular size. This type of relation is called a direct relation. An object with a size/distance ratio of about 1/57 has an angular size of 1°.

The ability of your eyes to distinguish detail is based on a characteristic of your eyes known as the resolution limit. The resolution limit can be described as a ratio. If an object's size/distance ratio is equal to or greater than your resolution limit, you can distinguish the object's shape. A telescope functions to increase the size/distance ratios of objects, or their features, so that the ratios exceed your resolution limit.

HOMEWORK

1. The Moon (diameter about 3,500 km) has an angular size of about 1/2 degree. Suppose a crater 225 km in diameter is in the middle of the full Moon. What is the crater's angular size?

2. Assume that on a baseball field the distance from the pitcher's mound to home plate is 19 m and that a baseball has a diameter of 7 cm.

   a) What is the angular size of the baseball as seen by the batter, who is standing at home plate, just as the pitcher throws it?

   b) What is the angular size of the baseball as seen by the batter when the ball is just 1 m away?

3. Neptune is 30 times farther from the Sun than is the Earth (the Earth-Sun distance is about 150 million km). Use the smallest size/distance ratio that you can distinguish to determine whether the Sun would appear to you as a disk or as a point of light if you were at Neptune. (The Sun's diameter is about 1,400,000 km.) Show the work you do to answer the question.

4. Compute the angular size of the Earth as seen from the Moon knowing that the Earth's diameter is about 1.3×10^4 km and that the Moon is about 4×10^5 km from the Earth. How does the angular size of the Earth as seen from the Moon compare with the angular size of the Moon as seen from the Earth? How many times larger is the former than the later?

5. An artist claims that the picture below is not a trick drawing. He says he was standing 10 m away from this house when he drew this picture of the crescent Moon. Did he draw the picture accurately? (Or is this a very strange house?) How do you know?

SELF-TEST

1. Assume that the size/distance ratio for your little finger is 1 to 50. If you are far enough from a sailboat so that your finger width just matches the height of the 8-m-tall sail, how far are you from the boat?

2. If you are 100 m from a flagpole, and if the flagpole appears to be three finger widths high, what is the height of the pole? Use a size/distance ratio of 1/50 for your finger.

3. The size/distance ratio for an angular size of 1° is about 1/60. How far must you place a 22-cm diameter basketball from you so that it appears to be 1° across?

4. If the 22-cm basketball were 40 m away from you, what would be its angular size?

Christopher Columbus: The Case of the Distance to China and the Size of the Earth

You have probably been told that when Columbus wanted to set sail west across the Atlantic, he had a hard time finding money and help because everyone thought the Earth was flat and any ship sailing too far would fall off the edge. (When you were younger, you may have thought of the Earth as a flat place; if you look now, you still might think it looks reasonably flat.) However, this story about Columbus is a myth. Like you, Columbus went to school, and even before 1492 people who learned geography and navigation also learned that the Earth is shaped like a ball. Not as many people went to school then as now, but certainly most of the people Columbus talked to knew that he could not sail off the edge of the Earth. One popular textbook of that time had three proofs that the Earth was spherical. The simplest proof pointed out that when a ship approaches a harbor, the people watching it from land see only the top of the mast at first; the rest of the ship doesn't become visible until it comes closer. If the Earth were flat, all of the ship would be visible as soon as it came within sight.

When Columbus planned his journey, no one in Europe knew that the North and South American continents existed. They thought that the ocean stretched uninterrupted from the European coast all the way around the globe to the Chinese coast. The real problem Columbus had with getting support for his trip came from trying to convince people the world was small enough to make the journey possible. He thought that the world was smaller than it actually is and, therefore, that his ships could reach their goal within 3 months. Other people thought it was bigger, and that the trip would take much longer—too long to bring enough food and water to keep the sailors alive. If you look at a map or globe of the Earth, you can see that Columbus was wrong about how far he had to go to reach Asia. It took him about 2 months to reach the West Indies (islands south and east of the North American continent); imagine how much longer it would have taken him to reach China! Columbus never knew that the land he found was not in Asia.

Are you convinced that the Earth is shaped like a ball? Why or why not?

*Find Europe, North America, and China on a map or globe. Compare the distance from Europe to North America across the Atlantic with the distance from Europe to China across the Atlantic, North America, and the Pacific. About how many times greater is the distance Columbus would have had to have gone to have **really** landed in China, compared to the distance he actually sailed?*

ACTIVITY 4.1   ESTIMATING SIZE AND DISTANCE

PURPOSE

To estimate the distance to an object in terms of its size, or to estimate the size of an object in terms of its distance, using equipment always available: your outstretched arm and little finger.

WHAT DO YOU THINK?

P1. *If you hold out your hand at arm's length, what part or parts of your hand or fingers will just cover the full Moon?*

P2. *How many Moon diameters will fit into the distance between the Earth and the Moon?*

MATERIALS

tape
1 one-dollar bill
1 meterstick or tape measure

PROCEDURE

A. Tape a one dollar bill to a wall with the *short side* of the bill *parallel* to the floor. See Figure 4.6.

B. Stretch one arm out to full length and make a fist, palm up. Straighten your little finger, keeping the rest of your hand closed in a fist. Position your hand so that your little finger is straight up and down. With your arm stretched in front of you, close one eye.

C. Stand far enough from the dollar bill so that the width of the upper joint of your little finger appears to just cover the width of the dollar bill. See Figure 4.6. (Hereafter, use of "little finger" or "finger" should be understood to mean the *width* of the upper joint of the little finger.) Place a piece of tape on the floor to mark your position.

D. Have another person measure the distance from your finger to your eye.

Keep your arm straight and horizontal! Be careful when the ruler is near your eye!

Figure 4.6

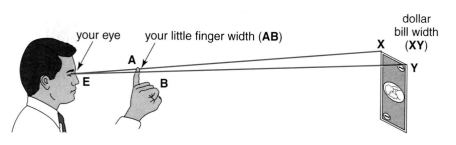

In Figure 4.6, the distance "AB" is the width of the upper joint of your little finger and the distance "XY" is the width of the bill. The distance from your eye to your finger is "EA" (or "EB") and the distance from your eye to the dollar bill is "EX" (or "EY").

1. *What is the distance from your finger to your eye in centimeters?*

E. Measure the width of the upper joint of your little finger.

2. *What is the width of your little finger in centimeters?*

F. Calculate the ratio of your "finger width" to your "eye-to-finger distance."

3. $\dfrac{\text{finger width}}{\text{eye-to-finger distance}} = ?$

The ratio of the size of your finger to its distance from your eye will be called the size/distance ratio for your finger width. This ratio is equal to one divided by the number of finger widths that fit into the distance between your eye and your finger. So, using the answer from question 3, you can state how many finger widths will fit into the distance between your eye and your finger.

G. Standing in the same position as in step C, have another person measure the distance from where you are standing (where your finger appears to just cover the dollar bill) to the dollar bill.

CAUTION   **Be careful when the ruler is near your eye!**

4. *What is the distance from your eye to the bill in cm?*

5. *What is the width of the bill in cm?*

6. *Calculate the ratio of your "dollar bill width" to the "eye-to-bill distance."*

$\dfrac{\text{dollar bill width}}{\text{eye-to-bill distance}} = ?$

How many dollar bill widths fit into the distance between you and the dollar bill (if you were standing at a position where your outstretched little finger just covers the dollar bill)?

7. *How "equal" to each other are your answers for questions 3 and 6?*

H. Repeat the procedure so that your partner can determine her or his own size/distance ratio for her or his finger width.

8. *Compare the size/distance ratio for your finger width to those of others in the class. What is the largest fractional difference between your ratio and that of another student? (For example, is the difference between your ratio and the other student's ratio one-tenth of your ratio?)*

I. Now stand at a position where the dollar bill is just covered by two little finger widths.

9. *Has the apparent size of the dollar bill increased, decreased, or stayed the same?*

10. *What is the distance between you and the dollar bill in centimeters?*

11. *How does the distance in question 10 compare to the distance found in your answer to question 4? Is it larger, smaller, or the same?*

J. Move to a position where the dollar bill is just covered by only half of your finger width.

12. *Has the apparent size of the dollar bill increased, decreased, or stayed the same?*

13. *What is the distance between you and the dollar bill in centimeters?*

14. *How does this distance compare to the distance found in your answer to question 4? Is it larger, smaller, or the same?*

K. Find an object outside your classroom window (such as a tree or a building) whose width you can just cover with the width of your little finger when your arm is fully extended.

15. *How many widths of the object would fit in the distance between you and the object?*

16. *Estimate the distance from you to the object in meters (m).*

17. *Measure the distance to the object directly. What is the result, in meters? How much different is it from your answer to question 16?*

L. Go outside on a clear night or day when the Moon is visible in the sky. Use your little finger with arm outstretched to measure the full diameter of the Moon.

18. *How many finger widths, or what fraction of a finger width, will just cover the Moon? (Even if the Moon is a crescent, you can estimate its full diameter by measuring from one tip of the crescent across to the other tip.)*

19. *Estimate the number of lunar diameters the Moon is away from you.*

20. *How do the answers to questions 18 and 19 compare with the predictions you made in questions P1 and P2?*

You now have a tool to determine the distance from you to some distant object if you know or can estimate the object's size. You can also determine the size of a distant object if you know or can estimate its distance from you. The homework questions are designed to help you practice using this tool.

HOMEWORK—SET A

FOR THESE QUESTIONS: *Use a size/distance ratio for a finger at arm's length of 1/50.*

1. You are standing in a park on a hill outside Boston, Massachusetts. At this position, the width of a little finger will just cover the height of the John Hancock building found in Boston. The visitor's guide to the city states that the Hancock building is 240 m (790 ft) tall. Estimate your distance from the building.

2. You are on a boat entering New York City Harbor. You observe that the towers of the World Trade Center appear about one little finger width tall. The guidebook to New York City states that the towers are 460 m (1,500 ft) tall. Estimate your distance from the towers.

3. You attend the launch of a space shuttle from Cape Canaveral, Florida. The observing site is 13 km (8 mi) from the launching pad. The shuttle (with fuel tank) appears about one-fourth of a little finger width tall. What is the height of the shuttle in meters?

   The distances to stars are so large that astronomers use the distance light travels in *1 year* as a unit of measure. This distance unit is called the *light-year* and equals 9.5 million million (9.5×10^{12}) km or about 6 million million (6×10^{12}) mi.

4. The Pleiades, a star cluster in the constellation of Taurus the bull, appears about one finger width big in the sky. If this cluster were about 7 light-years in diameter, how far away would the cluster be? Give your answer in light-years.

5. Another cluster in Taurus is the Hyades, which forms the "face" of the bull. This cluster appears to be about three fingers wide. If the Hyades were about 7 light-years in diameter, how many light-years would the Hyades be from us?

6. The only galaxy visible to people in the Northern Hemisphere is the Andromeda galaxy, in the constellation of Andromeda. The bright nucleus of the galaxy can be seen with the naked eye on a very clear, moonless night. This nucleus, which astronomers estimate to be about 30,000 light-years in diameter, appears about one finger width wide. How many light-years is this galaxy from us?

HOMEWORK—SET B

FOR THESE QUESTIONS: *Assume the Moon is 110 of its diameters away from the Earth.*

7. The picture at the left shows the Moon and Venus as they appeared together in the sky a few years ago.

   a) By taking measurements from the picture, determine the number of Venus diameters Venus is from the Earth.

   b) Given that the diameter of Venus is 12,100 km, what was the distance from the Earth to Venus when this picture was taken?

8. The largest apparent size of Mercury that we ever see in the sky is 1/150 the apparent diameter of the Moon. The diameter of Mercury is about 4,900 km. What is the closest that the Earth and Mercury approach each other?

9. On August 4, 1985, the Earth made its closest approach in 12 years to the planet Jupiter. The distance between the two planets was then about 600,000,000 km. Jupiter's image on a photograph taken then measured 1/40 of the apparent diameter of the Moon. Calculate the diameter of Jupiter in kilometers.

Photo by Byron Hogan, Clifton, NJ.

10. The above picture of the Moon and an airliner is a single photograph; it is not a double exposure. Is the airliner really almost as big as the Moon?

   a) Describe the situation that this photo recorded. Draw a diagram showing where the photographer, the plane, and the Moon were with respect to one another.

   b) What information would you need to determine the distance from the photographer to the plane? Try it! (Hint: A Boeing 747 airliner is about 80 m long.)

11. The picture below shows two photos of the Moon. One photo was taken when the Moon was closest to us and one when it was farthest from us. Measure the apparent diameter of the Moon in each photo.

   a) The diameter of the larger image is how many centimeters?

   b) The diameter of the smaller image is how many centimeters?

   c) The minimum distance from the Earth to the Moon is about 355,000 km (222,000 mi). Calculate the maximum distance from the Earth to the Moon.

ACTIVITY 4.2

SEEING DETAILS

PURPOSE

To determine the smallest distance that two objects can be separated and be distinguished by you as separate objects when you are a given distance from the objects.

WHAT DO YOU THINK?

P1. *How far could you get from a pair of headlights on a car before you began to see them appear together as a single blurred point of light?*

P2. *What is the diameter of the smallest crater that you can distinguish on the Moon?*

MATERIALS

Per team of two students
    Chart 4.1
    1 blank sheet of paper
    1 meterstick

PROCEDURE

Work in pairs for this activity.

A. Tape the "fantailed" Chart 4.1 to a wall in a well-lighted room.

B. Stand 10 m from the chart.

C. Have your partner hold a sheet of paper across the top edge of the chart. Tell your partner to move the paper very slowly down the chart, keeping the bottom of the paper horizontal. When you start to see the chart lines blur together just below the paper, tell your partner to hold the paper in place.

D. Your partner will read the line spacing printed on the chart nearest to the bottom of the paper.

1. Record this line spacing value in millimeters.

> *EXAMPLE*
> *When Ronnie, a typical student in a typical astronomy class, stood 10 m (10,000 mm) from the chart, she was just able to distinguish the separation of the lines spaced 3.0 mm apart. The smallest size/distance ratio Ronnie can distinguish is 3.0 mm (the line spacing) divided by 10,000 mm (the distance to the chart):*
>
> *3.0 mm/10,000 mm ≈ 1/3,300*
>
> *This ratio can be written as 1/3,300, the smallest size/distance ratio she can distinguish. This ratio is read as "1 to 3,300" and can also be written as 1:3,300. The smaller the size/distance ratio, the more detail your eyes can see.*

2. *What is the smallest size/distance ratio you can distinguish?*

E. Repeat steps B–D, standing at a different distance from the chart.

3. *What is the distance to the chart in meters?*

4. *Record the line spacing at which the chart lines blur.*

5. *What is the smallest size/distance ratio you can distinguish?*

6. *How do the answers to questions 2 and 5 compare? What is their fractional difference?*

Now you will determine how much detail your eyes can see when the lighting is dim.

F. Find a dark location where the lines on the chart are barely visible at a distance of 10 m.

G. Repeat steps B–D in this dark location, still standing 10 m from the chart.

7. *What is the smallest size/distance ratio you can distinguish?*

8. *How do the answers to questions 2 and 7 compare? What is their fractional difference?*

9. *Describe qualitatively how the amount of light affects your eyes' ability to see details.*

The size/distance ratio for your eyes determines how much detail you can see. Using the size/distance ratio method from Activity 4.1, you can estimate the "sharpness" (ability to see detail) of your eyesight. The example preceding question 2 gave a size/distance ratio of 1/3,300 for Ronnie. In Figure 4.7, E is the position of your eyes; X and Y are two side-by-side lights. Your distance from the lights is EX (or EY); the distance between the lights is XY.

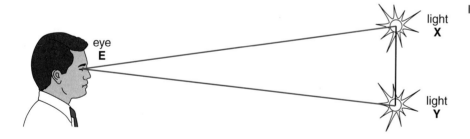

Figure 4.7

The smallest size/distance ratio Ronnie can distinguish shows that if she were closer than 3,300 m to the two lights separated by 1 m, she would see two separate lights. If she were farther away than 3,300 meters, she would see one light.

10. *How far apart would lights have to be for Ronnie to see two lights if she were standing 3,300 cm away from the lights?*

11. *How far apart would the lights have to be for Ronnie to see two lights if she were standing 6.6 km away from the lights?*

Use the smallest size/distance ratio you can distinguish to answer the following questions.

12. *What is the farthest you could be from two lights, separated by 1 cm, and still see them as two lights?*

13. *What is the farthest you could be from two lights, separated by 1 km, and still see them as two lights?*

14. *Describe how two lights, separated by 50 cm, would appear to you if you were standing 500 m from the lights. Show the work you do to solve this problem.*

15. *An automobile has headlights placed 1 m apart. If the car were driving toward you at night, how close to you would it have to be for you to tell it was a car and not a motorcycle?*

16. *The Moon is about 400,000 km (240,000 mi) from the Earth. What is the diameter of the smallest crater that you could distinguish on the Moon's surface?*

HOMEWORK

NOTE: **Be sure to put distances and sizes in the same units before making any calculations.**

Use the smallest size/distance ratio you can distinguish (see Activity 4.2, question 2) to answer the following questions.

1. Two marbles are separated by 15 cm. How far could you be from the marbles and still see them as separate objects?

2. Venus and the Earth can approach each other as closely as 40 million km (25 million mi). The Moon is about 400,000 km from the Earth. If you were on a spacecraft orbiting Venus at the time of Venus's closest approach to the Earth, would you be able to see the Earth and the Moon as separate objects? (Assume you are viewing the Earth and the Moon at their greatest separation.)

3. The imaging system of a reconnaissance satellite has a smallest size/distance ratio of about 1/4,500,000. The satellite orbits 240 km (150 mi) above the Earth's surface. If the satellite records the image of a truck convoy, how small could a number stenciled on the roof of a truck be and still be "readable" on the image?

EXTENSIONS

1. Look up the smallest size/distance ratios (sometimes called resolution limits) for a variety of animal species. Consider how such resolution limits relate to the habits and habitats of the animals.

NOTE: **Resolution limits may be stated in terms of angular size. See Table 4.1 in Chapter 4 for conversions.**

2. Research the structure of the human eye. What physical factors of the eye affect its resolution limit?

3. Study the radar mapping of the surface of Venus done by the *Pioneer Venus* spacecraft. What was the imaging system's resolution limit? What surface features were discovered with this system? What important information about the surface could not be obtained with this system? Compare this resolution to that for the *Magellan* spacecraft, which began its survey of Venus in 1990. (The *Pioneer Venus* survey began in 1978.) Articles about both surveys have been printed in periodicals such as *Astronomy*, *Scientific American*, and *Sky & Telescope*.

ACTIVITY 4.3   MEASURING ANGULAR SIZE

PURPOSE

To learn how to determine the apparent size of an object as an angle measured in degrees. Also, to learn how the size/distance ratio for an object is related to its angular size.

WHAT DO YOU THINK?

P1. *A quarter has a diameter of about 25 mm. How far from your eyes would a quarter have to be to have the same angular size as the Moon?*

MATERIALS

2 spherical objects of different sizes (a marble and a Ping-Pong ball, for example)
meterstick

PROCEDURE

You have learned how to determine the size/distance ratio for an object (Activity 4.1). Using the size/distance ratio, you can calculate the actual size of an object if you know its distance from you. For a celestial object, however, you do not know its size or its distance. The most obvious feature of an object is its apparent size—how large it *appears* to be. For apparent size, however, using units such as meters or feet is not appropriate.

To describe how large an object appears to be, you might compare it to some object you know, a baseball for example. But how large a baseball appears to be depends on how far it is from you; the greater its distance, the smaller its apparent size. So, in addition to saying the object looked to you to be as large as a baseball, you would have to indicate the distance from you to the baseball. Your description would end up something like this: "The object looks as large as a baseball looks at 3 meters." Suppose the person to whom you were giving the description couldn't imagine how big a baseball looks at 3 m (10 ft). (Can *you*?) Then your description wouldn't be very

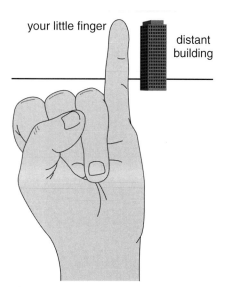

your little finger

distant building

Figure 4.8
Your little finger *appears* to be as wide as the distant building (see Figure 4.8). Therefore, your little finger's width and the building's width have the same angular size. If you moved your hand to the right, your little finger would just "cover" the distant building. (The building's height and your finger's length are *not* involved in this comparison.)

helpful. Fortunately, there is a convenient way to describe the apparent size of an object.

This method involves measuring the angular size of the object, that is, how many degrees (or fractions of a degree) the object "covers." The angular size of an object is related to the object's size/distance ratio. For small angles only, the angular size is directly proportional to the size/distance ratio. (For larger angles, the angular size becomes increasingly smaller, relative to the size/distance ratio.)

An object with a size/distance ratio of 1/57 has an angular size of about 1 degree (1°). Your little finger held at arm's length has a ratio of about 1/50 (Activity 4.1). Therefore, anything that you can just "cover up" with the width of your little finger has an angular size slightly greater than 1°. In Activity 1.1, you determined hand shapes that at arm's length equal 10° and 15°; anything that you can just "cover up" with one of these hand shapes has an angular size equal to the angular size of the hand shape. See Figure 4.8.

As a convenient approximation, you may assume that the size/distance ratio for an angular size of 1° is 1/60.

EXAMPLE 1

A ball has a diameter of 10 cm. How far away from you must it be to have an angular size of 1°?

The size/distance ratio for 1° is 1/60. Therefore, the ball must be 60 times its diameter from you:

$$10 \text{ cm} \times 60 = 600 \text{ cm} = 6 \text{ m}$$

Therefore, a 10-cm diameter ball must be at a distance of 6 m to have an angular size of 1°.

EXAMPLE 2

Suppose the 10-cm diameter ball is 8 m away. What is its angular size?

The size/distance ratio for the ball is 10 cm/8 m, or 10 cm/800 cm, which simplifies to 1/80. The size/distance ratio for 1° is 1/60. The ball's angular size is therefore only three-quarters as large as 1°:

$$1/80 \div 1/60 = 60/80 = 0.75$$

The angular size of the 10-cm ball when viewed from 8 m away is 0.75°, or 3/4° (three-quarters of a degree).

EXAMPLE 3

Suppose the 10-cm diameter ball is now 25 m away. What is its angular size?

The ball's size/distance ratio is 10 cm/25 m, or 10 cm/2,500 cm, which simplifies to 1/250. The size/distance ratio for 1° is 1/60. The ball's angular size is 0.24 times that of 1°:

$$1/250 \div 1/60 = 60/250 = 0.24$$

The angular size of the 10-cm ball when viewed from 25 m away is 0.24°, or about 1/4° (one-quarter of a degree).

A. Measure and record the diameter of each sphere.

1. *At what distance does the small sphere have to be from your eyes to have an angular size of 1°? Show your calculations. (See Example 1.)*

B. Place the small sphere at the distance determined in step A. Place the large sphere next to the small sphere.

2. *What is the size/distance ratio for the large sphere? Show your calculations. (See Example 2.)*

3. *What is the angular diameter of the large sphere? Show your calculations. (See Example 2.)*

C. Close one eye and look at both spheres, with your eye at the same level as the spheres. Notice that the two spheres do not appear to be the same size, because they are the same distance from your eye and their diameters are not equal.

4. *How far away from you must the large sphere be to have an angular size of 1°? Show your calculations. (See Example 1.)*

D. Place the large sphere at the distance calculated in your answer to question 4. Make sure the small sphere is at the position set in step B. Close one eye and look at both spheres, with your eye at the same level as the spheres.

5. *How do the angular sizes of the spheres compare? Does one appear larger than the other? If so, which one? Why?*

E. The Moon is at a distance of about 110 of its diameters from the Earth.

6. *What is the angular size of the Moon as seen from the Earth? Show your calculations.*

7. *How far would a quarter (24 mm in diameter), observed face on, have to be from your eyes to have the same angular size as the Moon? Show your calculations. Compare your answer to your prediction in question P1.*

About Light

WHERE DOES LIGHT GO?

While walking in the woods late one night, Peter saw a glowing campfire with a man sitting by it. The glow from the campfire allowed Peter to see the man's face.

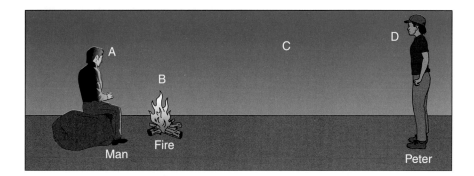

Peter began wondering about the fire and the light surrounding it. He asked the following questions to himself. Try to answer them.

1. Does light leave the fire?
2. Does light from the fire reach point A (the man)?
3. Does light from the fire reach point B (above the flames)?
4. Does light from the fire reach point C?
5. Does light from the fire reach point D (where Peter is standing)?

   Explain the reasoning behind each of your answers.

Preview: In this chapter you will be introduced to a model of how light behaves. This model predicts correctly how the apparent brightness of objects changes with your distance from them.

The only way astronomers can explore most of the universe is by studying the light that comes to the Earth from distant objects. The light that comes from the Sun is essential for life on Earth. But what is light? And why do light sources appear brighter or fainter depending on your distance from them?

How Light Behaves

It isn't obvious what light is. Somehow it just seems to be there. When light is there, you can see things. When it's not there, you can't. One way to try to make sense of something you don't understand is to make a model of it. The celestial sphere is a model that lets you make correct predictions about how the Sun and stars appear to move in the sky. You can also use a model of light to predict what you will see in many different situations.

Unlike the model you made of the celestial sphere, which you can hold in your hands, the model of light is not a "thing" but rather a way of talking and thinking about light. Models of light play a vital role in the design of cameras, telescopes, camcorders, and other optical equipment; without these models we would probably not have been able to build such devices.

You will use a model that represents light as consisting of particles— particles that travel very fast. The particles in this model are often called photons (from the Greek "photo" meaning "light"; see Figure 5.1). In accord with laboratory and other measurements of the speed of light, the model assumes that photons travel in space 3×10^5 (300,000) km each second; in air they travel slightly slower. Photons are something like the wind. You can only feel the wind directly when it touches you. But you use the idea of the wind to explain the movement of trees and clouds. You can't see photons traveling through space either, but you can use the photon model to explain what you can and cannot see.

Why use a model in which light is considered to be made up of particles? The following story gives one reason. A photographic negative consists of more than 10^6 (one million) "grains" of chemical that can be altered and thereby change color when light strikes them. (The "photo" in photographic is there for the same reason that it is in "photon.") Suppose a series of photographs is taken of a very dimly lighted object. For each successive photograph, the shutter of the camera is left open for twice as long as for the previous photograph. If the light is sufficiently dim, the first negative in the series will show, not a faint image of the entire object, but only a few scattered grains that have been affected by the light. Because only a few grains are altered, it makes sense to think of these grains as being changed in color by particles that strike the film at the locations of the grains. As the duration of each photograph increases, an image of the object begins to emerge on successive negatives. The final image in the series looks like a "conventional" photograph. It is made up of more than a million individually altered grains.

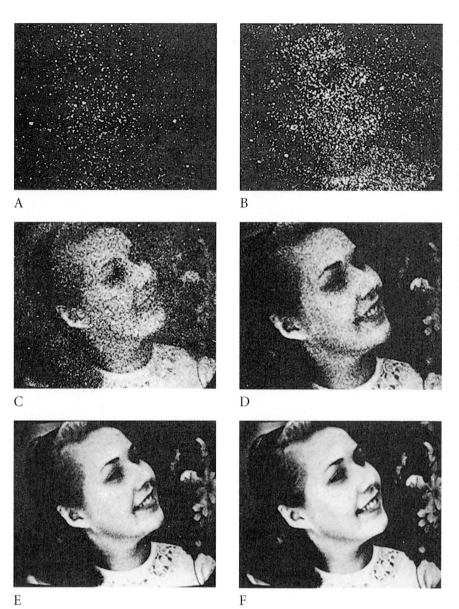

A

B

C

D

E

F

Figure 5.1

This series of photographs illustrates how an image is formed from many photons bouncing from an object (the woman and the flowers behind her).

The series shows the same image taken under increasing levels of illumination. Each spot on the photograph represents a single photon. Human eyes are not sensitive enough to detect individual photons as in pictures A–E, which were made using special electronic equipment. Humans see images like picture F where there are so many photons from the object reaching our eyes that the particle-like quality of the individual photons is not visible to us.

Other Models of Light

Physicists have developed other models of light. One model describes light in terms of waves, like waves in a pond. Some behavior of light makes most sense if you think about light as if it consisted of waves instead of particles. The photon model of light was invented by Albert Einstein (1879–1955) in 1905, although the word "photon" wasn't applied to his model until years later. Einstein was motivated to create a particle model of light to explain behavior similar to that of film described above. The modern photon model is actually a combination of a particle model and a wave model. In this book, you will concentrate on the particle aspect of photons.

How You See—An Explanation in Terms of the Photon Model

How does the photon model account for the fact that you can see things? In this model, the only time you see anything is when photons reach your eyes. If no photons from an object reach your eyes, you don't see the object. This model is very different from the one most people use when they think about light. You seem to see a distant mountain "over there" where the mountain is. In the photon model, the only "direct" contact you have with the distant mountain consists of the photons that travel from the mountain and reach your eyes. It will probably take a while for you to become comfortable using this model to predict the behavior of light. You might well also ask, "How do photons striking your eyes cause you to see something?" A good question. Unfortunately no one yet knows the answer in great detail.

What the Model Says about How Photons Behave

In the photon model, photons travel through space in straight paths. When photons pass from one medium, such as air, to another medium, such as water or glass, their paths change directions. This change in direction is how the model accounts for the appearance illustrated in Figure 5.2.

Figure 5.2
A ruler appears bent where it enters the water in a glass.

Other observations can be readily explained in terms of the photon model. For example, the straight paths of photons are consistent with the observation that you cannot see around corners (Figure 5.3). Since you cannot see through most objects, most objects do not allow photons to pass through them. Air and glass are two major exceptions. Objects like these, which allow most photons to pass through them, are called transparent.

The straight paths of photons also explain shadows—regions where there are fewer photons arriving from a source than are arriving in a nearby region (Figure 5.4). When a single light shines on an object that is not transparent, there is a region behind the object that photons traveling in straight paths from the source of light cannot reach directly. In such cases you are

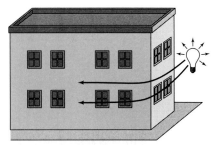

Figure 5.3
Photons would have to travel on curved paths to allow someone to see around the corner.

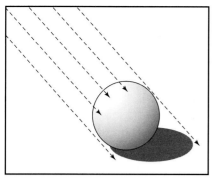

Figure 5.4
A shadow produced because photons from a source cannot reach the region behind the object.

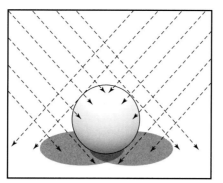

Figure 5.5
Photons from two sources producing two shadows.

usually aware of a shadow being behind the object. If there is more than one source of photons present, objects can have more than one shadow (Figure 5.5). If you are in a very large, dark room with only one source of light, shadows can be very dark. In most rooms there are several sources of light, as well as objects and walls from which photons can bounce (Figure 5.6), and "fill in" shadows, making them less dark.

In the photon model, photons travel until they strike something that absorbs them. If light traveled a long way, the model says that there must have been very little matter in the paths of the photons to absorb them. Since you can easily see the Sun even though photons from the Sun have to travel almost 150 million km before reaching your eyes, the model says that there must be very little matter in space to absorb photons traveling between the Sun and the Earth. In Chapters 10 and 14 you will find that you

Figure 5.6
Photons bouncing from objects in a room.

can see objects that are much much farther from you than the Sun is. The photon model thus calls for space to be largely "empty."

EXERCISE: How is the idea that photons travel in straight paths related to Occam's Razor (Chapter 1)?

Shadows are only one of the effects produced when photons strike an object. According to the model, photons behave in different ways when they strike different kinds of surfaces. Since you can see through air, glass, and some plastic, the model requires that air, glass, and some plastics allow some photons to pass through them—such objects are often called transparent; they are said to transmit light. What about objects you cannot see through? Here the model incorporates two quite different fates for photons. One of these possible fates is for the photon to be absorbed by an object that it strikes—the photon disappears. If a photon is neither absorbed by an object nor passes through it, the photon "bounces" from the object, traveling away in a direction different from the one it was traveling when it struck the object. If the photon bounces from the object, the process is called either scattering or reflection (see Figure 5.7). Mirrors, which are discussed in Chapter 6, reflect photons. Most other objects that do not reflect and are not transparent, absorb some of the photons striking them, and scatter the rest. Whether a photon will be scattered or absorbed cannot be predicted; it is a matter of probability (see Chapter 15).

What path does a reflected or scattered photon take? The model says that a photon behaves in the same way that a billiard ball behaves when it strikes the cushion on a billiard table after being hit "squarely." (If you have spent some time on pursuits other than academic, you may be familiar with this behavior.) Figure 5.8 shows the paths of several balls as they strike the cushion and bounce. Notice the angle each ball's path makes with the cushion before and after the bounce. We will refer to this behavior with the shorthand expression "angle in = angle out." Why do physicists and astronomers use a model in which photons in some circumstances behave like billiard balls? Light from a device called a laser (Figure 5.9) provides a good demonstration of the behavior of light when it strikes a mirror, suggesting one reason for the comparison between billiard balls and photons.

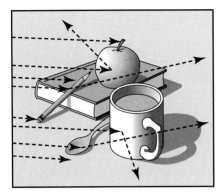

Figure 5.7
Objects absorbing and scattering photons.

How Big Is a Photon?

It might seem sensible to ask about the size of the particles called photons. But this question does not have a simple answer. Some circumstances are easiest to understand if photons were small, for example, the way individual microscopic grains on a photographic film are altered by light. Other cases seem to require photons that are large; these latter situations are better described by the model in which light is considered to be made up of waves rather than of particles. There is no way known to observe photons directly and see what they are "really" like; we can observe only the effects produced by photons. We will therefore leave the question of the size of photons unanswered. Light, like everything else, must remain in part a mystery.

Although for simplicity we say photons are particles, it would be more accurate to say that photons act like particles in some situations, but like waves in other situations. In this text we concentrate on the ways photons behave like particles, albeit somewhat strange particles—particles that do not break or get dented when they strike some objects, but disappear when they strike other objects and are mysteriously created by objects as diverse as the Sun and a firefly. To gain more understanding of the strange things we call photons, you should take advanced courses in physics.

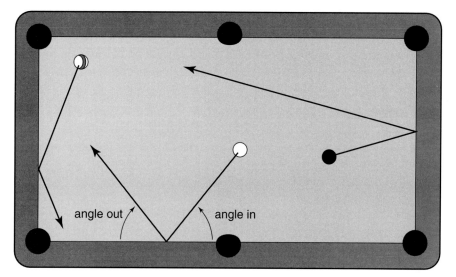

Figure 5.8
Balls striking and bouncing from a billiard table cushion.

angle out

angle in

But where do photons come from? How are they born? How do they die? The photon model provides answers to those questions; however these answers require understanding aspects of the model too advanced for this text. For now you will have to make do with knowing only that a source of light "emits" photons. In terms of the photon model, you can see an object either (1) if the object itself emits photons, or (2) if the object scatters photons that were originally emitted by some other object (Figure 5.10).

To summarize some of the characteristics of this model: photons can be created (emitted) and destroyed (absorbed). Photons in empty space travel in straight lines until they hit an object. When a photon strikes an object it can either be transmitted, absorbed, reflected, or scattered. If the photon is transmitted it passes through the object and continues on a straight path, but often in a different direction. If the photon is reflected or scattered, it sets off in a new direction, again on a straight path, until it hits another object. If the second object is your eye, you will see the first object. Remember, in terms of this model, the only time you see something is when photons enter your eyes. What you normally see is either a source of photons (a "light") or the last object that scattered the photons before they reached your eyes.

The photon model accounts for all the properties of light that you encounter in everyday life. You can use it to predict how light will behave in various circumstances. In fact, you will find that questions involving light are often much easier to answer if you think about photons. Ask yourself: From where do the photons come and to where do they go?

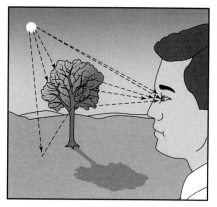

Figure 5.9
Light from a laser striking a mirror.

Figure 5.10
Paths of photons: some go directly from a source to the eye and others are scattered by an object toward the eye.

Using the Photon Model
Here is a story told in terms of the photon model. When the light in your bedroom is turned on, it emits a vast number of photons each second (approximately 10^{20}, that is about 100,000,000,000,000,000,000 photons). Photons travel very fast, so the room instantly seems filled with photons flying in every direction. The photons travel in straight lines until they hit furniture, walls, floor, or ceiling. Some photons are absorbed by these objects and other photons bounce from the objects they hit and strike other objects

About Light ✳ **101**

before they are absorbed. If the photons that bounce from the bed reach your eyes directly, you see the bed. If photons that bounce from the bed strike only the back of your head, you would have to turn around to see the bed. If photons that strike the bed then strike the rug before entering your eyes, you see the rug, not the bed. We will describe in Chapter 6 the fate of photons that hit mirrors.

What happens when you turn off the light? The photons that are bouncing around keep bouncing until they are absorbed. Since the photons are traveling very fast, they strike many objects in rapid succession and thereby get absorbed very quickly. The room is dark once again.

EXERCISE: To get some idea about how fast photons must be absorbed, turn off the light in your bedroom and try to get into bed before all the photons are absorbed and the room is dark.

EXERCISE: Draw a diagram using photon paths to show how you are able to see the lights in your classroom, how you are able to see the Sun, and how you are able to see the Moon.

EXERCISE: Draw a diagram using photon paths to show how you are able to see another student in your class.

EXERCISE: Draw a diagram using photon paths to show how you are able to see a car in the street when you look out a window.

QUESTION: It is daytime. You are in a room with windows, but it is cloudy and you cannot see the Sun. No light is turned on in the room you are in. Yet you can see perfectly well. Where do the photons come from?

Apparent Brightness and Distance

Astronomers must decode the light from distant objects to tell them most of what they know about the universe. One of the first things they measure is the apparent brightness of distant objects.

Although you may never have thought much about it, you know that the farther away from you a light is, the fainter it appears to be. The headlights on cars, street lights, and the lights in the windows of houses and apartments, appear fainter the farther away they are from you. You could of course say that the lights are not really fainter, they only seem fainter as you move farther from them. We will use the words "apparent brightness" to mean how faint or bright a light source appears to you, the observer. A particular light appears less bright, that is, appears fainter, the farther it is from you.

Lightbulbs are usually marked in watts: 60 watts, 75 watts, 100 watts, etc. In the photon model, the wattage can be thought of as a measure of the rate at which the bulb uses electricity to produce photons. Normally, the higher the wattage, the more photons the bulb emits each second. A typical lightbulb does not do a very good job of producing photons, however; instead it converts much of the electricity it uses into heat, which is why it is not a good idea to touch a lighted bulb. (You will not have to worry here about what electricity and heat are; we leave detailed discussions of them for a course in physics.)

If a 100-watt bulb and a 60-watt bulb are placed side by side, normally the 100-watt bulb will appear considerably brighter to you. But a 100-watt bulb 10 m away from you appears much fainter than a 100-watt bulb 1 m away. So the apparent brightness of a lightbulb depends on two factors: the rate at which the bulb emits photons, related to its wattage, and how far away the bulb is from you.

The Inverse Square Law

In Activity 5.1 you make use of a simple device for measuring the apparent brightness of light—a wax photometer. Experiments with a wax photometer reveal that, as long as your distance to the photometer remains unchanged, the apparent brightness of the wax diminishes as the distance between the photometer and the light source increases. However, doubling the distance does not halve the apparent brightness. Apparent brightness diminishes with the square of the distance from the source: doubling the distance quarters the apparent brightness. This behavior is sometimes called an inverse square law—inverse because greater distance yields lower apparent brightness. If we define our units properly, and know how wattage relates to emission of photons, we can write this inverse square law as

$$\text{apparent brightness} = \frac{\text{wattage}}{\text{distance}^2}$$

The apparent brightness varies in proportion to the wattage and inversely in proportion to the square of the distance.

How does the photon model account for this observed behavior? Imagine a light bulb inside a transparent sphere (Figure 5.11). According to the model, huge numbers of photons (approximately 10^{20}) are emitted each second by the bulb and pass through the surface of the sphere. By dividing this number of photons by the area of the sphere, you can find the number of photons that pass each second through a "unit" area on the surface of the sphere. For example, if 10^{20} photons pass each second through a surface whose area is 10^3 cm², you can find the number of photons that pass each second through each square centimeter by dividing the number of photons by the area:

10^{20} photons/10^3 cm² $= 10^{17}$ photons/cm²

The size of the unit area depends on the units in which the area of the sphere is measured—square centimeters, square inches, square kilometers, etc. The smaller the unit area, the more of them there are for a given surface and the smaller the number of photons that pass each second through a unit area.

Now imagine that you place this first transparent sphere inside a second transparent sphere with twice the radius of the first sphere (Figure 5.12). Further, imagine that while the photons are traveling through space, their number does not increase or decrease. Therefore, all of the photons passing through the first sphere will continue on straight lines and pass through the surface of the second sphere. The number of photons passing through each sphere per second is the same, but the area of the second sphere is larger than the area of the first sphere. As a result, fewer photons will pass each second through each unit area (for example, square centimeter)

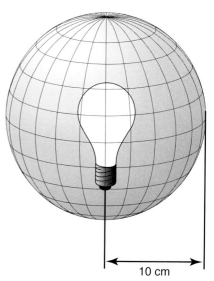

Figure 5.11
One sphere surrounding a bulb.

10 cm

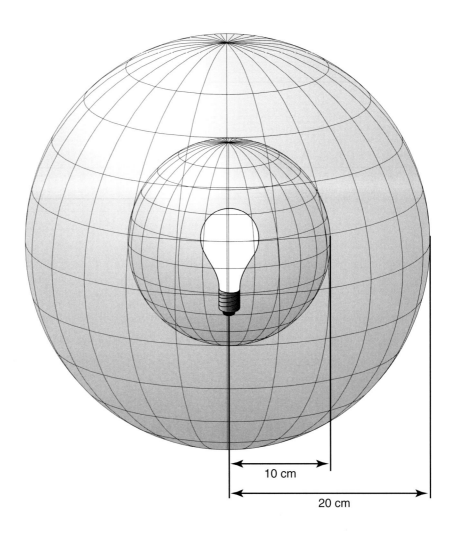

10 cm

20 cm

of the surface of the larger sphere. The surface of the second sphere* is 4 times larger than the surface of the first sphere; therefore only one-fourth as many photons pass each second through a unit area on the surface of the second sphere as through a unit area on the first sphere. At twice the distance from the source, a unit of area gets struck by one-fourth the number of photons. One-fourth the number of photons each second results in one-fourth the apparent brightness. This imaginary experiment shows how the photon model explains that an object moved to twice its former distance from you appears to you to be only one fourth as bright. By a similar argument, you can see that a source moved to 3 times its distance would appear one-ninth as bright.

In general, if you move N times as far from a bulb, only $1/N^2$ as many photons from the bulb will reach your eyes each second.

---

*The area of a sphere = $4 \times \pi \times radius^2$. Imagine two spheres are centered on the bulb, one inside the other. The smaller sphere has a radius of 10 cm and the larger sphere has a radius of 20 cm. The surface area of the smaller sphere is $4 \times \pi \times 10\ cm \times 10\ cm = 400\ \pi\ cm^2$. The surface area of the larger sphere is $4 \times \pi \times 20\ cm \times 20\ cm = 1,600\ \pi\ cm^2$. The surface area of the larger sphere is 4 times that of the smaller sphere. Therefore at the distance from the bulb of the larger sphere, the same number of photons "cover" 4 times more area than they did when they were at the distance of the smaller sphere from the bulb (see Figure 5.12).

HEADS UP!

In talking about apparent brightness, we have assumed that the pupil of each of your eyes does not change in size no matter how far you are from a source of light. We have also assumed that your eyes and brain translate the number of photons per second that strike your pupils into perceived brightness. Both of these assumptions are only approximations. For example, in a darkened room with a single source of light, the pupils of your eyes tend to get larger as you move farther from the source. As a result, your eyes gather more photons each second than they would have gathered if the pupils had remained the same size. This involuntary behavior makes it hard to use your eyes to judge apparent brightness accurately. To make quantitative measurements you therefore use a device called a photometer whose "pupil" does not change size. It is also much easier to judge when two objects appear equally bright, rather than to judge when one appears to be twice, or one-fourth, etc., as bright as the other. In Activity 5.1 and the activities in Chapter 10, you take advantage of your ability to judge when two objects are equally bright.

PROBLEM: If you move 4 times farther from a source of photons, how will the apparent brightness of the source change?

SOLUTION: The second position for your eyes is 4 times farther away from the bulb than the first. The apparent brightness changes inversely with the square of the distance over which the photons travel, so at the greater distance the apparent brightness is $1/4 \times 1/4 = 1/16$ times the apparent brightness at the closer distance. Only 1/16 as many photons would enter your eyes at the greater distance, assuming the size of your pupils did not change.

IMPORTANT DIFFERENCE! The angular size of an object discussed in Chapter 4 depends directly on the size of the object and inversely on the distance of the object from you. The apparent brightness discussed in this chapter depends directly on the wattage of the source and inversely on the square of the distance between you and the source of photons. These two relations are very different. If you want to use these two relations properly you must understand and remember this difference.

Light is still mysterious, but with the photon model you can at least predict how light behaves in certain circumstances.

SUMMARY

The photon model is a very useful way to understand and predict the behavior of light. In this model, light consists of particles called photons. Photons are emitted by all objects, but only some objects emit photons of visible light at a sufficiently high rate for us to see them. Photons normally travel on straight paths until they reach another object. When this happens the photons are transmitted, scattered, reflected, or absorbed by an object. If the photons are not absorbed, they travel on new paths, which are also straight. You can only see an object if it emits photons or scatters photons that reach your eyes.

Measurements show that when a source of light is located N times the distance from an observer, the source appears only $1/N^2$ as bright. The photon model explains these measurements as due to photons from a source spreading out; they pass successively through (imaginary) spheres whose areas increase as the squares of their distances from the source increase. These areas thus increase with the square of the radii of the spheres, that is, with the square of the distances over which the photons travel. Since apparent brightness decreases as distances increase, the relation of apparent brightness to distance is called an inverse square relation (see Figure 5.13), which contrasts with the simple inverse relation between angular size and distance (see Figure 5.14).

Figure 5.13
The number of photons per unit area decreases as the distance increases. Of the four photons that pass through the square at 10 cm, only one passes through the square at 20 cm, at twice the distance, only one-fourth the number of photons will strike the square.

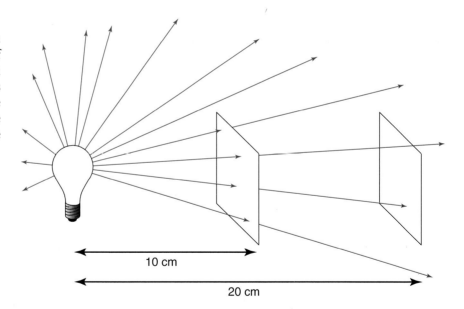

10 cm

20 cm

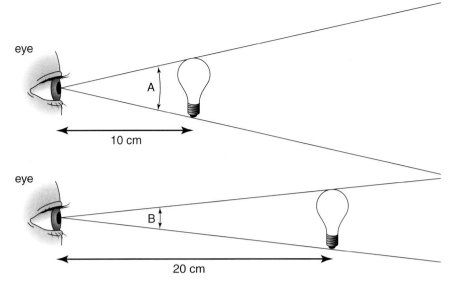

Figure 5.14
The angular size of the bulb also decreases as the distance increases, but the angular size of the bulb at 20 cm (B) is one-half as large as its angular size at 10 cm (A).

HOMEWORK

1. Over a year, the Earth-Sun distance averages about 1.5×10^8 km. How long does it take on average for sunlight to travel from the Sun to the Earth? If the Sun were to cease emitting photons at noon your time on a particular day, when would it get dark on the Earth?

2. A very small source of light exists at the center of a series of concentric transparent spherical shells with radii of 1 m, 3 m, and 5 m. If X photons pass through a $1 m^2$ window in the first shell, how many photons will pass through a $1 m^2$ window in each of the second and third spherical shells?

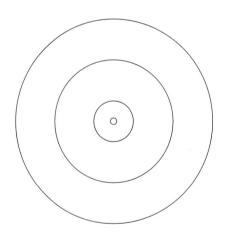

3. On a camera, the nearly circular iris in the lens may be opened or closed. The iris has settings called "*f* stops," and they regulate the number of photons that pass through to the film. Opening the iris one *f* stop—*lowering* the *f* number—lets in twice as many photons as were let in by the preceding *f* stop; closing the iris one *f* stop—*raising* the *f* number—lets in one half as many photons as were let in by the preceding *f* stop. What is the ratio of the "open" area in the lens for one *f* stop to the "open" area in the lens for the next smallest opening?

SELF-TEST

1. Describe the path of a photon.

2. If a 5-cm square of cardboard is placed 50 cm from a lightbulb and is then moved to a distance of 100 cm, how many lightbulbs would be needed at the source to make the cardboard at the 100-cm distance appear as bright as it did at the 50-cm distance? Assume the cardboard has the same orientation to the bulbs at 100 cm as it did to the single bulb at 50 cm. How many lightbulbs at the source would be needed to make the cardboard appear as bright at a distance of 200 cm as it did at the 50-cm distance?

About Light ✳ **107**

3. Even in the darkest room you can often see the outlines of furniture after you have been in the room for a while. Is there light in the room at those times? If so, where does it come from?

4. It is night and someone is shining a flashlight on the wall of a building. You cannot see the flashlight, but you can see the illuminated wall. Is light reaching your eyes?

ACTIVITY 5.1

JUDGING APPARENT BRIGHTNESS AT VARIOUS DISTANCES

PURPOSE

To determine how the apparent brightness of a source of light changes as its distance from the viewer changes.

WHAT DO YOU THINK?

Show your math and box your answers, labeling answers with proper units of measurement.

In front of the classroom you can see two 200-watt bulbs lighting up a paraffin block. The paraffin block is called a photometer. It is a device that enables you to compare the apparent brightness of two sources of light. (You will soon build your own photometer.) See Figure 5.15. Each light is the same distance from the photometer. Since both lights appear equally bright, as "seen" by the photometer, both sides of the photometer also appear equally bright. Your teacher will now move the bulb on the left side to a distance of 2 m from the photometer. Notice that the left side of the photometer now looks dimmer.

Figure 5.15

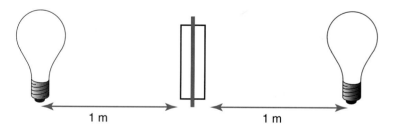

P1. *How many 200-watt bulbs do you think you would have to place on the left side at this 2-m distance so that the sides of the photometer would again look equally bright? (See Figure 5.16.) Explain your answer.*

Figure 5.16

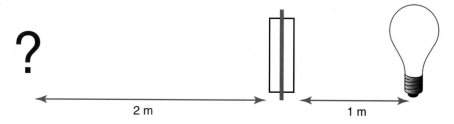

✳ The Universe in Your Hands

P2. *Saturn is about 10 times farther from the Sun than is the Earth. How will the apparent brightness of the Sun as seen at Saturn compare to its apparent brightness as seen at the Earth?*

MATERIALS

1 pair of scissors
2 pieces of 20 cm × 25 cm (8 in. × 10 in.) cardboard
1 meterstick
1 sheet of paper printed with grid of squares
masking tape
1 200-watt unfrosted bulb with clamp socket
1 knife for cutting cardboard
1 sheet of black paper with one small white square

PROCEDURE

Work in pairs for this activity.

A. Cut a square hole 5 cm on a side out of the center of a piece of cardboard. Carefully cut out the small white square on the black sheet of paper. Tape this sheet onto the piece of cardboard so that the square is over the hole.

B. Tape the sheet with the grid of squares to the other piece of cardboard.

C. Turn on the 200-watt bulb and turn off the room lights. Hold the single square opening at a distance of 10 cm from the bulb. Make sure this piece of cardboard is *perpendicular* to the bulb's filament. (See Figure 5.17.)

Figure 5.17

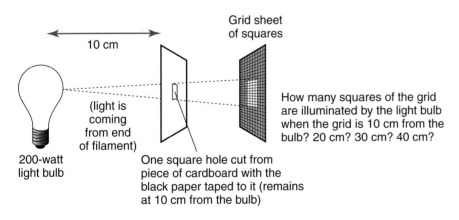

Grid sheet of squares

10 cm

(light is coming from end of filament)

200-watt light bulb

One square hole cut from piece of cardboard with the black paper taped to it (remains at 10 cm from the bulb)

How many squares of the grid are illuminated by the light bulb when the grid is 10 cm from the bulb? 20 cm? 30 cm? 40 cm?

Table 5.1	
Distance from bulb (cm)	number of grid squares illuminated by light passing through square hole
10	
20	
30	
40	

D. Now place the grid of squares against the square opening. Line up a square on the grid with the square opening.

E. The light coming through the square opening is now illuminating one square on the grid paper. Make a table for your observations (see Table 5.1 for an example). Record a number "1" for one illuminated grid square when the grid is at a distance of 10 cm from the bulb.

F. While your partner holds the square at a distance of 10 cm from the bulb, move the grid paper to a distance of 20 cm from the bulb. See Figure 5.17. Keep the cardboard with the square hole and the cardboard with the grid parallel to each other. Be sure the end of the filament is pointed at the hole. Count the number of squares on the grid illuminated by the light passing through the square hole. Record this number in your copy of Table 5.1.

G. Repeat step F for the grid paper at distances of 30 cm and 40 cm from the bulb, and record the numbers in your table.

1. *What fraction of the light passing through the square hole falls on* **one** *of the illuminated squares on the grid sheet when the grid sheet is 10 cm from the lightbulb?*

2. *What fraction of the light passing through the square hole falls on* **one** *of the illuminated squares on the grid sheet when the grid sheet is 20 cm from the lightbulb?*

3. *What fraction of the light passing through the square hole falls on* **one** *of the illuminated squares on the grid sheet when the grid sheet is 30 cm from the lightbulb?*

Using the results from the preceding discussion, set up and complete a chart like Chart 5.1 to a distance of 100 cm.

Chart 5.1

distance in cm   10   20   30   40   50   60   70   80   90   100

fraction of light reaching one square of grid paper   1

Now we want to determine the number of bulbs at different distances that would produce the same apparent brightness as one bulb at a distance of 30 cm (1 ft). Refer to your Chart 5.1 to answer the following questions.

4. a) *When the grid sheet was 20 cm from the bulb, what fraction of the light passing through the square hole falls on one illuminated square on the grid sheet?*

   b) *How many identical bulbs would have to be placed at the position of the original bulb for this square (at a distance of 20 cm) to appear as bright to you as it did at 10 cm?*

5. a) *If the grid sheet were 50 cm from the bulb, what fraction of the light passing through the square hole would fall on one illuminated square on the grid sheet?*

   b) *How many identical bulbs would have to be placed at the position of the original bulb for this square (at a distance of 50 cm) to appear as bright to you as it did at 10 cm?*

6. a) *If the grid sheet were moved to a position 9 times farther from the bulb than is the square hole, what fraction of the light passing through the square hole would fall on one illuminated square on the grid?*

b) *How many identical bulbs would have to be placed at the position of the original bulb for this square (at 9 times the original distance) to appear as bright to you as it did at 10 cm?*

Using the results from the preceding questions, set up and complete another chart, labeled Chart 5.2, to a distance of 100 cm. This chart is similar to Chart 5.1 except that it shows the number of identical light-bulbs at various distances that would produce an apparent brightness equal to that of one bulb at 10 cm.

Use Chart 5.2 to answer the following questions (assume that all the bulbs are identical).

7. *How many bulbs at 30 cm from you will produce the same apparent brightness as one bulb at 10 cm?*

8. *How many bulbs are needed to produce the same apparent brightness as one bulb when they are at 5 times the original distance from you as was the one bulb?*

9. *How many bulbs are needed to produce the same apparent brightness as one bulb when they are at 10 times the distance from you as was the one bulb?*

10. *How many bulbs would you have to place at a distance of 100 m from you to produce the same apparent brightness as one bulb at a distance from you of 25 cm?*

11. *How many bulbs would you have to place 1 km away from you for you to observe the same apparent brightness as you do for one bulb placed 50 cm away from you?*

12. *If the Sun were to change suddenly and appear 100 times brighter than it does now, how far would we have to go away from the Sun so that it would appear as bright as it normally does?*

13. *The planet Mars is 1.5 times farther from the Sun than is the Earth. How would the apparent brightness of the Sun at Mars differ from its apparent brightness as seen from the Earth? How many times brighter or dimmer would the Sun appear to be?*

14. *Neptune is 30 times farther from the Sun than is the Earth. How would the brightness of the Sun at Neptune differ from its apparent brightness as seen from the Earth? How many times brighter or dimmer would the Sun appear to be?*

15. *Mercury is on average 4/10 as far from the Sun as is the Earth. How would the average apparent brightness of the Sun at Mercury differ from its apparent brightness as seen from the Earth? How many times brighter or dimmer would the Sun appear to be?*

About Mirrors and Lenses

WHAT DO YOUR FRIENDS KNOW ABOUT TELESCOPES?

Before the next class meeting, interview some friends who are not in this class. Ask them the following questions, making sure that you write down their responses as completely as possible. Provide your friends with paper so that they can make sketches if they want to. Bring the answers and drawings to the next class meeting and be prepared to talk about them.

1. Imagine that an astronomer decides to look at the North Star through a telescope. Do you think that the North Star would look bigger, smaller, or the same size through the telescope? Do you think that the North Star would appear brighter or dimmer, or have the same apparent brightness?

2. You buy a telescope at a department store because you want to look at the planets. Trace the circle at the far right; on the tracing, draw what you think Saturn would look like when you look through your telescope.

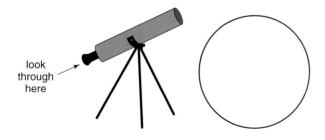

3. Using the same department store telescope described above, you try to observe Saturn by looking through the wrong end of the telescope. Trace the circle; on the tracing, draw what you think Saturn would look like when you look at it through the wrong end of the telescope.

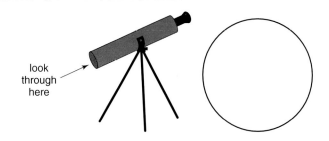

If the image of Saturn filled the above circle when you looked through the correct end of the telescope, about how much of this circle would be filled by Saturn's image now?

FORMING IMAGES

Jack wants to form a sharp image of a lightbulb on a white movie screen. He will attempt to form an image four different ways. Look at each technique that Jack will try and answer these four questions for each case:

    a. Do you think that Jack will be able to form a sharp image of the lightbulb on the movie screen? (Y or N)

    b. If a sharp image is formed, will it be right-side up or upside down?

    c. If a sharp image is formed, will it appear to be brighter or dimmer, or have the same apparent brightness as the lightbulb itself (when you stand equally far from both)?

    d. Will it be possible for Jack to produce a sharp, *magnified* image using this method?

CASE I. Jack uses a *glass lens* and varies its distance between the bulb and the screen:

CASE II. Jack uses the *top half of a glass lens* and varies its distance between the bulb and the screen:

CASE III. Jack uses a *sheet of aluminum foil* with a tiny hole in the center and varies its distance between the bulb and the screen:

CASE IV. Jack uses *nothing* in between the lightbulb and the screen, but varies the distance between the bulb and the screen:

Preview: In this chapter you will learn how to use the photon model to predict some of the ways mirrors and lenses affect light.

In Activity 6.2, you found that if you hold a lightbulb in front of a screen, you do not see an image of the filament on the screen. However, if you make a pinhole in a piece of cardboard and place it between the bulb and the screen, you do see an image of the bulb on the screen (Figure 6.1). How are these quite different observations explained by the photon model?

Think about a firefly representing a single point-source of photons (imagine that the firefly's light stays "on"). Large numbers of photons are emitted each second by the firefly. Each photon travels in a straight path. Different photons in general strike different locations on the screen. (Figure

Figure 6.1
A lightbulb, a pinhole, and a screen.

light bulb

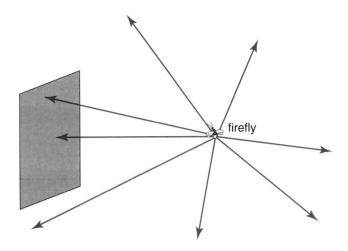

6.2 shows the paths of a few of these photons.) Now imagine that a piece of cardboard containing a pinhole is placed between the firefly and the screen (see Figure 6.3). As you saw in Activity 6.2, this procedure causes an image of the source of light to be formed on the screen. In the photon model, if the pinhole is sufficiently small, a photon from a point source of light can only reach a single point on the screen.

Figure. 6.3
A firefly, a pinhole, and a screen.

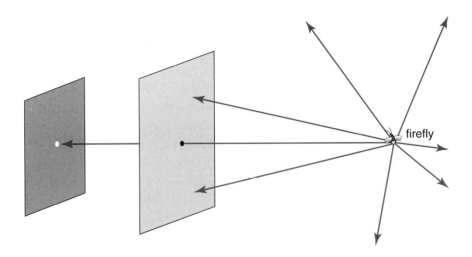

Now imagine that you add a second point source of light (Figure 6.4). Again, according to the photon model, some photons from the first point source reach one point on the screen (most, of course, never reach the screen). Some photons from the second point source can only reach a different point on the screen (again, most never reach the screen). Since, in this model, photons travel in straight lines until they strike a surface, photons passing through the pinhole from the bottom source can only reach a point nearer the top of the screen, and photons passing through the pinhole from the top source can only reach a point nearer the bottom of the screen: The model predicts that the image formed by a pinhole is upside down. From Activity 6.2, you know that this is indeed what happens.

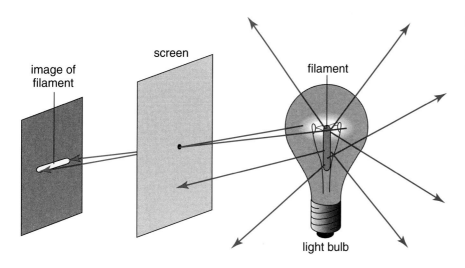

QUESTION: What would happen if you removed the cardboard with the pinhole? Would you still see on the screen an image of each of the two point sources of light? Explain your answer in terms of the photon model.

QUESTION: If the two sources had been side by side instead of one above the other when the cardboard was between the sources and the screen, how would the image differ from the image seen in the original arrangement? (Hint: Draw the path of the photons as seen from overhead.)

By imagining that the two sources of light are from the same object, such as the filament of a clear lightbulb, you can see how a pinhole forms an image of an extended object as well as of a number of point sources (Figure 6.5). This approach allows you to describe the formation of an image by a pinhole in terms of the photon model.

Figure 6.5
One light source can act as multiple point sources to form an image through a pinhole.

QUESTION: A piece of cardboard with a pinhole is placed between a lightbulb and a screen. The image of the filament on the screen is upside down and left-right inverted. When the screen is moved to half its original distance from the cardboard, the image of the filament is half as large. Make a sketch of the filament of a bulb, showing the paths of the photons emitted by the filament that pass through the pinhole and strike the screen. Explain why, according to the photon model, the image is smaller when the screen is closer to the pinhole than when the screen is farther from the pinhole.

In Activity 6.2 you may have observed that the image formed by a pinhole appears brighter as you move the screen closer to the pinhole and fainter as you move the screen farther away. Let us see how you might explain this behavior in terms of the photon model. In this discussion, we will assume that your eye is always the same distance from the screen, even though we talk about moving the screen. Light from the image therefore travels the same distance to your eye in every case. If you viewed the screen from different distances, the apparent brightness of the image would change even if the screen remained the same distance from the cardboard.

You know from Chapter 5 that the photon model explains apparent brightness in terms of the rate at which photons arrive on a unit of area at the location of the observer. The rate is all important—the more photons that strike a unit of area in any given time interval, the brighter that area will appear.

In this example, "the observer" is the screen. You are observing the screen, but your distance from the screen does not change and so any change in apparent brightness is not produced by a changing distance between you and the screen. Since the image is smaller when the screen is closer to the pinhole, the photons passing through the pinhole and then hitting the screen are confined to a smaller area on the screen. More photons thus strike each unit of area in the illuminated part of the screen—therefore the image appears brighter when the screen is closer to the pinhole.

EXERCISE: Write a brief statement using the language of the photon model to explain why an image appears fainter if you move the screen farther from the pinhole while you remain the same distance from the image.

What Mirrors Do

In Chapter 5 you learned what the photon model says about photons that strike a surface: angle in = angle out. If the surface is "smooth," it behaves like a mirror. But what is a smooth surface in terms of the photon model? The cushions of a billiard table, for example, are not smooth as far as photons are concerned; the cushions do not act like mirrors. Smoothness can be described in terms of the paths of photons as they first approach and then leave a surface.

In Figure 6.6 the paths of three photons traveling on parallel paths are represented. Notice that these photons are still traveling parallel to each other after they bounce from the surface. In Figure 6.7 the photons also bounce from the surface at the same angle at which they encounter the surface. But in this figure, each photon encounters the surface at a different angle and so leaves the surface in a different direction. Photons that were traveling on parallel paths before they reached the surface are no longer traveling on parallel paths after they leave the surface.

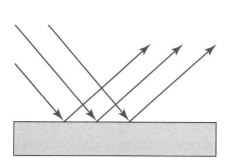

Figure 6.6
Photons on parallel paths hitting a smooth surface.

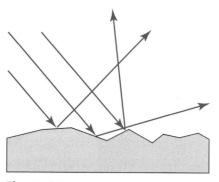

Figure 6.7
Photons on parallel paths hitting a rough surface.

If photons traveling on parallel paths before they strike a surface travel on nearly parallel paths afterward, the surface is said to be smooth and the photons are said to be reflected. If photons traveling on parallel paths before they strike a surface are traveling on paths far from parallel ("every which way") afterward, the surface is said to be rough and the photons are said to be scattered. Of course, smoothness and roughness are relative terms and there are conditions between the ideal, but never achieved, conditions of "perfectly smooth" and "perfectly rough." Some parts of a surface can also be smoother or rougher than other parts. The definition of smooth only applies to flat (uncurved) surfaces, but these are the surfaces you will be concerned with most in this course.

The paths of photons traveling parallel to each other define an angle with respect to a smooth surface (see Figure 6.8). This angle is the "angle in" in the rule "angle in = angle out." If the photons are not traveling on parallel paths after they bounce from the surface, there is no single angle out, but instead many angles out (or "angle outs" if, like the televison and radio announcers, you talk about "time outs" in football and basketball). Since you cannot see the paths of photons, you will usually use the definition of smooth for a mirror in the following way: photons striking the surface of a mirror will obey the "angle in = angle out" rule.

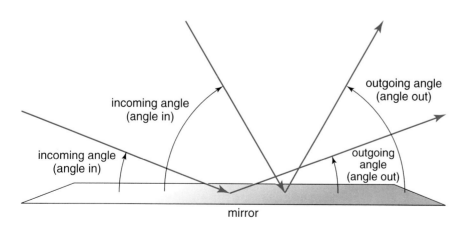

Figure 6.8
"Angle in = angle out."

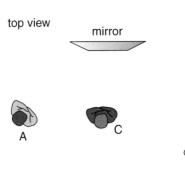

Figure 6.9
An overhead view of three people standing in front of a mirror.

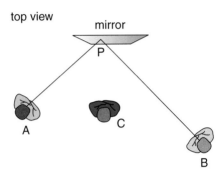

Figure 6.10
Lines AP and BP make the same angle with the mirror.

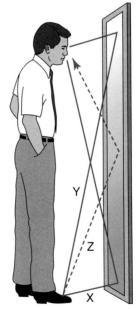

Figure 6.11
Three paths from foot to mirror to eye; only one follows the angle in = angle out rule. Only that one describes a possible path for photons.

Look at Figure 6.9. Could a person at point A see a person at point B in the mirror? Could a person at point A see a person at point C in the mirror? One way to answer those questions is to arrange three people and a mirror in the same way they are shown in the figure and discover what each person can see by asking them. Another way to answer those questions is to use the photon model. Since you are dealing with a mirror, you know that the angle in = angle out rule applies. "Could a person at point A see a person at point B in the mirror?" In terms of the photon model this question becomes, "Can a straight line be drawn from A to some point P on the mirror, in such a way that the line from P to B makes the same angle with the mirror that the line from A to P makes?" (see Figure 6.10). If you can draw AP and PB in this way, A can see B.

QUESTION: If A can see B, can B see A?

QUESTION: Could a person at point A see a person at point C in the mirror?

QUESTION: "Angle in = Angle out" is a prediction of the photon model; can you think of some ways to determine how well this prediction fits your observations?

In Activity 6.1 you explored some of the ways mirrors affect light. You can now describe these effects in terms of the photon model. For example, using the photon model, you can explain why you can see all of yourself in a mirror that is only one-half your height. Here is how you might do it. You know that in the photon model, you can only see your feet if photons coming from your feet enter your eyes. If you are standing in front of a mirror, where do photons from your feet that enter your eyes bounce from the mirror? Figure 6.11 shows some possible paths that photons might take in traveling from your feet to your eyes. According to the photon model, however, photons striking a mirror travel in such a way that angle in = angle out. In Figure 6.11 only the path marked "Z" meets this requirement. Therefore path "Z" describes a path that a photon could take in traveling from your feet to your eyes according to the model. Photons from your feet that strike the mirror below this point never reach your eyes, so they play no role in your seeing your feet.

QUESTION: Does the amount of yourself you can see in a mirror depend on how far you stand from the mirror? Draw diagrams to justify your answer in terms of the photon model.

According to the photon model, a mirror changes the direction in which a photon is traveling. You explored some of the effects of mirrors in Activity 6.1. One way to make an image appear brighter is to use several mirrors to change the paths of photons that otherwise would not contribute to the image (see Figure 6.12). This technique is one that astronomers use in building telescopes. In most cases, however, instead of using many flat mirrors, they use one curved mirror which is able to direct even more photons to an image, making the image brighter (see Figure 6.13). Thus astronomers can observe an object that would not be visible without a mirror to gather large numbers of photons from the object. The larger the area of the mirror, the more photons it can direct to the image. A properly curved mirror is

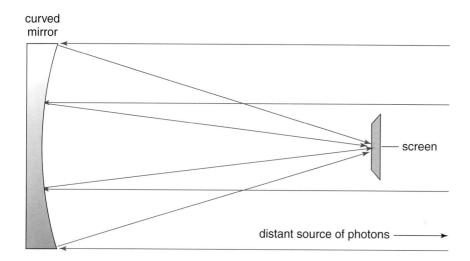

top view

mirrors

screen

mirrors

distant source of photons ⟶

curved mirror

Figure 6.13
One curved mirror can also direct photons onto a screen.

screen

distant source of photons ⟶

advantageous because it acts like many thousands of carefully positioned small flat mirrors. In the largest telescopes in the world (as of 2000), located in Hawaii, astronomers combined many mirrors, each of which is curved (see Figure 6.14).

Describing a Lens in the Photon Model

When a piece of cardboard with a pinhole in it is placed between a point source of light and a screen, the image formed on the screen appears dim. The image appears dim because only a relatively small number of photons reach the screen per second—most strike the cardboard and are absorbed, or never reach the cardboard at all (refer back to Figure 6.3). In doing Activity 6.2 you may have discovered that when you made the pinhole larger the image became less sharp—if you made the pinhole large enough, the image disappeared altogether.

About Mirrors and Lenses ✳ **121**

Figure 6.14
The Keck I Telescope in Hawaii.

QUESTION: Using the photon model, describe why the image produced by a pinhole disappears if the pinhole is made large enough.

It is unfortunate that you cannot make a pinhole as large as you like and still obtain an image, because a large pinhole would allow more photons per second to reach the screen and the image would appear brighter. How can you produce a brighter appearing image that isn't blurry? In Activity 6.2 you discovered some of the properties of lenses. You might have noticed that a lens produces an image that appears brighter than an image produced by a pinhole. In terms of the photon model, a lens acts much like a mirror—a lens changes the direction in which photons are traveling. By changing the path of photons, a lens allows photons to reach the image that otherwise would not have reached it. (See Figure 6.15.) When more photons reach the image per second, the image appears brighter, assuming, as usual, that we stand at the same position relative to the screen.

Lenses must be carefully designed to direct photons from an object to proper places on its image. The direction in which a photon is traveling changes when the photon leaves one medium, such as air, and enters

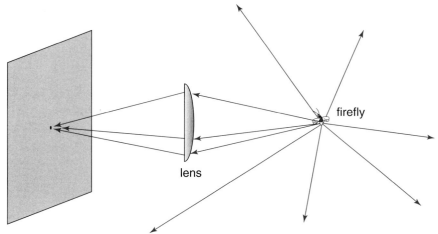

another medium, such as glass. The photon's path alters direction again when it returns to the first medium (see Figure 6.16). The amount of the overall change in path direction depends on the exact composition of the glass or plastic used in the lens and must be calculated very accurately if a lens is to work properly.

A lens has one disadvantage relative to a pinhole, however. As you have discovered, a pinhole can form a sharp image on a screen placed at many different distances from the pinhole, but a lens forms a sharp image on a screen only when the screen is placed at or near a certain distance from the lens. You found in Activity 6.2 that this "certain distance" depends on how far the lens is from the object whose image is being formed. If an object is relatively close to the lens, its image is farther from the lens than if the object were relatively far from the lens. You can explore the relation between the "object distance" and the "image distance" using the materials in Activity 6.2.

Figure 6.16
A photon's path changes when the photon passes from one medium to another.

SUMMARY

The photon model provides a simple way to predict the behavior of mirrors and lenses. In this model, photons travel through space on straight paths. When a photon strikes a mirror, the mirror changes the direction of the photon's path. The angle a photon's path makes with a mirror's surface before the photon bounces from it is the same as the angle the photon's path makes with the mirror after the photon bounces from it (angle in = angle out). Similar, but somewhat more complicated, rules allow opticians to design lenses; other factors must be considered for the design of optical systems to be used in space (see Figure 6.17).

Pinholes can form images of objects on screens "behind" the pinholes. Lenses also form images of objects, but a lens, in contrast to a pinhole, has to be positioned "just right" between an object and a screen for the image to be sharp.

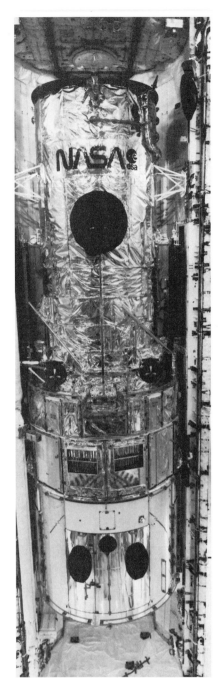

Figure 6.17
This photograph shows the Hubble Space Telescope, still in the cargo bay of the Space Shuttle, being readied for placement in orbit around the Earth.

HOMEWORK

1. A pinhole camera is set up with the distance from the pinhole to the film equal to 25 cm. It is set up on a picnic table and is used to take a picture of a flagpole located 20 m away. The flagpole is 4 m tall.

   a) How tall is the image of the flagpole on the film?

   b) The pinhole is enlarged slightly by twirling the very sharp point of a pencil in the original pinhole. How will this affect the resulting picture?

   c) If you increase the distance from the pinhole to the film to 50 cm, what effects, if any, would you see on the picture?

2. When a lens replaces the pinhole of a pinhole camera, how does the appearance of the image change?

3. Show with a diagram, like the one below, that the shortest vertical flat mirror you need to be able to see your whole image as you stand upright is exactly one-half your height. No calculations are necessary, only the diagram.

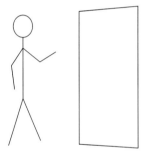

SELF-TEST

1. After you constructed your pinhole tube, you used it to view the filament of a lightbulb. If the filament had been 1.5 cm long, the pinhole 10 m from it, and the tube length 35 cm, what size image would have been produced on the tracing paper?

2. Using the same pinhole tube, you view another lightbulb that has a 2-cm-long filament. If your tube is 30 cm long, and you have a 0.5-cm image on the tracing paper, how far will the pinhole be from the filament?

3. When you use your telescope to look at something on the opposite side of your classroom and then take it outside to look at something on the horizon, do you have to make it longer or shorter to focus the image? Why?

ACTIVITY 6.1   INVESTIGATING MIRRORS

PURPOSE

To observe how light is reflected by a single flat mirror and combinations of flat mirrors.

WHAT DO YOU THINK?

P1. *An injured student had to lie flat on his back in bed. He asked his sister to position the flat mirror from his dresser so that the mirror would reflect the light from a TV screen onto the ceiling over his head. Was the student able to watch TV this way?*

MATERIALS

1 flashlight with removable cover
1 sheet of graph paper
1 piece of dark paper and scissors (optional: see step J)
1 chalkboard eraser (optional: whiteboard eraser)
1 white cardboard screen, about 15 cm × 15 cm (6 in. × 6 in.)
1 pen or pencil
1 clear 200-watt lightbulb, with socket mounted on a flat base
1 meterstick
6 flat mirrors, 2.5 cm × 2.5 cm (1 in. × 1 in.) each, mounted on wooden blocks

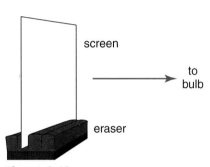

Figure 6.18

PROCEDURE

A. Place the lightbulb near one end of a table.

B. Use the eraser as a base to support the screen by slipping the screen into the middle crease of the eraser. When the eraser is placed flat on a table, the screen should be upright, like a miniature movie screen. Place the screen on the table as far from the lightbulb as possible. Position the screen so that it faces the bulb. See Figure 6.18.

C. Turn on the bulb. Place one of the mirrors so that it is halfway between the bulb and the screen, but *not* in line with the bulb and screen; see Figure 6.19. Turn the mirror so that it faces the bulb. Then slowly turn the mirror until light reflected from the mirror shines on the screen. Move the mirror to try to get an image of the bulb on the screen. (You may also turn and move the screen.) Record your observations. Turn off the bulb when you are done.

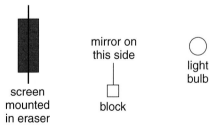

Figure 6.19
View from above the table of the setup in step C.

DO NOT TOUCH THE BULB WHEN IT IS ON OR FOR A FEW MINUTES AFTER YOU TURN IT OFF. YOU MAY BE BURNED.

CAUTION

1. *What are your observations from step C?*

D. Position the mirror about 50 cm (18 in.) from one edge of the table, with the mirror facing toward that edge. Lay a pencil or pen in front of the mirror with one end pointing at the mirror. Lower your head so that it is level with the mirror and look at the mirror. Refer to Figure 6.20.

Figure 6.20

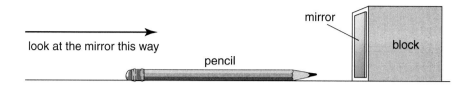

look at the mirror this way · pencil · mirror · block

2. *Where does the image of the pencil appear to be located? Does the image exist where it appears to be, that is, are photons reaching your eyes from the image's apparent location?*

E. Pick up the mirror and look at yourself in it. Move the mirror away from your face.

3. *How did the appearance of your face change as the mirror was moved away from it? Can you position the mirror so that you or a friend can see all of your face in the mirror?*

F. Experiment with positioning the mirror to determine if your entire body can be seen in the mirror. Let a partner be the observer, if necessary.

4. *Did you find a position for the mirror so that your entire body was visible in the mirror? If so, describe the positions of the mirror and the observer with respect to your body. (How far was the mirror from you? Were you the observer or was your partner? If your partner was the observer, where was she or he located?)*

G. With a partner, try arranging mirrors (any number) so that one of you can see the other in a mirror without being seen by the other person, who is trying to see you by looking in one of the mirrors.

5. *Describe the results of step G.*

H. Place a mirror so that it reflects the light from the bulb onto the white screen. Place a second mirror next to the first mirror and turn the second mirror so that it reflects the light from the bulb to the same spot on the screen as the first mirror. Continue with this procedure, adding as many mirrors as you can.

6. *How, if at all, did the apparent brightness of the spot of light on the screen change as more mirrors were used?*

7. *Sketch the final arrangement that you made with the mirrors in step H.*

I. Darken the room. Hold the flashlight in one hand and stand about 3 m (10 ft) from a smooth wall. Turn on the flashlight and aim it at the wall.

8. *Describe the pattern formed on the wall by the light from the flashlight.*

J. Turn off the flashlight. Take off the flashlight's cover and remove the shiny, cone-shaped reflector. (If you cannot remove the reflector, cut a piece of dark paper so that it covers the reflector, but not the bulb.) Replace the cover. Repeat step I.

9. *How does the pattern of illumination on the wall in this step compare to that in step I?*

10. *By considering the results of steps H, I, and J, can you draw any conclusion about the purpose of the reflector in the flashlight? If so, what do you think is the purpose of the reflector?*

11. *List some other light sources in which you expect to find reflectors similar to the one in the flashlight. Place an "X" next to each of these light sources that you* **know** *has a reflector in it.*

K. Position the bulb so that it is about 30 cm (12 in.) higher than the tabletop. (A stack of books can be used to support the bulb.) Place a mirror on a sheet of graph paper about 3 m (10 ft) from the bulb. (It may be necessary to place the bulb and the mirror on separate tables so that they are 3 m apart.) Position the mirror so that it reflects light from the bulb onto the part of the graph paper between the bulb and the mirror. Refer to Figure 6.21. Place a second mirror next to the first and adjust its position so that light reflected by the second mirror shines on the same spot on the graph paper as does the light reflected by the first mirror. Add a third mirror in the same manner as the second. Add three more mirrors, one at a time. Use a pen or pencil to make a mark on the graph paper where the front of each mirror touches the paper. Connect these marks with a smooth line.

Figure 6.21

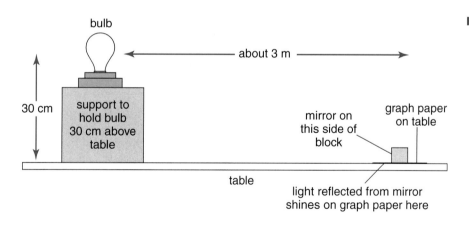

12. *What happened to the brightness of the spot of light on the paper as mirrors were added in step K? How, if at all, did each of the following change as mirrors were added: the shape of the spot of light, the area covered by the spot of light?*

13. *How do your results from step K compare with your results from step J?*

14. *Describe the shape of the line that you drew in step K that connected the mirror position marks. What, if any, relation do you see between the shape of the flashlight reflector in step J and the shape outlined by the mirrors in step K?*

ACTIVITY 6.2

INVESTIGATING PINHOLES AND LENSES

PURPOSE

To make images with pinholes and with lenses; to compare the images made by a pinhole and a lens.

WHAT DO YOU THINK?

P1. *What differences in appearance, if any, are there between an image created by a pinhole and an image created by a lens?*

MATERIALS

1 clear 200-watt lightbulb, with socket mounted on a flat base
1 chalkboard eraser (optional: whiteboard eraser)
2 pieces of thin cardboard, about 10 cm × 10 cm (4 in. x 4 in.)
1 pen or pencil
1 white cardboard screen, about 15 cm × 15 cm (6 in. x 6 in.)
masking tape
1 large convex lens, 45 mm (1.75 in.) diameter
1 meterstick
1 small convex lens, 18 mm (0.75 in.) diameter
1 ruler
1 pin

PART A   PINHOLES

PROCEDURE

A. Use the pin to make a small hole in the center of one piece of thin cardboard.

B. Tape a piece of masking tape slightly more than 2 m (80 in.) in length onto a flat, horizontal surface such as a tabletop or a floor. Use the meterstick to mark the tape every 10 cm, starting with 0 cm at one end of the tape and ending with 200 cm near the other end.

C. Place the base holding the lightbulb on the tape so that the center of the bulb is at the 100-cm mark. Do *not* turn on the bulb.

D. Use the eraser as a base to support the screen by slipping the screen into the middle crease of the eraser. When the eraser is placed flat on your work surface, the screen should be upright, like a miniature movie screen. Place the screen at the 0-cm mark on the tape so that the screen faces the lightbulb.

E. Turn on the bulb.

 **CAUTION** DO NOT TOUCH THE BULB WHEN IT IS ON OR FOR A FEW MINUTES AFTER YOU TURN IT OFF. YOU MAY BE BURNED.

✳ The Universe in Your Hands

1. *What do you see on the screen?*

F. Place the cardboard square with the pinhole flat against the screen, facing the bulb. Slowly move the pinhole away from the screen, making sure that the light from the bulb shines through the pinhole and onto the screen. As you move the pinhole away from the screen, keep looking at the screen. Turn off the bulb when you are done.

2. *Describe what happened to the image on the screen as the pinhole was moved farther from the screen. Your description should include the height of any image seen; its sharpness or how fuzzy it looks; and its relative brightness, for example, "very bright," "faint," "hard to see," etc.*

G. In step F, the distance between the pinhole and the screen increased, but the distance between the pinhole and the bulb decreased because the bulb was not moved. To remove the effects, if any, caused by the decreased pinhole-bulb distance, repeat step F, but move the bulb each time you move the pinhole so that the pinhole-bulb distance does not change. Describe what you see on the screen. Turn off the bulb when you are done.

DO NOT TOUCH THE BULB WHEN IT IS ON OR FOR A FEW MINUTES AFTER YOU TURN IT OFF. YOU MAY BE BURNED.

3. *Are the results of step G identical to those of step F? If the results are not identical, discuss any differences in the images. (For example, when the pinhole was the same distance from the screen in steps F and G, was there any difference in the heights of the images?)*

H. Use a pen or pencil to punch a hole through the center of the second cardboard square. Twist the pen or pencil around inside the hole to make sure the edge of the hole is smooth and rounded.

I. Repeat steps F and G with the "large" pinhole. Record your observations.

4. *Does the size of the hole affect the image? If so, describe how the image is affected. (Is the image brighter, larger, etc.?)*

PART B   LENSES

PROCEDURE

A. Place the lightbulb at the 200-cm mark on the tape. Position the screen at the 0-cm mark. Do *not* turn on the bulb.

B. Pick up the large lens, being careful to hold it by the edge to prevent your fingers from smudging it. Look closely at the lens and notice that one side curves outward slightly while the other side is flat. Turn on the bulb. Hold the lens in front of the screen with the flat side facing the screen. Move the lens slowly away from the screen while looking at the screen. If an image is visible, describe it, including its height, its changes in apparent brightness, and its sharpness. Record your observations. After making these observations, turn the lens so that the curved side faces the screen, repeat your observations, and record your data. Turn off the bulb when you are done.

1. *Did reversing the lens affect what you saw? If it did, what differences did you observe? (For example, when the lens was reversed, was the image brighter?)*

2. *How do the two sets of results obtained with the lens in step B above compare to the results obtained with the pinhole in step F of Part A? Does the lens form images in the same way as the pinhole?*

3. *How do the results obtained with the lens in step B compare to the results obtained with the mirrors in step H of Activity 6.1? How is the lens similar to the flashlight reflector in step J, Activity 6.1? How do the lens and reflector differ?*

C. Place the lens flat on this text. Stand up and look at the text through the lens. Lift the lens slowly away from the page towards one eye.

4. *How did the appearance of the letters of the text change as the lens was moved farther from the page?*

D. Hold the lens close to one eye and look through the lens at an object at least 4 m (13 ft) away from you. Continue to look through the lens as you move it slowly away from your eye, until the lens is as far away as your arm can stretch.

5. *How did the appearance of the object change as the lens was moved away from your eye?*

E. Repeat step B with the small lens, recording your observations. Turn off the bulb when you are done.

 **CAUTION** **DO NOT TOUCH THE BULB WHEN IT IS ON OR FOR A FEW MINUTES AFTER YOU TURN IT OFF. YOU MAY BE BURNED.**

6. *How do your results with the small lens compare to your results with the large lens (step B)?*

F. Repeat step C with the small lens.

7. *How did the appearance of the letters of the text change as the lens was moved farther from the page? How do the results obtained with the small lens compare to those obtained with the large lens?*

G. Repeat step D with the small lens.

8. *How did the appearance of the object change as the lens was moved away from your eye? How do the results obtained with the small lens compare to those obtained with the large lens?*

H. Turn on the bulb and hold the large lens in the position where it creates the sharpest image of the bulb filament on the screen. (The filament is the tightly coiled piece of wire inside the glass bulb.) Use the pinhole card as a shield to cover different portions of the lens (lower half, upper half, righthand side, etc.). Turn off the bulb when you are done.

9. *What happened to the image when each different portion of the lens was covered?*

ACTIVITY 6.3   BUILDING AND USING A PINHOLE TUBE

PURPOSE

To build a pinhole tube and use it to make terrestrial and astronomical measurements.

WHAT DO YOU THINK?

P1. *How many Sun diameters fit between the Earth and the Sun?*

PART A BUILDING A PINHOLE TUBE
MATERIALS

> 2 paper-towel tubes, one of which fits inside the other
> 1 small sheet of aluminum foil (large enough to fit over the end of the tube)
> 1 piece of millimeter tracing graph paper (about 10 cm x 10 cm)
> 1 200-watt unfrosted lightbulb with clamp socket
> 1 ballpoint pen or a straight pin
> 1 meterstick
> 3 rubber bands
> 1 pair of scissors

PROCEDURE

Refer to Figure 6.22 for steps A and B.

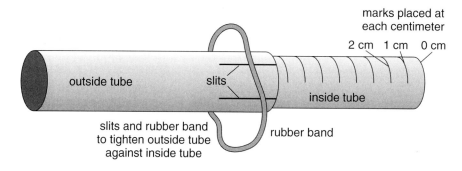

Figure 6.22

A. Be sure your two paper-towel tubes fit together easily. Measure the length of the outer tube. Cut four slits equally spaced around the circumference of the outside tube with each slit being about 2 cm long. Slide the inside tube into the outside tube (into the end with the slits) and wrap a rubber band tightly around the cut end of the outside tube to prevent the inside tube from slipping out.

B. Push the inside tube farther into the outside tube until the ends of both tubes are even with each other. Pull the inside tube out 1 cm. Use the end of the outside tube to guide your drawing of a line on the inside tube. Label this line as "1 cm." Pull the inside tube out another centimeter. Again, draw a line on the inside tube using the outside tube as a guide. Label this line "2 cm." Continue this procedure until the inside tube falls out of the larger tube or until the inside tube becomes too loose to be stable. As you slide the two tubes apart, you should now be able to read the total length of the pinhole tube by adding the centimeter reading on the inner tube to the length of the outer tube. See Figure 6.22.

Refer to Figure 6.23 for steps C–E.

Figure 6.23

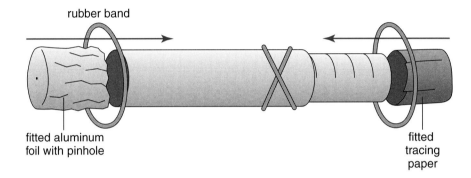

rubber band

fitted aluminum foil with pinhole

fitted tracing paper

C. Place the aluminum foil over the end of the outside tube which does not have the slits. Use a rubber band to hold the foil in place. Be careful to keep the foil smooth over the end of the tube.

D. Using either a straight pin or a ballpoint pen, slowly and carefully punch a small hole in the center of the aluminum foil. Check that the pinhole is round and not a linear rip; if the foil was ripped, use a new piece and try again.

E. Place the graph paper or tracing paper over the exposed end of the smaller tube. Hold the paper in place with a rubber band and be careful to keep the paper smooth over the end of the tube.

Refer to Figure 6.24 for steps F–H. Figure 6.24 shows the arrangement as seen from above.

Figure 6.24

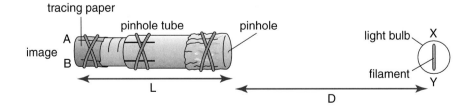

tracing paper

pinhole tube

pinhole

image

light bulb

filament

F. Place the 200-watt lightbulb at one end of the room. Take care to keep the length of the tube perpendicular to the long axis of the bulb's filament. This experiment will work best if the walls, floor, and ceiling are as dark as possible. (The dark color will make the filament easier to see.) *Do not turn on the bulb yet.*

G. *Keep bulb off.* Measure the length of the filament (line XY in Figure 6.24). To make the measurement, look straight down on top of the bulb and hold a ruler against the glass. Close one eye and estimate the length straight across (the filament will probably be slightly curved).

Refer to Figure 6.24 for the following questions.

1. *What is the length of the filament (XY) in cm?*

H. Turn on the bulb. Stand across the room from the bulb and aim the pinhole at the bulb, keeping the pinhole tube horizontal and perpendicular to the filament of the bulb. Slowly adjust the position of the tube, moving it around until you can see an image of the bulb's filament on the tracing paper; it will appear as a small, bright line. Slide the smaller tube in or out until the image of the filament is sharply focused on the paper. Keep the pinhole tube in this position, with the image of the filament focused on the tracing paper, to answer questions 2–4.

DO NOT TOUCH THE BULB WHEN IT IS ON OR FOR A FEW MINUTES AFTER YOU TURN IT OFF. YOU MAY BE BURNED.

2. *What is the length of the tube from the pinhole to the tracing paper (**L**) in centimeters?*

3. *What is the distance between the bulb filament and the pinhole (**D**) in centimeters?*

4. *What is the length of the filament's image on the tracing paper screen (**AB**) in centimeters?*

5. *What is the size/distance ratio for the filament from the point of view of the pinhole?*

6. *What is the size/distance ratio for the image from the point of view of the pinhole?*

7. *How do the ratios in questions 5 and 6 compare? Which is larger, or are they equal?*

8. *Do you think your answer to questions 7 will always be true for any image?*

9. *Based on your answer to question 7, how do the angular sizes of the image and of the filament compare? Which is larger, or are they equal?*

10. *Do you think your answer to question 9 will always be true for any image?*

Discuss the results of Part A with your classmates before continuing to Part B.

YOU CAN NOW USE YOUR PINHOLE TUBE TO ESTIMATE THE DIAMETER OF THE SUN!

BE CAREFUL NEVER TO LOOK DIRECTLY AT THE SUN!!!

PART B ESTIMATING THE DIAMETER OF THE SUN

MATERIALS

Per team of two students

pinhole tube from Part A

PROCEDURE

Work in pairs for this activity; each pair has one tube.

A. Take the pinhole tube outside on a sunny day. Extend the tubes to their greatest possible length without their coming apart.

B. Aim the pinhole end of the tube towards the Sun. Slowly adjust the position of the tube, moving it around until you see a bright disk on the graph paper. This disk is the image of the Sun.

 **CAUTION**   **LOOK ONLY AT THE GRAPH PAPER, NOT AT THE SUN!**

1. *Measure and record the length of the tube from the pinhole to the tracing paper in millimeters.*

2. *Measure and record the diameter of the Sun's image in millimeters.*

3. *Calculate the number of solar image diameters that, if placed "end-to-end," would fill the length of the tube. (Divide the answer from question 1 by the answer from question 2.)*

4. *How many solar diameters is the Sun from the Earth? (Hint: Remember Activity 4.1.)*

5. *Given that the Sun is 150,000,000 km from the Earth, calculate the diameter of the Sun.*

EXTENSIONS

1. You can determine the size/distance ratio for the Sun by using a mirror instead of a pinhole tube. You will need

   1 small, flat mirror
   1 piece of chalk
   a sunny day
   1 tape measure
   an outside wall that you can mark on with chalk

 **CAUTION**   **WARNING: NEVER LOOK AT THE SUN IN THE MIRROR!**

Take the mirror outside. Stand so you are facing, and at least 15 m (50 ft) away from, the shaded wall of a building. The Sun must also be visible either in front of you or to your side. Position the mirror so it reflects an image of the Sun onto the wall you are facing. Prop up the mirror so the image is steady and walk to the wall. Use the chalk to trace the outline of the reflected image of the Sun on the wall.

With the mirror still propped in place, measure both the diameter of the outlined solar image on the wall and the distance from the wall to the mirror with the tape measure.

a) What is the diameter of the solar image in millimeters?

b) What is the distance from the mirror to the image in millimeters?

c) How many solar diameters distant is the Sun from us?

d) How does the number in (c) compare to the number you obtained using the pinhole tube (Part B, question 3)?

2. Repeat Part B one night when there is a full Moon to find the size/distance ratio of the full Moon instead of the Sun. Replace the paper on the tube from Part B with a new piece. (You may need to cover your head and the end of the tube with a jacket to see the Moon's image clearly. Watch your step!)

a) How does the size of the Moon's image compare to the size of the Sun's image? Is it bigger, smaller, or the same size?

b) How does the size/distance ratio for the Moon compare to the size/distance ratio for the Sun? Is it bigger, smaller, or the same size?

ACTIVITY 6.4   BUILDING AND USING AN ASTRONOMICAL TELESCOPE

PURPOSE

To build a simple telescope and use it to make terrestrial and astronomical observations.

WHAT DO YOU THINK?

P1. *If you were to replace the aluminum foil in a pinhole tube with a lens, how would the image on the tracing paper change (if it were to change)? (Would the image be brighter or dimmer? bigger or smaller? right-side up or upside down? clearer or fuzzier? as those formed by the pinhole tube?)*

PART A BUILDING A SIMPLE TELESCOPE

MATERIALS

    1 pinhole tube from Activity 6.3
    1 pair of scissors
    1 200-watt unfrosted lightbulb with clamp holder
    masking tape
    small piece of clean, thin cloth or facial tissue
    1 meterstick
    1 large lens (NOTE: To avoid scratching the lens, place it on a piece of paper or cloth.)

Figure 6.25

PROCEDURE

Refer to Figure 6.25 for the following instructions.

A. Remove the aluminum foil from your pinhole tube.

B. Pick up the large lens, being careful not to smudge it with your fingers. Fit the flat side of the lens snugly against the front of the outer tube, making sure it is positioned perpendicular to and centered on the tube. Wrap a piece of masking tape around the end of the tube to make a collar that holds the lens firmly in place. Fold the tape around the edge of the lens. Use a second piece of tape if necessary. (You should be able to shake the tube without the lens loosening.)

C. Stand about 3 m from the 200-watt bulb. With the room lights off, aim the lens end of the tube at the bulb. Slide the smaller tube in and out until a clearly focused image of the bulb's filament appears on the tracing paper.

1. *Measure and record the distance from the lens to the tracing paper in centimeters.*

2. *Describe the image you see on the tracing paper.*

D. Take your telescope to the side of the room farthest from the bulb. Move the smaller tube inside the larger one, until the image of the filament is focused on the paper.

3. *What is the distance of the paper from the lens in centimeters?*

4. *Is this distance larger or smaller than it was when you were closer to the bulb?*

5. *If you wanted to project a clear image of a very distant object, would the telescope length have to be longer or shorter?*

E. Aim the lens end of the telescope out a window at a distant object, such as a tree, that is silhouetted against the sky. Adjust the sliding tube until the image is focused clearly on the paper.

6. *Measure and record the length of the telescope—the distance from the tracing paper to the lens—in centimeters.*

7. *Is the length of the telescope larger or smaller now than the length you found in the answer to question 3?*

When a very distant object is brought into focus, the distance from the paper to the lens is called the focal length of the lens. Focal length is defined as the distance at which a lens (or mirror) will focus light from a very distant source to a point.

8. *In what ways are the images projected in steps C, D, and E similar? How do they differ?*

You have now built a telescope that is fundamentally the same as one that an astronomer might use. Astronomers seldom use telescopes to view the sky with their eyes. Far more often, they use telescopes for taking pictures or gathering light that is analyzed with special equipment. The lens (or in most astronomical telescopes, a mirror) collects the light coming from a distant object. When taking astronomical pictures, the image can be focused on a sheet of photographic film or on an electronic device; the tracing paper on your tube takes the place of a piece of film or an electronic device. In this way, the telescope acts as a camera.

Photographic film was not invented until the mid-1800s. Before then, astronomers looked through their telescopes and made drawings of what they saw. You will now convert your telescope so that you can look through it. Then you will make some astronomical observations similar to those made by Galileo in 1610.

PART B   ADDING AN EYEPIECE TO YOUR TELESCOPE

MATERIALS

telescope from Part A
1 foam lens holder
1 meterstick
small piece of clean, thin cloth or facial tissue
1 small lens (NOTE: To avoid scratching the lens, place it on a piece of paper or cloth.)

PROCEDURE

Refer to Figure 6.26 for steps A and B.

Figure 6.26

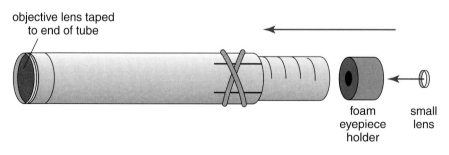

A. Remove the tracing paper from the end of the telescope.

B. Using the small piece of cloth or tissue to prevent smudging, push the small lens into the foam lens holder. With the curved side of the lens facing into the tube, squeeze the foam holder and press the lens/holder assembly into the end of the smaller tube. Be sure the lens is positioned perpendicular to the end of the tube. (You may have to twist the holder to position the lens properly.) The large lens is called the objective lens of the telescope, or more simply the objective. The small lens is called the eyepiece, or the ocular.

CAUTION

The telescope with the eyepiece does two things: (1) the objective lens forms a very small image of a distant object near its focal point, and (2) the eyepiece acts like a simple magnifying glass, enlarging that small image.

Magnifying objects also magnifies motion. To prevent vibration, secure your telescope to some object or hold it snugly against a post or a tree. You might even want to try to invent a way to secure the telescope tube to a camera tripod to prevent the images of objects from "dancing around."

The rest of this activity consists of suggested objects to view with your telescope. Always indicate the date, time, and viewing conditions for any observation; this will provide you with a good record should you make telescope viewing a habit! Draw what you see through the telescope in a circle representing the field of view of the telescope.

Clear skies! (Astronomy's version of "good luck.")

View the Moon through your telescope. The best time is near its crescent or quarter phases. During the full Moon, the lack of shadows makes seeing craters difficult.

1. *Draw a circle to represent your view through the telescope and make some sketches of what you can see. Indicate if you are seeing craters and/or mountains. Record the date, the time, and the weather conditions.*

If Jupiter is currently visible in your nighttime sky, try to observe it. (Your teacher will provide information about its visibility and location.)

2. *Make some sketches of what you can see. Record the date, the time, and the weather conditions.*

The Pleiades is a cluster of stars found in the "shoulder" of the constellation Taurus, the bull. On a clear night, it is easily visible to the naked eye. When it is visible at a convenient time, locate and observe it with your telescope.

3. *Make some sketches of what you can see. Record the date, the time, and the weather conditions.*

The second star from the end of the handle of the Big Dipper (in Ursa Major, the big bear) is really two stars that appear close together. The star that appears brighter is Mizar; the other is Alcor.

4. *Make some sketches of what you can see. Record the date, the time, and the weather conditions.*

Find the winter constellation of Orion, the hunter. If you are not familiar with the appearance of this constellation, refer to a celestial sphere, or to your star finder. The three stars in the center of the rectangle of stars are called the "belt stars." Below the belt is a bright fuzzy

 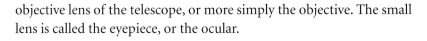

area called the Great Nebula. This appears as the "tip of the sword" hanging from the hunter's "belt." Locate and observe Orion and the "tip of the sword."

5. *Make some sketches of what you can see. Record the date, the time, and the weather conditions.*

PART C   CALIBRATING YOUR TELESCOPE

PURPOSE

To determine the calibration scale for your telescope and to estimate the distances to some objects using this scale and your telescope.

MATERIALS

telescope from Part B
1 meterstick
tape

PROCEDURE

A. Looking through the eyepiece, or ocular, aim the objective end of the telescope at some distant object. Adjust the telescope length until you see a focused image of the distant object.

1. *Measure and record the distance from the objective to the eyepiece in centimeters.*

2. *Describe the image you have viewed.*

B. Tape a meterstick vertically against a wall where it will be 5 to 10 m from a table or desk. Position your telescope on the table or desk and focus on the meterstick. (Tape the telescope down so it will give a stable image.)

3. *How many **millimeters** of the meterstick are visible in the field of view of the telescope?*

4. *How far, in **meters**, is the meterstick from the objective lens of your telescope?*

C. Divide your answer to question 3 by your answer to question 4.

5. *Record this number. (Remember to label the units.)*

   The number in question 5 is the telescope's calibration scale. This scale is a size/distance ratio. The scale tells you the size of an object in millimeters that fills the field when viewed at a distance of 1 m. This scale can be used to determine an object's size when the distance is known or the distance to the object when the size is known.

D. Secure your telescope as in step B and focus it on a large object on the opposite side of the room. Carefully observe what portion of the object fills the field of view of the telescope.

6. *What is the distance from the objective lens to the object you are viewing in meters?*

7. *Using the telescope's calibration scale, calculate in millimeters the width of the portion of the object you observed that fills the field of view.*

8. *Check your work by measuring the width of the portion of the object you observed. Using this measured width and the telescope's calibration scale, calculate the distance between the objective lens and the object you are viewing. What is the difference between this calculated distance and the measured distance? If the difference (error) is less than 1/10 the measured distance, your calculated distance is as accurate as can be expected for this experiment.*

HOMEWORK

BACKGROUND FOR QUESTION 1: Every pair of binoculars is marked with two sets of numbers. (See Figure 6.27.) One set of numbers indicates the magnification and the front-lens diameter. For example, the label "7 × 50" (which is read "7 by 50") means that an object seen through the binoculars appears 7 times (7×) larger than it would without the binoculars and that each front lens is 50 mm in diameter.

Figure 6.27

The second set of numbers gives a viewing scale for the binoculars. For example, the label "525 ft at 1,000 yds" means that at a distance of 1,000 yards, an object 525 ft across will fill the field of view of the binoculars.

Diagraming your answers may help you solve the following problems.

1. The following questions refer to the binoculars shown in Figure 6.27.

    a) What is the calibration scale for the binoculars? (See steps B and C in Activity 6.4, Part C for help.)

b) How tall would a parade float be if its height filled the field of view when it was a football-field length (100 m or about 300 ft) away from the binoculars?

c) If a 2-m-tall (about 6 ft, 8 in.) person's image were to just fill the field of view, how far away would the person be standing?

The following problems refer to Activity 4.2, Seeing Details. Since binoculars or telescopes (with eyepieces) increase the apparent diameter of a distant object, you can see more detail than with just your eyes. The magnification of a telescope or binoculars tells you how much more detail you can see: a 10× (10 power) telescope lets you see 10 times more detail than you can see with your eyes alone. It is as if the distance factor of your resolution limit (Chapter 4) has been increased 10 times, although your eyes have *not* changed.

EXAMPLE

In Activity 4.2, we learned that our friend Ronnie's eyes have a resolution limit of 1/3,300. She can see two lights separated by 1 m at any distance closer than 3,300 m.

With a 10× telescope, Ronnie could go up to 10 times that distance, or 33,000 m (20 mi) away from the lights and still see two points of light. Or she could see two lights separated by 0.1 m (10 cm) at a distance of 3,300 m.

This information will be useful to answer some of the following questions:

2. Write down the resolution limit of your eye.

3. With your naked eye, what is the smallest diameter crater that you can see on the Moon, which is about 400,000 km (240,000 mi) from you?

4. If you were to use 7 × 50 binoculars, what would be the diameter of the smallest crater you could see on the Moon?

5. Would the binoculars shown in Figure 6.27 allow you ever to see the Earth and the Moon as separate points of light if you were at Venus near its closest approach to Earth (40 million km)? Show how you got your answer.

6. If you were orbiting at a distance of 480 km (300 mi) above the surface of the Earth, what would be the diameter of the smallest object that you could see on the Earth's surface?

7. What would be the diameter of the smallest object on the Earth's surface visible to you from this orbit using 11 × 80 binoculars?

QUESTIONS TO TEST YOURSELF

1. How do the size/distance ratios calculated in Activities 4.1 and 6.3 relate to the ratio used for the telescope calibration scale calculated in Activity 6.4, Part C?

2. If you know the focal length of your telescope and the width of the image it creates, what else would you need to know to calculate the distance between the telescope and the object on which the telescope is focused?

Earth, Moon, and Sun

WHAT DO YOU BELIEVE ABOUT THE MOON?

Below is a partial list of some beliefs that people have about our Moon. Some of these beliefs are true while others are not. Which of these statements do you believe is true?

1. The Moon spins.
2. There is a side of the Moon that never receives sunlight and is always in darkness.
3. You see the Moon because it scatters light from the Sun toward you.
4. The Moon changes phase when it passes through the Earth's shadow.
5. The Moon changes phase when clouds or planets block our view of part of the Moon.
6. When people in Washington, D.C., see a crescent Moon at night, people in Hawaii will see a full Moon later that same evening.

HOW BIG IS THE SUN?

Which do you think is larger—the radius of the Sun or the distance from the Earth to the Moon?

Preview: In this chapter you will apply what you learned in Chapter 4 and learn some new ways to measure the diameters of the Earth, Moon, and Sun, and to determine how far away the Moon and Sun are from the Earth. You will build scale models of the Earth, Moon, and Sun. You will use your Moon journal from Chapter 2 to learn about the phases of the Moon. You will then apply what you have learned about the Earth, Moon, and Sun to learn about solar and lunar eclipses.

Scale Models

You have built a model of the celestial sphere (abbreviated CS), but this is not a scale model. Why not? The Sun, Moon, and stars are all represented as lying on the CS, but as you will see, all these objects are at very different distances from the Earth. In a scale model, each distance in the model would be the same fraction of the corresponding distance in the system being modeled.

What does it mean to say that a model airplane is a scale model? (See Figure 7.1.) Suppose you measure the length of a model airplane and find it to be 25 cm (10 in.). If the length of the full-sized airplane is 7 m (23 ft), then, clearly, 25 cm in the model represents 7 m = 700 cm in the airplane; equivalently, 1 cm in the model represents (700/25) = 28 cm in the airplane. In this scale model every length is therefore 28 times smaller than the corresponding length in the airplane. If you measure the wingspan of the model and find it to be 40 cm (16 in.), you can figure out what the wingspan of the airplane is by multiplying by 28. If you measure the propeller on the airplane and find it to be 1.8 m, you can figure out how big the propeller of the model must be by dividing by 28.

Figure. 7.1
A Piper Cub.

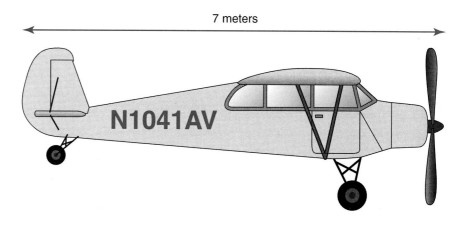

7 meters

N1041AV

QUESTION: What is the wingspan of the airplane in meters?
To build a scale model of the Earth, Moon, and Sun system, you need to know the diameters of each object and the distances between them, as well as how they are arranged in space. Since for this system you cannot determine diameters and distances by using a ruler or tape measure, you will need some other ways to measure them.

How Big Is the Earth?

Determining the radius of the Earth is harder than you might think. Here you will learn one way. But first some preliminaries.

You know from using your model of the CS that if you were standing at the North Pole and looked directly overhead you would see the North Star 90° above the horizon. If you start walking southward from the North Pole, the North Star would appear to sink lower and lower in the sky. At a point halfway between the North Pole and the equator, you would see the North Star at an angle from the horizon of 45°. By the time you reached the equator, the North Star would be on the horizon (see Figure 7.2).

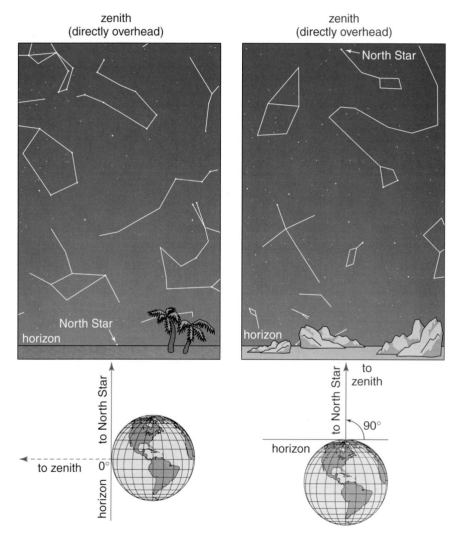

Figure. 7.2
The North Star as seen from the equator and from the North Pole.

QUESTION: What would happen to the apparent position of the North Star in the sky if you continued traveling southward?

The latitude of the North Pole is 90°. The latitude of the equator is 0°. The latitude of a point halfway between the North Pole and the equator is 45°. There is a simple relation between latitude and the angle from the horizon to the North Star: The angle from the horizon to the North Star (see Figure 7.3) is equal to the latitude of the location from which the observation is

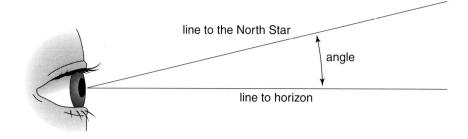

line to the North Star

angle

line to horizon

made. (You can remember this relation by thinking of the angle from the horizon to the North Star, as measured at the North Pole.) This relation is quite accurate because the Earth is nearly spherical and because the North Star is very far away and is nearly directly over the North Pole.

Ninety degrees of latitude span the Earth from the pole to the equator (one-fourth the Earth's circumference). If you know, say, the distance that corresponds to a degree of latitude, you can then easily determine the circumference of the Earth.

Suppose you know a city that is directly south (or north) of another city; if a straight road runs between them, you can use a car to determine the relevant distance between the cities. You know that the angle between the North Star and the horizon as measured from each city corresponds to the latitude of the city. By subtracting the two latitudes you can find the number of degrees separating the two cities. From the distance between the two cities you can find the distance that corresponds to a degree of latitude by simple division. Knowing this number and the number of degrees in a circle, 360, you can then calculate the circumference of the Earth. The radius, r, then follows by use of the formula, $2\pi r$, for the circumference of a circle.

Let's consider a numerical example. In one town, the students measure the angle of the North Star above the horizon and find it to be 33.0°. They then travel directly to another town, due north, and find it to be 1.00×10^3 km (1,000 km, 620 mi) away. In this second town, they again measure the angle from the horizon to the North Star and find it to be 42.0°. See Figure 7.4.

The difference in latitude between the two towns can now be found by subtracting the angle from the horizon to the North Star for one town from that from the other town. This difference in the two angles is equal to 42.0° − 33.0° = 9.0°. Therefore, the difference in latitude between the two towns is 9°. This difference in latitude corresponds to 1×10^3 km, the distance between the towns. If 9° corresponds to 1,000 km, 1° must correspond to 1,000/9.0 = 110 km. Since there are 360° in a circle, the circumference of the Earth must be 110 km per degree × 360° = 40×10^3 km (approximately 25,000 mi). What is the Earth's radius? What is its diameter? What is a simpler way you could have calculated the Earth's circumference from the latitude difference and distance between these two towns?

How Far Away Is the Moon and How Big Is It?

You now know the size of the Earth. Another step in building the scale model is to determine the distance to the Moon and the size of the Moon. Let's first consider a method to measure distance that depends on observing objects simultaneously that are at different distances from you.

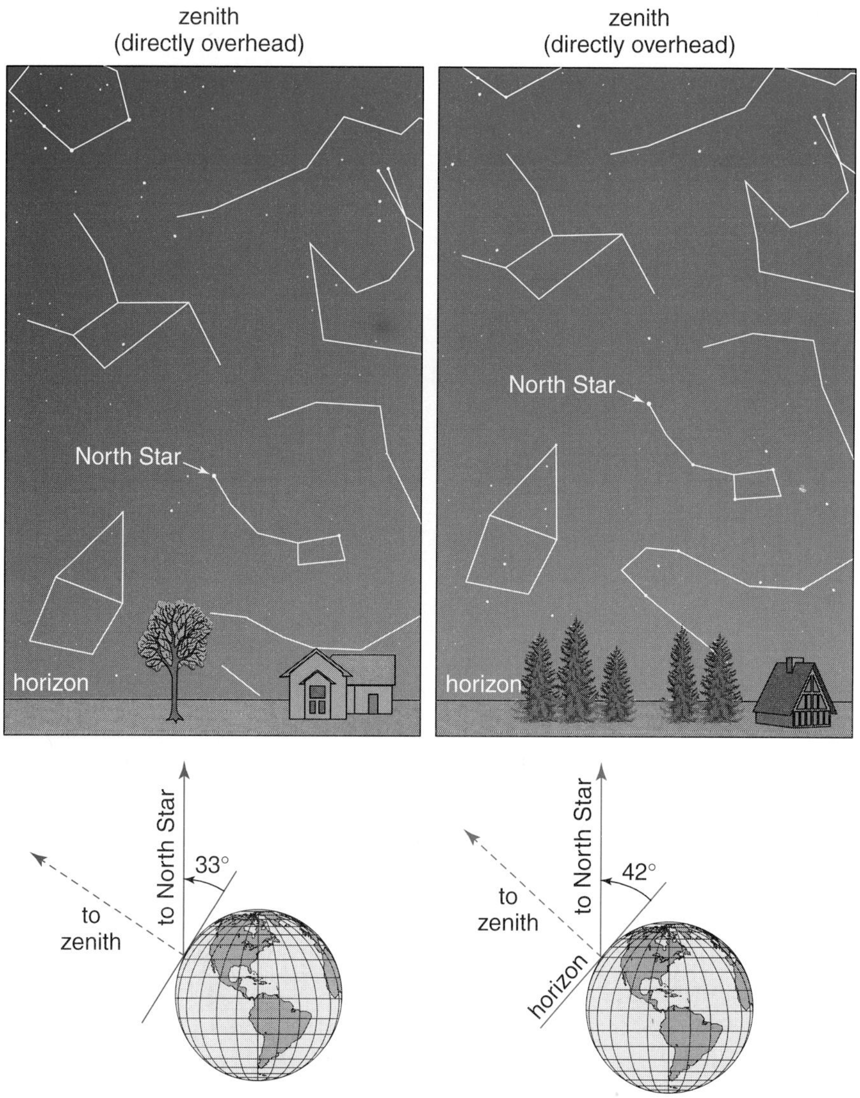

zenith
(directly overhead)

zenith
(directly overhead)

North Star

North Star

horizon

horizon

to North Star

33°

to
zenith

to North Star

42°

to
zenith

horizon

Figure. 7.4
The North Star as seen from two towns, 33° above the horizon (left) and 42° above the horizon (right).

EXERCISE: Face an object from a distance of approximately 3 m (10 ft) and notice its position against a more distant background. Now move approximately 1 m (40 in.) to the left or right of your original position and observe the apparent position of the object against the background. Write a description of what you see on a separate sheet of paper or in your notebook. Move closer to the object and repeat your observations. Move farther away and step farther to the left and right. Write descriptions of what you see (Figure 7.5). Given your results, you should be able to imagine that a quantitative method could be developed to determine the distance to a nearby object by viewing it against a distant background, if you repeat the observation from different places.

When you look at a nearby object from two different positions, the object appears to line up with different, more distant points. This apparent shift in the position of an object due to the observer's changing the position of viewing is called "parallax" and can be used to determine the distance to the object being observed. If two people observe the Moon at the same time from different locations and record their observations accurately, such as by

Figure. 7.5
A person looking at an object and the background from different positions.

 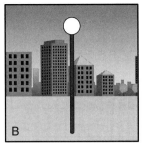 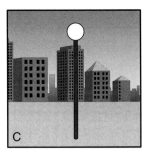

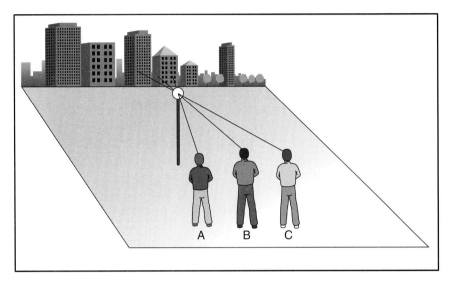

taking a photograph of the Moon, then the photos can take the place of one person changing position. The location of the Moon in the sky, relative to the background stars, will be different in the two photographs, just as the streetlight appeared at different places against the background in Figure 7.5, when viewed from different positions. You can use this parallax effect to determine the distance from the Earth to the Moon. A more modern and far more accurate method, based on radar signals, is discussed in Chapter 8. Using this modern method leads to an average value of about 380,000 km (240,000 mi) for the distance from the Earth to the Moon. Astronomers have also used this method to measure the distances to some of the stars closest to the Earth (see Chapter 10).

QUESTION: What is the diameter of the Moon?

If you and some friends were on the Moon, you could find its diameter with the same method you used to find the diameter of the Earth. However, because Polaris is not directly over the "North Pole" of the Moon, you would use a different star to determine the latitudes of different places on the Moon. The star overhead at the North Pole of the Moon does not appear as bright as Polaris, which might make your task more difficult. Of course, you could use a star overhead at the South Pole of the Moon instead . . .

Unfortunately, or perhaps fortunately, you are not on the Moon, so you will have to find another way to determine its size. Since you know the distance to the Moon, and the size/distance ratio for the Moon, it is very easy to determine the diameter of the Moon. The average distance between the center of the Earth and the center of the Moon is about 3.8×10^5 km

(2.4 x 10^5 mi). The size/distance ratio for the Moon is 1/110 (see Chapter 4), which means that the Moon is 110 of its diameters away from the Earth. The Moon's diameter, therefore, is equal to the distance to the Moon divided by 110:

$$\text{diameter of the Moon} = 3.8 \times 10^5 \text{ km}/110$$
$$= 3.5 \times 10^3 \text{ km}$$

which is about 2.1 x 10^3 mi.

How Far Away Is the Sun and How Big Is It?

Determining the distance to the Sun accurately baffled astronomers for centuries. Using Kepler's relation (see Chapters 9 and 10), they were able to determine accurately the ratio of the average distance of any planet from the Sun to the average distance of any other planet from the Sun. So by defining the distance from the Earth to the Sun as one astronomical unit (a.u.), astronomers automatically knew the distance from the Sun to every planet in these units.

On Earth, we use distance units such as kilometers (and miles). How many kilometers are there in an astronomical unit? That was the key question. To answer it, all one had to do was measure the distance from any one planet to any other planet in kilometers. Not so easy, until powerful radar systems were invented. With these, signals were beamed to Venus, the echoes were detected, and the round-trip time measured. These signals, being a form of light, travel at 3 $\times$ 10^5 km/sec as measured on the Earth (see Chapter 5); thus, the round-trip time could be converted to kilometers and the astronomical unit in kilometers could be, and was, determined. The result yielded nearly 1.5 $\times$ 10^8 km (9.3 $\times$ 10^7 mi) for the average distance of the Earth from the Sun.

With this distance in hand, we move to the next question.

QUESTION: What is the diameter of the Sun?

You can use the same method to determine the diameter of the Sun as you used to determine the diameter of the Moon. You know that the size/distance ratio for the Moon is 1/110; the corresponding ratio for the Sun must also be about 1/110, since the Sun and Moon appear to be the same angular size (see Chapter 4 for a review of angular size). The average distance from the Earth to the Sun must therefore equal about 110 Sun diameters. The Sun's diameter is thus equal to this average distance divided by 110:

$$\text{diameter of the Sun} = 1.5 \text{ x } 10^8 \text{ km}/110$$
$$= 1.4 \text{ x } 10^6 \text{ km}$$

which is slightly under 9 $\times$ 10^5 mi.

Now that you have examined the relative diameters of the Earth, Moon, and Sun and the distances that separate these objects, you can study some of the interesting phenomena associated with them. In Activity 2.1 you observed the Moon for 2 weeks, recording its appearance (phase) and its location in the sky. In Activity 7.2, you use your Moon observations and your knowledge of the Earth-Moon-Sun system to investigate why the Moon has phases and why the phases appear in the pattern you observed.

Figure 7.6

The shadow of the Earth is shown in a side view (upper drawing) and as it would appear if it were projected onto a giant movie screen placed "behind" the Earth in space (lower drawing). In the upper drawing, paths are shown for photons leaving from two points on the Sun's surface. No photon leaving the Sun's surface from between points 1 and 2 can reach the inner region of the Earth's shadow. However, some photons from between points 1 and 2 can reach the outer region of the shadow. Since the outer region of the shadow receives some sunlight, it is not as dark as the inner region, which does not receive any sunlight.

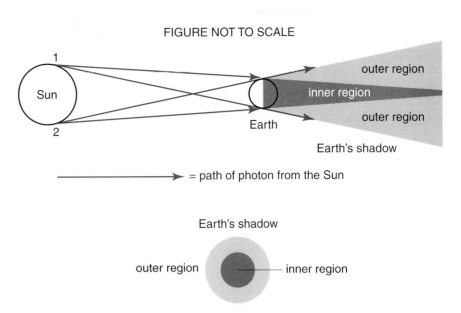

FIGURE NOT TO SCALE

outer region
inner region
outer region

Sun

Earth

Earth's shadow

⟶ = path of photon from the Sun

Earth's shadow

outer region — inner region

The pattern of the Moon's phases arises from its motion around the Earth, which determines the Moon's position in the sky relative to the Sun's. Eclipses are more spectacular events associated with the Moon's motion and the Sun. How do eclipses happen and what chance do you have of seeing either type of eclipse?

Lunar Eclipses

A lunar eclipse occurs when the Moon passes through the Earth's shadow. That sounds simple enough. Since the Sun is always "on," the Earth always has a shadow extending into space. Because the Sun is not a point source of photons, the Earth's shadow has an inner and outer region (see Figure 7.6; also see Chapter 5 for a discussion of shadows). If an observer on the Moon were in the center of this shadow, the observer could not see the Sun at all. When near the edge of this shadow, an observer on the Moon could see part of the Sun. Here by "shadow," we mean the inner region from which no part of the Sun can be seen. If the Moon passes through this shadow as it travels around the Earth, the Moon becomes invisible. Remember, the Moon is only visible because it scatters photons from the Sun toward the Earth; the Moon produces no visible light of its own. Thus, when sunlight is completely blocked from reaching the Moon, you cannot see the Moon.

The Moon can pass through the Earth's shadow only when the Moon is on the other side of the Earth from the Sun. From Activity 7.2, you know that this position corresponds to a full Moon. The Moon must therefore be full when a lunar eclipse occurs. But a full Moon occurs once every 29.5 days, usually without a lunar eclipse happening. In fact, it might seem almost impossible that you could have a full Moon occurring in the same place as a lunar eclipse: a full Moon requires sunlight to reach the Moon, but a lunar eclipse can occur only if the Moon passes through the Earth's shadow. But lunar eclipses do happen only during a full Moon, so it is not impossible. Why not?

Think back to Activity 7.2, when you were moving the ball around your head to model the Moon's motion around the Earth. When you got to

Earthshine

The Earth, like the Moon, scatters sunlight. Sunlight scattered by the Earth is called "earthshine." Earthshine sometimes shines on the Moon. In turn, some of that earthshine is scattered by the Moon back toward the Earth. This scattered earthshine is very dim. However, the part of the Moon lit only by earthshine can sometimes be seen, especially when the Moon appears as a thin crescent and it is nighttime. You may then be able to see the rest of the Moon, faintly visible compared to the bright crescent portion that is scattering light from the Sun toward the Earth. An observer on the part of the Moon lit only by earthshine could see the Earth (see Figure 7.7), but not the Sun.

Figure 7.7
The Earth, as seen from the Moon, has phases, too.

the full-Moon position, you probably noticed that your head blocked the light from the bulb—the ball was in the shadow of your head. How did you solve the problem? You may have held the ball a little higher, so it was above the shadow of your head. Then you could have seen the side of the ball facing you fully "lit up," like a full Moon. When you made that little adjustment to the ball's position, you were actually modeling something that happens with the real Moon.

Look at your celestial sphere (CS). There is a line traced on the CS representing the ecliptic, the apparent yearly path of the Sun around the Earth. This line also traces the path of the Earth's shadow (why?). Imagine that the ecliptic is the path of the Moon around the Earth. If you move a marker on the ecliptic to represent the Moon's motion around the Earth, you can see that the Moon marker is exactly on the opposite side of the Earth globe from the Sun marker at the full Moon. That puts the Moon in the Earth's shadow every time there is a full Moon.

But what if the Moon's path on the CS differed slightly from the ecliptic, while still being a circle on the CS like the ecliptic? Then the Moon's path would be "tilted" from the ecliptic so that the Moon's path crossed the ecliptic at only two points opposite each other on the CS. As a result, most of the times when the Moon was on the opposite side of the Earth from the Sun, the Moon would be above or below the Sun's apparent path. Only rarely would the Moon be at one of these two crossing points when the Sun was at the other. See Figure 7.8. Thus, most of the time the Moon would be above or below the Earth's shadow, resulting almost every month in a full Moon without a lunar eclipse.

In fact, observations of the Moon's position against the background of the stars have shown that the Moon's path is "tilted" from the ecliptic. Only when the Moon marker is on the opposite side of the Earth from the Sun

Earth, Moon, and Sun ✳ **151**

Figure 7.8
In this figure, the celestial sphere is viewed from the side and slightly above the plane of the celestial equator. The Moon's path and the ecliptic are drawn in the figure and also separately on the right-hand side of the figure; the plane of the ecliptic has been shaded to show more clearly how the Moon's path is "tilted" from the ecliptic. (This figure may be easier to understand if you have your celestial sphere handy.)

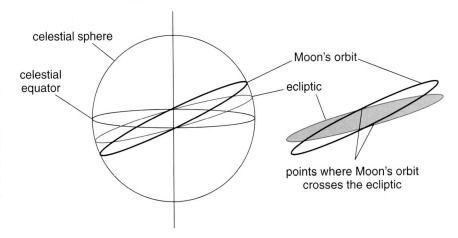

and at one of the two points where the Moon's path crosses the ecliptic (putting the Moon in the Earth's shadow) can a lunar eclipse occur. This situation normally occurs twice a year, about 6 months apart, when the Moon is at one crossing point and the Sun is exactly opposite the Moon on the CS. The Moon must be at a crossing point so that it can be in the Earth's shadow. The Earth's shadow can be at a crossing point only if the Sun is at the opposite crossing point. Since the Moon and the Sun are opposite each other on the CS, the Moon is full. Because (1) the ecliptic and the Moon's path cross on the CS at only two points, and (2) it takes the Sun a year to complete one trip along the ecliptic, the Sun passes through a crossing point only once every 6 months. Thus, all the "pieces" needed for a lunar eclipse come together only twice a year, and only during a full Moon.

You cannot draw a circle on the CS to represent the Moon's path, as you can for the Sun's apparent motion (the ecliptic), because the Moon's path is not a "fixed" circle, that is, a circle that does not change its position on the CS. In a manner somewhat similar to a Hula-Hoop, the Moon's path wobbles around the Earth, slowly changing the points where its path crosses the ecliptic. (This "wobble" is too complicated to explain in detail in this book. Basically, the Earth and the Sun are having a "tug of war" with the Moon, which causes the path of the Moon around the Earth to shift back and forth. However, the "tug of war" is not nearly severe enough to send the Moon crashing into the Earth or the Sun.)

Due to the variable speed with which the Moon moves along its orbit around the Earth, and the differences in the extent of the Earth's shadow at the Moon's orbit, the Moon can take as long as several hours to pass through the shadow. The exact path the Moon takes through the shadow can also vary; most of the time the Moon does not entirely enter the shadow, resulting in a partial lunar eclipse. See Figure 7.9.

How likely are you to see a lunar eclipse when one occurs? The only requirements are that (1) you be on the side of the Earth facing the Moon when it passes through the Earth's shadow, which could be almost anywhere on the nighttime side of the Earth, and (2) the sky be clear. (You may also have to stay up late; a lunar eclipse can occur anytime between sunset and sunrise and last for several hours. Totality, when the Moon is completely within the Earth's shadow, can last for more than an hour.) There have been

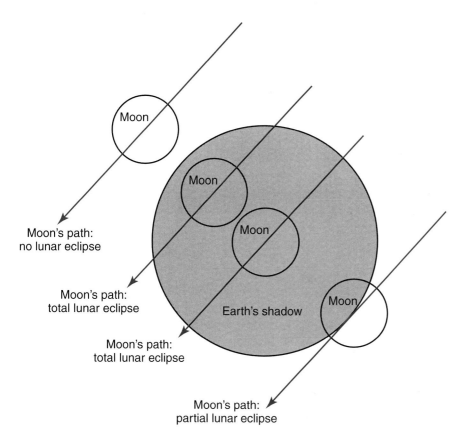

Figure 7.9
The diagram shows some possible paths of the Moon through the Earth's shadow as seen from a location on the nighttime side of the Earth. Of the two paths shown for the Moon during a total eclipse, which path would produce the longer eclipse? Why?

some total lunar eclipses visible from where you live since you were born, probably at least one in the past 5 years or so. If you haven't seen one yet, you will have many opportunities during your life. And it is perfectly safe to view a lunar eclipse—you are only looking at the Moon, which you have done before. You can safely view the Moon during a lunar eclipse through binoculars or a telescope (you observed the Moon with your telescope as part of Activity 6.4).

Solar Eclipses

Many people who have seen a total solar eclipse think that it is the most spectacular event in nature. Solar eclipses have been mentioned before in this book as being caused by the Moon passing in front of the Sun. Now for some details.

For the Moon to pass in front of the Sun, the Moon must be directly between the Earth and the Sun. Referring again to Activity 7.2, you know that the Moon is in the new phase when this arrangement occurs. Just as with the full Moon and lunar eclipses, you do not have a solar eclipse with every new Moon. The reason is similar to that for lunar eclipses: as you view the sky, the Moon usually passes above or below the Sun, not in front of it. However, as with lunar eclipses, about twice a year the Moon passes in front of the Sun, creating a solar eclipse. Recall that a lunar eclipse occurs when the Moon and the Sun are at opposite crossing points on the CS. Since the Moon travels completely around the CS once a month, it takes the Moon about 2 weeks to travel from one crossing point to the other one. Thus, the conditions for a solar eclipse usually occur either 2 weeks before or 2 weeks

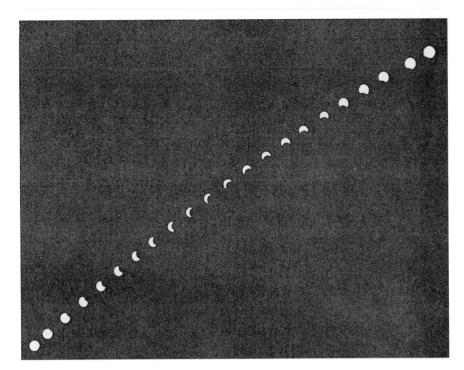

Figure. 7.10

A partial solar eclipse. This picture is a multiple exposure photograph. Each exposure was taken about 6 minutes after the one before it to show the change in the portion of the Sun blocked by the Moon.

after a lunar eclipse. However, most people will not observe both the lunar and solar eclipses (unless they do some traveling).

During a total solar eclipse, a small part of the Earth is in the shadow of the Moon. As the Moon moves in its path and the Earth turns, the Moon's shadow moves across the surface of the Earth at about 3,000 km/hr (2,000 mi/hr). Because the distance between the Earth and the Moon varies, the diameter of the Moon's shadow on the Earth can also vary, from essentially zero up to about 350 km (about 200 mi). The combination of shadow speed and shadow diameter determines how long you will see the Sun completely covered by the Moon (7.5 min is the maximum). You must stand in the Moon's shadow to see a total solar eclipse; if you stand slightly outside the shadow's path, you will see only part of the Sun covered by the Moon, a partial solar eclipse. (See Figure 7.10.) If you are far from the path of the Moon's shadow, you will not see the Moon block the Sun at all.

Your chances of seeing a total solar eclipse are not nearly so good as for seeing a total lunar eclipse. There probably has not been a total solar eclipse visible from where you live since you were born. The last total solar eclipse visible from the United States occurred in 1991 over the island of Hawaii. The last total solar eclipse visible from the continental United States was in 1979. The next total solar eclipse visible from the United States will be in 2017, followed by another one in 2024. However, there will be a number of partial solar eclipses visible from the United States before 2017. To see a total solar eclipse before 2017, you will have to travel. Remember, you have to stand in the Moon's shadow to see a total solar eclipse. For any one location on the Earth, an average of more than 300 years elapses between times when the Moon's shadow passes over that location.

A variation of a total solar eclipse is an annular, or "ring," eclipse. Because the Moon's orbit is not exactly a circle, the distance between the Moon and the Earth varies. An annular eclipse occurs when the Moon

Figure 7.11

An annular eclipse of the Sun.

passes directly in front of the Sun, but when the Moon is at or near its farthest distance from the Earth (see Figure 7.11). In this situation, the Moon has a smaller angular size (see Chapter 4) than the Sun and cannot cover up the Sun completely. Part of the Sun's surface remains showing as a ring around the Moon.

Viewing a solar eclipse of any type can be dangerous because you cannot look safely at the Sun without special protection for your eyes. (*No* type of sunglasses, including "glacier" and "UV blocking" styles, is safe for viewing the Sun.) Even if only a small part of the Sun is not covered up by the Moon, the sunlight can still damage your eyes. Only when the Sun is completely covered by the Moon is it safe to look at the Sun with unprotected eyes. Using binoculars or a telescope to view a solar eclipse is very dangerous and can only be done with special filters fitted to the instrument.

NEVER USE A TELESCOPE OR BINOCULARS TO VIEW THE SUN. **CAUTION**

SUMMARY

The sizes of the Earth, Moon, and Sun can be determined indirectly, that is, you do not have to travel around the object to measure its size. Knowing the size/distance ratios for the Moon and Sun allows you to determine either their size or their distance from the Earth, if you know the other quantity. The distance from the Earth to the Moon can also be determined by using parallax. Parallax is the apparent change in the position of an object with respect to a more distant background caused by a change in the position of the observer.

The Moon's phases follow a regular pattern. The Moon's phases are the result of the Moon's motion around the Earth, causing the Moon to appear in different positions in the sky relative to the Sun's position. Knowing the phase of the Moon, you can estimate the time of moonrise or moonset.

When the full Moon passes through the Earth's shadow, there will be a lunar eclipse. A lunar eclipse is relatively simple to observe: you need only be on the nighttime side of the Earth when the eclipse occurs. When the shadow of the new Moon touches the Earth, there will be a solar eclipse. To see a solar eclipse, you must stand in the Moon's small shadow; solar eclipses are infrequently observed at any particular place on the Earth because the Moon's shadow does not cover a large area on the Earth and because solar eclipses do not occur very often.

1. Two observers decide to measure the size of the Earth. They are located on a north-south line 550 km apart and decide to measure the angle of the North Star above the horizon at the same time. One observer measures the North Star to be at an angle of 30° and the other observer measures it to be at an angle of 35°.

   a) What is the latitude of each observer? Before answering, draw a sketch showing a cross section of the Earth as a circle with two straight lines from the observers to where they perceive the North Star to be located, one straight line from each observer toward the North Star. Label the angular height of each sight line.

   b) What is the difference between the two latitudes? From this difference in the latitudes and the distance between the observers, calculate the circumference of the Earth.

2. Suppose you measured the angular size for a crater on the Moon observed from the Earth and found it to be 0.1°.

   a) What is the diameter of the crater?

   b) How many times wider is the Moon than the crater?

3. The picture below shows the imaginary planet, Voltar, and its three moons. All three moons lie in the plane of Voltar's equator. *You are high above the north pole of the planet, looking down.* Voltar's sun is located 200 million km away, to the (very!) far left in this diagram.

   How do you think these three moons will look to the people of Voltar? For example, could all three moons be seen from some location on the planet at the time this picture was "taken"? Imagine yourself at a specific location on Voltar's surface; draw the appearance of each of the moons you see, and explain the reasoning behind your predictions.

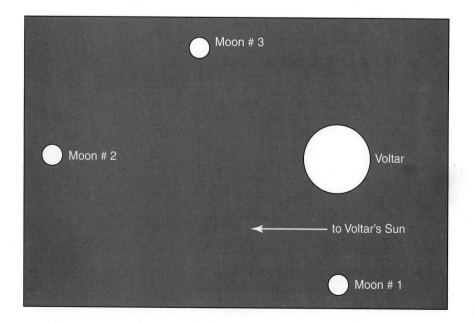

SELF-TEST

1. How many times smaller is the Earth-Moon diameter ratio than the Sun-Earth diameter ratio?

2. How many times smaller is the Earth-Moon distance than the Earth-Sun distance?

3. What phase does the Moon exhibit when it appears 90° west of the Sun in the morning sky? Explain your answer with a diagram.

4. What phase does the Moon exhibit when it appears 90° east of the Sun in the evening sky?

5. If you look up at the Moon and see a waxing crescent phase, what phase of the Earth would an astronaut standing on the Moon see?

BENJAMIN BANNEKER (1731–1806)

When Benjamin Banneker, a son and grandson of freed slaves, began studying astronomy on his own, he practiced what he learned by calculating the times of sunrise and sunset, the phase of the Moon, and the apparent positions of some of the planets and stars on each day of the year. Tables with the information have appeared in almanacs for hundreds of years; the word "almanac" comes from old Arabic words about predicting the weather from the positions of the stars (not a useful practice, see Chapter 15).

Before clocks and watches became common items, people used tables of sunrise and sunset to keep track of time. Sailors used the information to help them navigate, and farmers decided when to plant and harvest based on information about the seasons. In the 1700s, almanacs in America also included stories, essays, proverbs, recipes, and other assorted information in addition to the astronomical data (the table of such astronomical data is called an ephemeris). For people with little opportunity to find many magazines, newspapers, or books (and definitely no radio or television!), almanacs provided entertaining and educational reading material.

Banneker lived his whole life in Maryland. He owned a tobacco farm and spent most of his time working to produce that crop. He also had strong interests in mathematics, music, and things mechanical. When he was 22, he built a working clock by himself with no instructions (he borrowed a watch to use as a model), but he didn't begin to study astronomy until he was 58.

At first Banneker made his astronomical calculations for his own enjoyment and experience, but as he developed accuracy and confidence in his work, he decided to find a publisher and publish an almanac. Just before he finished the tables for a 1792 almanac, he left home for the only time in his life to participate in the land survey for the new capital of the young United States: Washington, D.C. Although Banneker didn't travel very much, his almanac did; Lewis and Clark used Banneker's almanac on their famous expedition across America.

Although Banneker and his family were free, most Black people in 18th century America were slaves. Abolitionists, people who worked to abolish slavery, supported Banneker's work. His first almanacs included essays about the injustice of slavery written by prominent people of the time, including Thomas Jefferson. On the next page is a reproduction of part of the title page of one of his almanacs.

Benjamin Banneker's

PENNSYLVANIA, DELAWARE, MARYLAND and VIRGINIA
Almanack
and
EPHEMERIS
for the YEAR of Our LORD
1792;

**Being ... Leap Year, and the sixteenth year
of American Independence,
which commenced July 4th, 1776.**

*Containing the Motions of the Sun and Moon, the true places and
aspects of the Planets, the Rising and Setting of the Sun, and the
Rising, Setting, and Southing Place and Age of the Moon, etc., the
Lunations, Conjunctions, Eclipses, Judgments of the Weather,
Festivals, and other remarkable days. . . . several useful Tables and
valuable Recipes; various selections from the commonplace Book of
the Kentucky Philosopher, an American sage; with interesting and
entertaining Essays in Prose and Verse, the whole comprising a
greater, more pleasing and useful variety than any work of the kind
and price in North America.*

ACTIVITY 7.1   MAKING SCALE MODELS OF THE EARTH, MOON, AND SUN

PURPOSE

To build scale models of the size and distance relations of the Earth, Moon, and Sun to help you understand how the distances between these objects compare with their sizes.

WHAT DO YOU THINK?

Your teacher will draw a circle to represent the Sun at one end of the board. You, along with each of your classmates, should draw another circle on the board to represent the Earth. Try to draw it to the same scale as the Sun. In other words, if the teacher's circle were the size of the Sun, what size would the Earth be and how far would it be from the Sun?

P1. *How many times bigger than the Earth's diameter is the Sun's diameter?*

Now repeat this exercise, this time for the relation between the Earth and the Moon. Your teacher will draw a circle to represent the Earth. Draw a circle to represent your best guess of the corresponding size of the Moon and its distance from the Earth.

P2. *How many times bigger than the Moon's diameter is the Earth's diameter?*

MATERIALS

an assortment of different size spheres
1 meterstick
1 classroom Earth globe, 30-cm or 40-cm diameter (12- or 16-in. diameter)

PROCEDURE

A. Take one sphere from the box of spheres provided by your teacher. Your classmates will do the same so that each of you will have a different size sphere. Look around the room and find someone whose sphere, along with yours, would represent a scale model of the Earth and the Moon.

B. When you have found a partner, move your spheres apart until they are separated by the distance you think the Earth and Moon would be separated if they were the sizes of the spheres. If you are having difficulty, read the following example.

EXAMPLE

The Earth is about 13,000 km in diameter. The Moon is about 3,500 km in diameter. Therefore, the Earth's diameter is nearly 4 times the Moon's diameter. Thus, if your Moon-sphere is 12 cm in diameter, the Earth-sphere should be about 48 cm in diameter. The Earth-Moon distance averages about 400,000 km. Therefore, it would take about 115 Moon-sized spheres, placed side-to-side, or about 1,400 cm (14 m or about 45 ft), to represent the distance between the Earth and the Moon.

1. *Measure and record the diameters of the objects you used for the Earth and the Moon.*

    model Earth = ? cm   model Moon = ? cm

2. *Show the calculations you made to find the proper scale distance between the models of the Earth and the Moon.*

    model distance = ? cm

C. Place your model of the Moon at its proper scale distance from the model of the Earth.

D. Use the classroom Earth globe to answer the following questions.

3. *At the scale of the globe, what is the diameter of the Moon?*

4. *At the scale of the globe, what is the distance from the Earth to the Moon?*

5. *The Space Shuttle orbits 480 km (300 mi) above the Earth's surface. How far would this orbit be above the surface of the globe if the shuttle's orbit were at the same scale as the globe?*

6. *Some satellites, such as are often used for telephone and television communications, must stay (nearly) directly above the same spot on the Earth. If a satellite can be placed in a circular orbit at an altitude of 36,000 km (22,000 mi) above the Earth's equator, it will complete one full orbit in 24 hours. In this way the satellite appears to stay over the same spot on the Earth's surface, and is therefore called a "geostationary" satellite. How far from the globe's surface would these geostationary (or geosynchronous) satellites be if they were at the same scale as the globe?*

7. *How many times greater is the distance of the Moon from the center of the Earth than is the distance of a geosynchronous satellite from the center of the Earth? How many times greater is the distance of a geosynchronous satellite from the center of the Earth than is the shuttle when it is in orbit?*

    To begin to get a sense of the distance from the Earth to the Sun, you will need the following information:

    The Earth is about 13,000 km (8,000 mi) in diameter.

    The Moon is about 3,500 km (2,200 mi) in diameter and orbits the Earth at an average distance from it of 400,000 km (240,000 mi).

    The average distance from the Earth to the Sun during a year is 150,000,000 km (93,000,000 mi).

    The Sun is about 1,400,000 km (875,000 mi) in diameter.

8. *How many times larger than the Earth's diameter is the Sun's diameter?*

9. *How many solar diameters would fit between the Sun and the Earth?*

E. Choose two spheres, one as a scale model of the Earth, and the other as a scale model of the Sun. Measure their diameters.

10. *Approximately how far apart must these spheres be for the distance between them to be at the same scale? Show your calculations.*
    model Earth diameter = ? cm
    model Sun diameter = ? cm   model Earth-Sun distance = ? cm

F. Separate your spheres by the scale distance found in your answer to question 10. If your classroom is not large enough, move out into the hallway or out to the school yard (with your teacher's permission).

For the previous questions, you measured the diameters of the model Sun, Earth, and Moon and calculated their corresponding distances from each other. You can also calculate their diameters if you start by knowing the distances between them.

EXAMPLE

If your classroom were 15 m long (about 50 ft), how large would a model Earth sphere and a model Sun sphere have to be if the model Sun were to be placed at one end of the room and the model Earth placed at the other?

It takes about 107 Sun diameters to fill the space between the Sun and the Earth. (This number is called a *scale factor*.) 15 meters (1,500 cm) divided by 107 (the scale factor) equals about 14 cm. Thus, a sphere would have to be 14 cm in diameter to represent the Sun.

It takes about 109 Earth diameters to match the diameter of the Sun. Since the Sun is therefore 109 times larger in diameter than is the Earth, you have to divide 14 cm by 109 to calculate how large the model Earth would be. The answer is about 0.1 cm (or 1 mm), or about the size of the head of a pin!

G. Measure the length of your classroom, and let this length represent the scale distance between the Earth and the Sun.

11. *What is this scale Earth-Sun distance (the classroom length) in centimeters?*

12. *Following the example given above, calculate the diameters that the Sun and the Earth would have, if they were at the same scale as the distance between them, when they are placed at opposite ends of your classroom.*
    model Sun diameter = ? cm   model Earth diameter = ? cm

13. *Following the same reasoning as in your answer to question 12, estimate how far the Moon would be from the Earth in your scale model.*

14. *List some common objects that are either about the same size as your model Sun or as your model Earth. (For example, would a softball be about the size of your model Sun?)*

ACTIVITY 7.2   MODELING THE PHASES OF THE MOON

PURPOSE

To use the information from your Moon journal (Activity 2.1) to predict changes in the appearance of the Moon and to predict the rising and setting times of the Moon.

WHAT DO YOU THINK?

Cut out the pictures of the Moon on your handout. Choose the picture that you think best represents the appearance of the Moon 3 days after the new Moon. Tape it onto the square labeled "day 3." Tape the remaining pictures onto the squares in the sequence that you think represents the rest of the Moon's cycle to 26 days after the new Moon.

P1. *If the Moon appeared as in picture B on your handout, at what time on that day would it be highest in the sky?*

PART A   IDENTIFYING THE PHASES OF THE MOON
MATERIALS

Moon journal from Activity 2.1
1 pencil or pen
1 pair of scissors
1 Styrofoam ball 6.5 cm (2.5 in.) in diameter
Chart 7.1
stapler
2 handouts for What Do You Think? activity
transparent tape
1 cardboard sheet, 22 cm x 28 cm (8.5 in. × 11 in.)
1 light source (clear 200-watt lightbulb), with clamp socket

PROCEDURE

A. Place the 200-watt lightbulb as high as possible in the front of the room. Be sure no one blocks the light. This bulb should be the *only* source of light in the room; it will represent the light of the Sun.

B. Sit or stand at a place with plenty of arm room and face the bulb. You should be about 2 to 3 m away from the bulb. Your head represents the Earth (but not to scale).

C. Stick a pencil or pen into the Styrofoam ball. This ball represents the Moon (also *not* to scale). Hold the pencil upright in your left hand with the ball at eye level. Extend your arm toward the light source and move the ball from right to left. This movement represents the motion of the Moon around the Earth. Notice how the shape and size of the lit part of the ball appears to change.

D. Chart 7.1 is a diagram showing an overhead view of a person holding a ball as described in step C. The 16 small circles surrounding the head on the chart represent the positions of the Moon in its orbit around the Earth at about 2-day intervals.

E. Repeat step C, but this time stop and observe the ball in each of the 16 positions shown on the drawing.

F. With a pencil, darken in the large white disks to match the appearance of the ball at each position. *Be sure that what is shaded on the sphere is what is darkened on your diagram.* After darkening one circle, rotate the sheet clockwise to the next circle, to keep the circle that you are darkening at the top.

G. When you have filled in all the disks on the chart, cut the outer circle along the dark line and cut the lines between each darkened circle. *Do not cut the inner edge of the circle.*

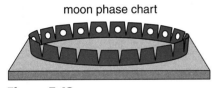

moon phase chart

Figure 7.12

H. Each disk is now a separate tab. Fold each gray tab up so it is perpendicular to the sheet. You now have a model showing the phases of the Moon. It is based on the Moon's position relative to the Earth and Sun. (In this model the person's head is always facing the Sun.)

I. Staple or tape the chart to the sheet of cardboard. The finished device should look like Figure 7.12.

The names of the phases of the Moon for days after new Moon are as follows:

Day Number	Name of Phase
0	NEW MOON
0 to 7.5	WAXING CRESCENT MOON
7.5	FIRST QUARTER MOON
7.5 to 15	WAXING GIBBOUS MOON
15	FULL MOON
15 to 22.5	WANING GIBBOUS MOON
22.5	LAST QUARTER MOON
22.5 to 30	WANING CRESCENT MOON

Some explanation of terms: "Waxing" means gradually increasing in size; "gibbous" means rounded, between half and full; and "waning" means gradually decreasing in size.

J. Write the name of each lunar phase under the picture of it on Chart 7.1.

Use your finished chart to answer the following questions.

1. *For each of the diagrams on the next page, identify the phase of the Moon and the number of days after the new Moon.*

2. *If you saw only a picture of the Moon, how could you tell where the Sun was, relative to the Moon, when the picture was taken?*

3. *If you were to see the first quarter Moon today, what phase would you see 2 days later?*

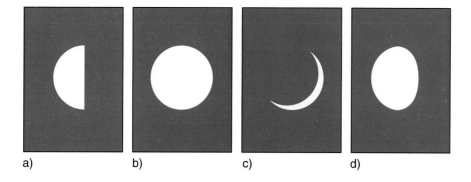

a)   b)   c)   d)

4. *If you were to see the first quarter Moon today, what phase would you have seen 10 days ago?*

5. *At the first quarter Moon, does the Moon appear to the left or to the right of the Sun when you are in the United States?*

6. *At the first quarter Moon, is the angle formed by the line from the Earth to the Sun and the line from the Earth to the Moon greater than, less than, or equal to 90°?*

7. *If it were a full Moon today, how many days later would the Moon be in its last quarter phase?*

8. *If the Moon were in its last quarter phase, in what phase would the Earth appear to be if you were standing on the Moon?*

9. *If you were standing on the Moon and saw the Earth in its full phase, in what phase would the Moon be as seen from the Earth?*

10. *If you looked at the eastern horizon and saw the full Moon just rising, in what direction would you look to see the Sun?*

11. *An inmate is planning to break out of prison. On August 2nd the prisoner sees a first quarter Moon. The inmate has read "Basic Escape Planning" by O. ver daWaal and knows that getting caught is what ruins most escapes. A dark night would help the inmate avoid detection. Based on the Moon phase sighting above, on what date should the prisoner try to get out? Explain your choice of date.*

12. *a) Refer to the predictions you made in the What Do You Think section in this activity. Compare your picture sequence with the phase drawings on Chart 7.1. Make corrections as needed.*

     b) Write the phase name under each photograph.

13. *Refer to the journal of Moon drawings from Activity 2.1. Label the pictures you drew with the proper day number and phase name.*

PART B   TIMING MOONRISE, MOONNOON, AND MOONSET

PURPOSE

To construct a device to determine the phase of the Moon and the location of the Moon in the sky for a given day of the month and time of day.

MATERIALS

Chart 7.1 from Part A
Chart 7.2
Chart 7.3
Tape or paste
Pin or tack

PROCEDURE

A. Cut out the Earth Time circle diagram on Chart 7.2.

B. Tape or paste this circle onto the center circle of your Moon Phase chart (Chart 7.1) from Part A. Be careful to match the phases printed on Chart 7.2 with those you wrote on the Moon Phase chart. *"New Moon" should be in the same direction as the Sun.*

C. Note the 16 small circles on Chart 7.2. Circle 1 has the time "Noon" written above it. Turn the chart around to small circle 5. Write "6:00 p.m." above this circle. Write "Midnight" above small circle 9.

1. *What time should be written above small circle 7?*

D. Write this time and also write the proper times above the other *numbered* small circles.

E. Cut out the Time/Horizon Pointer diagram in Chart 7.3 and pin or tack it to Chart 7.2, the Moon Phase combination. Chart 7.3 should turn freely around the pin. The time that the pointer shows is the time when the Moon is being observed.

The following Moon problems deal with the relations among three quantities: (1) the *phase* of the Moon, (2) the *time* (approximate *standard time*) of the observation, and (3) the *position* of the Moon in the sky. If you know any two of these quantities, you can find the other using this device. These procedures might seem somewhat like magic. But they can be understood, based on what you learn in this chapter. Can you figure them out?

EXAMPLE 1

At *noon* where in the sky would you see the first quarter Moon?

Turn the pointer so it points at *noon*. Find the first quarter Moon. According to the pointer device, the Moon is near the *eastern horizon*, which means the Moon would be rising at *noon*.

EXAMPLE 2

At what time would the waxing gibbous Moon be in the southwest?

Find the waxing gibbous Moon. Turn the pointer circle until this Moon is halfway between south and west. Notice the time at which the *time* pointer is pointing. It is *midnight*.

Use this device to answer the following questions:

2. *If the Moon were to set at 3:00 p.m., what would be its phase?*

3. *If the Moon were rising at midnight, what would be its phase?*

4. *If the Moon were at its highest at 9:00 p.m., what would be its phase?*

5. *When does the last quarter Moon rise?*

6. *When does the waxing crescent Moon set?*

7. *If the Moon were full, at what time of day would it be highest in the sky?*

   Key to diagrams:

   the Sun

   the Moon (in various phases)

8. *From the diagram of the Moon below, identify the phase of the Moon and the approximate time of day.*

   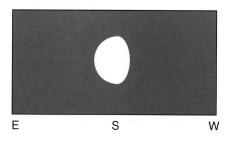

   E   S   W

9. *Explain the problem(s) with the diagram below and indicate at least one way you could correct the problem(s):*

   E   5 p.m.   W

1. For each of these three diagrams of the Moon, identify the phase of the Moon and the approximate time of day.

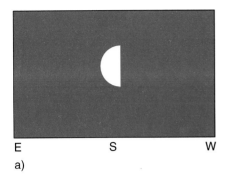

E   S   W
a)

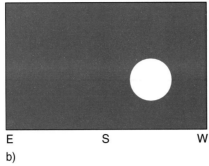

E   S   W
b)

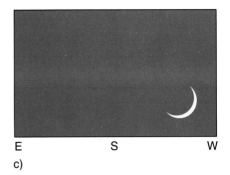

E   S   W
c)

2. Explain the problem(s) with each of the following three pictures and indicate at least one way each of these pictures could be corrected.

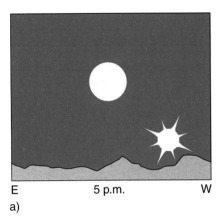

E   5 p.m.   W
a)

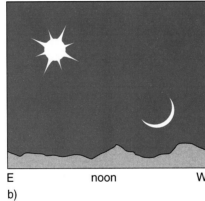

E   noon   W
b)

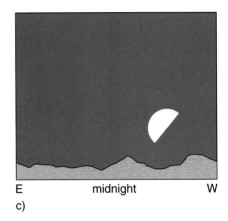

E   midnight   W
c)

DISCUSSION QUESTIONS

1. If the Moon were at first quarter tonight, when would it next be at first quarter?

2. How long does it take for the Moon to make one orbit of the Earth?

3. Study the pictures of the Moon's phases from the beginning of this activity. Does the Moon always keep the same face pointed at the Earth?

4. If you were standing in the center of the part of the Moon visible from the Earth, would you see the Earth rise and set?

5. The picture above shows how Venus would appear through a telescope on the Earth on five different dates. When the "full" Venus was seen, it was in the sky very close to the Sun. Venus was also seen very near the Sun in the sky when it was a thin crescent. The fact that Venus undergoes phases was first observed by the Italian astronomer Galileo. He claimed that the phases meant Venus orbited the Sun, not the Earth. The Moon also has phases and goes around the Earth. Why would Galileo believe these observations were proof that Venus goes around the Sun?

EXTENSIONS

1. There have been at least two TV programs with names referring to the Moon: "The Honeymooners" and "Moonlighting." What are the origins of the words "honeymoon" and "moonlighting"? (The words existed long before the shows.) List other words and phrases that refer to the Moon and try to determine their origins. Why do you think "moon" turns up so often in our daily language?

2. Have another student move the Styrofoam ball in a circle around the 200-watt bulb so that it is about two-thirds as far from the bulb as you are. (If you are 3 m from the bulb, have your friend keep the ball 2 m from the bulb.) This setup is a model of the motion of Venus as seen from the Earth. (Discussion question 5.)

   a) Draw the sequence of phases that you would see if the ball were to move counterclockwise around the bulb (imagine you are looking down on the bulb and ball setup from the ceiling).

   b) How does Venus's phase sequence compare to the Moon's phase sequence?

3. Discuss the phases that Jupiter undergoes as seen from the Earth. (Try setting up a ball and bulb model to work out your answer.) Hint: Jupiter's average distance from the Sun is about 5 times the Earth's average distance from the Sun.

4. a) Diagram the positions of the Moon, the Sun, and the Earth for a lunar eclipse.

   b) In what phase is the Moon during a lunar eclipse?

   c) Why do we not see a lunar eclipse once every month?

   d) Find the dates for the next partial and total lunar eclipses for your area.

5. a) Diagram the positions of the Moon, the Sun, and the Earth for a solar eclipse.

   b) In what phase is the Moon during a solar eclipse?

   c) Why do we not see a solar eclipse once every month?

   d) Find the dates for the next partial and total solar eclipses for your area.

CHAPTER 8

The Paths of the Planets

CAN YOU HELP SUSAN?

Susan is building a scale model of the solar system as a school science project. *She wants to use a basketball to represent the Sun.*

1. Susan has collected the following objects to possibly use as corresponding scale models of some of the nine planets:

    bowling balls
    tennis balls
    golf balls
    marbles
    grains of sand

    Pick two or three of the nine planets and choose the object that you think Susan should use to *most closely* match the scale size of the planet (you may use the same object more than once).

2. When Susan assembles her scale model of the solar system, how far away from the basketball do you think she should place each of the objects you chose to represent planets?

JOURNEY TO PLUTO

Write a brief (2–3 page) science fiction story in which you travel from the Earth to the distant planet Pluto. Include information about the type of spaceship you used, how fast your ship traveled, how long the journey took, and what objects you encountered as you went on your journey.

Preview: In the last chapter, you built a scale model showing the relative distances between, and relative sizes of, the Earth, Moon, and Sun. In this chapter you will build a scale model that includes the other planets as well. You will also learn about models proposed over the years to account for the motions of the planets. (Appendix 2 contains brief descriptions of the planets and their moons.)

The apparent motions in the sky of the pinpoints of light called planets (Greek for "wanderers"), as well as of the Moon and Sun, fascinated people for millennia. Trying to understand why these wanderers appeared to move among the stars as they did was a challenge to scientists—astronomers, mathematicians, and physicists—for at least as long as history has been recorded. Over the last few centuries critical advances in our understanding of gravitation and important developments of mathematics resulted directly from attempts to meet this challenge. In this chapter, we first describe briefly the early history of studies of the apparent motions of the planets and then describe how astronomers determine the relative distances of the different planets from the Sun. With the development of powerful radar systems in the last half of this century, astronomers can now detemine the "absolute" distances of the planets from the Sun. That is, the astronomical unit (Chapter 7) can be determined by radar in terms of kilometers and so relate astronomical to Earth scales of distances. We leave to the next chapter a discussion of the theory of gravitation used to explain the observed motions of the Sun, Moon, and planets.

In earlier times people could see the sky at night more clearly than now because there were fewer lights. People followed the apparent motions of objects in the sky. They noticed that the stars moved regularly across the sky and that the return of the seasons brought the same stars into the same positions each year. They also realized that some of the brighter "stars" moved in more complex patterns across the sky. Strangely, the brightest such object in the morning sky was never seen on the same days as was the brightest such object in the evening sky. Ancient people finally figured out that this "morning star" and this "evening star" were the same "star." The Romans called this "star" Venus. They noticed that Venus never strayed very far from the Sun in the sky and that another "star," Mercury, stayed even closer to the Sun. The "stars" Mars, Jupiter, and Saturn, on the other hand, often appeared in the opposite part of the sky from the Sun.

The ancients also noticed other characteristics of these "wandering stars" or planets; they changed in apparent brightness as they moved against the background of "fixed stars." Mars, Jupiter, and Saturn appeared brightest when they were in positions opposite to that of the Sun in the sky. Moreover, sometimes the planets seemed to stop their motion against the stars, move backward, and then move forward again. Very confusing.

Early Models of Planet Motions

One of the first tasks undertaken by ancient astronomers was to figure out and understand the pattern of the motions of the planets in the sky. The Greek philosopher Aristotle (384–322 B.C.E.) developed a model for these motions in which the Sun, Moon, and planets were attached to spheres surrounding the Earth. He believed, in particular, that the Sun, Moon, and

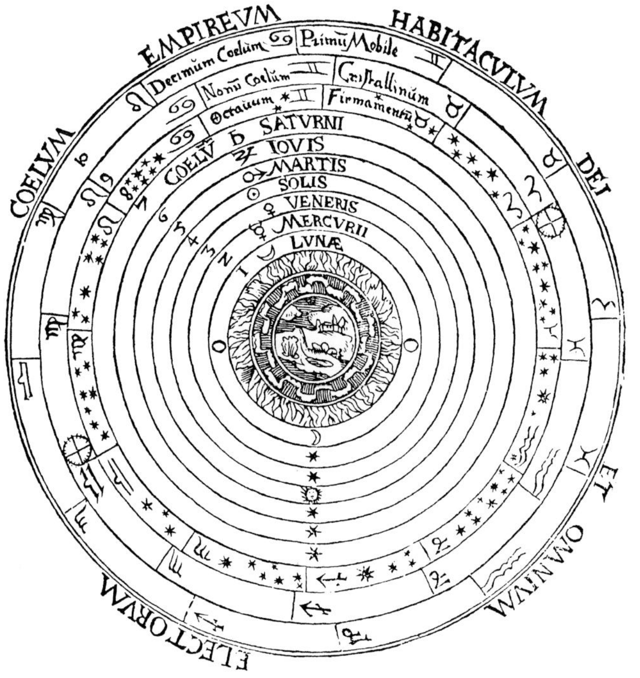

Figure 8.1
Diagram of Aristotle's model of the heavens.

planets moved in circles because circles are a "perfect" form suitable for the heavens (see Figure 8.1). This model, however, provided a poor description of the motion of the planets: The circles were no help in predicting when the planets would change direction and begin to move "backward" against the background of the stars, or when they would resume their original direction of motion. The model also failed to predict that the apparent brightnesses of the planets would change as their positions changed relative to the Sun's. Better models were clearly needed.

Ptolemy (TALL-eh-mee), a Greek astronomer who lived in Alexandria, Egypt, in the second century C.E., developed a model that succeeded in predicting the complex motion of the planets and, to some extent, their changing apparent brightnesses. In Ptolemy's model the planets move in a very complicated way involving what were called "epicycles." Ptolemy's model was used to predict the motion of the planets for more than 1,400 years (see Figure 8.2). But it was not the kind of model that Occam later had in mind.

In both Aristotle's and Ptolemy's models, the Earth was considered to be at the center of the universe, everything in the heavens moved around the Earth. Not until almost 1,500 years later did a new view take deep roots. The Polish astronomer Nicholas Copernicus (1473–1543) realized that the motion of the planets could be described more simply if the Sun, rather than the Earth, were at the center of the planet-Sun system. The model Copernicus developed was still rather complicated compared with the model we use today and still retained some epicycles. Copernicus's model was about as good as Ptolemy's model in predicting the behavior of the planets. It was a major advance, however, in one important aspect: Copernicus's model allowed the relative distances between the planets and the Sun to be determined; Ptolemy's model did not. See Figure 8.3.

Figure 8.2
Diagram of Ptolemy's model of the
heavens.

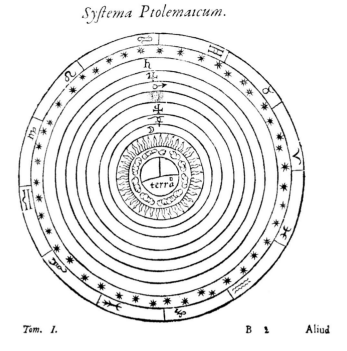

Figure 8.3
Diagram of Copernicus's model of the
heavens.

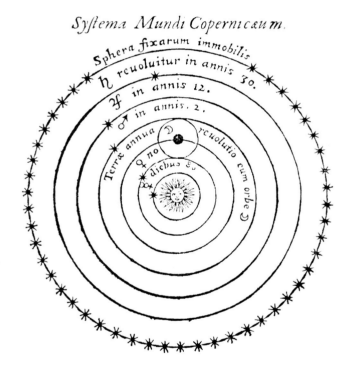

Our understanding of the motions of the planets then started to
increase rapidly. The German astronomer Johannes Kepler (1571–1630)
developed the modern model of these motions. In this model, as in Copernicus's model, the Sun is in the center, rather than the Earth. But in Kepler's
model the planets move in elliptical paths, rather than in circular paths.
Kepler, like Ptolemy and Copernicus before him, was very reluctant to give
up the idea that the planets must travel in circular orbits. However, no matter how hard he tried, Kepler could not match circular or oval orbits with
the observations of the planets made by Tycho Brahe (see Chapter 2). After

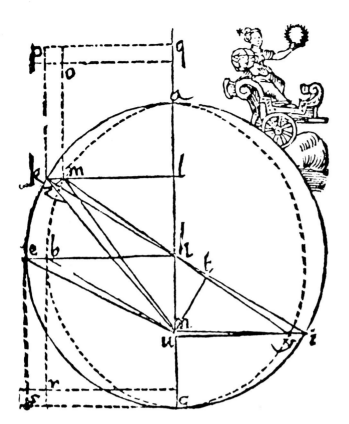

Figure 8.4
Diagram of Kepler's model of the heavens.

many failures, he finally tried elliptical orbits. Without Tycho's very careful observations, Kepler would never have made his discovery about elliptical orbits. This apparently small change allowed Kepler to eliminate epicycles. Although Kepler's model has the planets moving in ellipses, these ellipses are almost circular and only very close study shows the slight differences (see Figure 8.4). For example, the Earth's distance to the Sun changes by only about 3% between the times it is closest to and farthest from the Sun.

Scale Model of the Planetary System

You will now construct your new scale model by first adding two planets, without knowing their distances from the Sun. This scale model will build on the one you made of the Earth, Moon, and Sun in Chapter 7.

It is easy to use measurements of the positions of Mercury and Venus with respect to the Sun to make a scale model of their orbits. We know these planets are closer to the Sun than is the Earth because their positions in the sky, as seen from the Earth, are never very far from the position of the Sun. We know all the other planets are farther from the Sun than is the Earth because they can appear in all parts of the sky, relative to the sky position of the Sun; for example, they are often seen on the opposite side of the sky from the Sun.

Astronomers early on used the method you used in Activity 8.1 to find the relative distances from the Earth to Mercury, Venus, and the Sun. Now, however, they have a way to measure directly the distances between the Earth and many of the planets. They use radar.

A radar sends out a burst of "radio" photons. (Different kinds of photons will be discussed in Chapter 11; see also the Glossary for a description

Figure. 8.5
The Millstone Hill radio telescope in Westford, Massachusetts; the first used to measure the distance from the Earth to Venus.

of radio photons.) When these photons strike an object some are scattered and some are reflected (see Chapter 5) back to an antenna; using sophisticated equipment, radar astronomers can determine the time it takes for these photons to make this roundtrip. These photons take nearly the same amount of time to reach the object as they do to return. By knowing the speed at which photons travel, from laboratory measurements on the Earth, astronomers can then compute how far away the object is. This technique has been used to measure the distance from the Earth to the Moon (see Chapter 7) and to many planets.

If the Sun had a solid surface, like the Moon, we could use radar to determine directly and accurately the distance to the Sun. Because the outer part of the Sun is made of very hot gases, it is not a very good radar "target." But radar can be used to determine the distance from the Earth to the Sun by other means.

Very powerful radars have sent radio signals to the planet Venus and have detected the reflected photons (see Figures 8.5 and 8.6). Let's consider a simple example.

QUESTION: A radar was used to send radio signals from the Earth to Venus when Venus came its closest to the Earth. The echoes of these signals were detected 300 sec later. How far away was Venus from the Earth at that time?

If the round-trip time for these radio photons was 300 sec, the time it took for the photons to travel from the Earth to Venus was approximately

$$300 \text{ sec}/2 = 150 \text{ sec}$$

Since photons travel at 3.00×10^5 km/sec (300,000 km/sec or 186,000 mi/sec) in 150 sec a photon will travel

$$1.5 \times 10^2 \text{ sec} \times 3.0 \times 10^5 \text{ km/sec} = 4.5 \times 10^7 \text{ km},$$

Figure. 8.6
The orbits of Venus and the Earth drawn to scale showing the distance between the Earth and Venus.

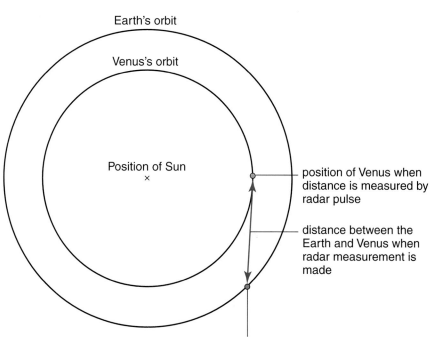

Earth's orbit

Venus's orbit

Position of Sun
×

position of Venus when distance is measured by radar pulse

distance between the Earth and Venus when radar measurement is made

position of the Earth when radar pulse is sent to Venus and the reflected pulse is detected (the Earth moves a very small distance in its orbit compared to the distance to Venus during the time it takes for the radar pulse to travel to Venus and back)

✳ The Universe in Your Hands

which is a good approximation to the distance from the surface of the Earth to the surface of Venus when Venus passes close to the Earth in its orbit.

Using the method just described, you can thus determine the distance to Venus. If you return to your scale drawing of the orbits of Mercury and Venus from Activity 8.1, you will see that if you know the distance from the Earth to Venus at any one time you can find the distance to the Sun. By combining many radar measurements of the distances to Mercury, Venus, and Mars, and to the *Viking* spacecraft, which landed on Mars in 1976, astronomers have been able to determine the distance from the center of the Earth to the center of the Sun very accurately, the error being less than 1 km, or less than 1 part in 100 million.

Using measurements of the sizes of planets and of their distances from the Sun, you can build a scale model of the solar system.

SUMMARY

People observe that Mercury and Venus move rapidly with respect to the background stars and never stray far from the Sun. Several models have been used to explain the motion of these planets and the others in our solar system. The best known models were proposed by Aristotle, Ptolemy, Copernicus, and Kepler.

The scale distances to the planets and their sizes can easily be set up in a model so that the overall scale of the solar system can be seen. From this scale model, the relatively small sizes of the planets compared to the size of the Sun, and the large distances between the planets, become clear. The distance between the Earth and some planets can be determined directly by measuring the round-trip travel times of radar signals sent from the Earth to these planets.

1. The Sun's size/distance ratio as seen from Jupiter is 1/572. Compute the angular diameter of the Sun as observed from Jupiter.

2. Imagine you are observing the Sun from Neptune. Make the appropriate calculations to find

    a) the angular diameter of the Sun as you see it.

    b) the Sun's apparent brightness as compared to its value when viewed from the Earth.

3. Two telescopes, each of 5.0 m focal length, are used to photograph Mars at the same time but from two locations on the Earth that are 4,500 km apart. The images are superimposed, giving a 0.4 mm separation in the position of Mars with respect to the background stars. Given that you do not know the orientation of the line between these two locations and the direction to Mars, what could be the greatest distance from the Earth to Mars at the time of these observations?

4. Assume the limit of detail that your eyes can see is 0.017°, which means that the eyes can see a spherical object as a disk if the distance to the object is no more than about 3,600 times the object's diameter. What is the farthest planet from the Sun on which you could see the Sun as a disk?

SELF-TEST

1. Compare the angular size of the Sun as viewed from its nearest planet, Mercury, with the angular size of the Sun as seen from the planet Saturn.

2. Using your scale model, estimate the distance humans have traveled into the solar system to date and how many times farther you will have to travel if you go to Mars.

ACTIVITY 8.1   PLOTTING THE ORBITS OF MERCURY AND VENUS

PURPOSE

To use observations of Mercury and Venus to plot their orbits around the Sun.

MATERIALS

Table 8.1
Chart 8.1
1 metric ruler
1 protractor
1 drawing compass
1 sharpened pencil with eraser

PROCEDURE

A. Chart 8.1 represents the orbit of the Earth around the Sun. Although the Earth's orbit is not a perfect circle, at the scale of Chart 8.1 you could not tell the difference. The dates on the orbit mark the position of the Earth in its orbit on the first day of each month. For the purpose of this activity, we will assume that the Earth moves at a constant speed around the Sun and that all months have 30 days. Thus, the 360° circle representing the Earth's orbit can be divided into 30° segments, each segment representing 1 month and each degree along the circle representing the distance traveled by the Earth along its orbit in 1 day. That the number of degrees in a circle, 360, and the number of days in a year, 365, are nearly the same is not a coincidence. An early estimate of the length of a year was 360 days, so it was quite natural that 360 was used to subdivide a circle into smaller portions.

B. From observations of the motions of both Mercury and Venus on the sky, astronomers inferred that these planets orbit the Sun inside the orbit of the Earth: Neither planet appears in the sky very far from the Sun. The greatest angular distance between the Sun and Mercury or Venus, as viewed from the Earth, is called the angle of greatest elongation. These angles have been measured by astronomers; some results are shown in Table 8.1.

As Mercury and Venus orbit the Sun, so does the Earth. All of the planets orbit the Sun in a counterclockwise direction as viewed from above the North Pole of the Earth (and as indicated by the dates on the Earth's orbit on Chart 8.1). Mercury or Venus can be seen from Earth either to the left (east) of the Sun or to the right (west) of the Sun, depending upon the positions of the planet and the Earth in their orbits. An important assumption allows you to plot the position of the planet in its orbit when it is at greatest elongation: If a line is drawn from the Earth in the direction of the planet, the planet will probably be on that line at the point where the line passes nearest the Sun. If

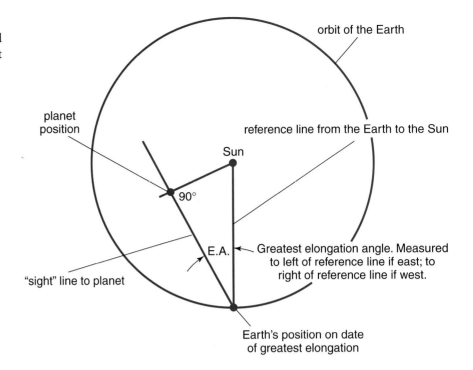

Figure 8.7
Greatest elongation angle. Measured to left of reference line if east; to right of reference line if west.

orbit of the Earth

planet position

reference line from the Earth to the Sun

Sun

90°

E.A.

Greatest elongation angle. Measured to left of reference line if east; to right of reference line if west.

"sight" line to planet

Earth's position on date of greatest elongation

another line is drawn from this point to the Sun, the second line will form a 90° angle with the first line. See Figure 8.7.

C. Using the information in step A, locate the position of the Earth in its orbit on Chart 8.1 for each of the dates of greatest elongation for Mercury. The year does not matter in plotting the Earth's position: the Earth is very nearly at the same point in its orbit on the same date from one year to the next. But the year *does* matter for the position of Mercury and Venus, so label each point with the date, including the year.

D. Use a sharp pencil to draw a faint line (you'll want to erase it later) to the Sun from each point labeled on the Earth's orbit. These are your reference lines for measuring the angles of greatest elongation.

E. Start with the first greatest elongation date for Mercury, 8 January 1989 (for the rest of this activity, when we refer to "elongation," we mean greatest elongation). The elongation angle is 19° east. That means Mercury was located in the sky 19° to the left of the Sun. Center your protractor on the 8 January point on the Earth's orbit, measure 19° to the left from the reference line along the protractor, which should be set to point toward the Sun, and make a mark on the chart at the 19° point. Now use the pencil and ruler to draw a "sight" line from the 8 January Earth position through the mark. Next, place the base line of your protractor along the sight line. Slide the protractor base along the sight line until the 90° mark on the protractor lines up with the Sun. Mark a point on the sight line where the center mark of the protractor is located on the sight line. This mark is the position of Mercury on 8 January 1989. *Do not label this point with the date.* Such a label would only confuse you later when you connect all 13 points to trace out the orbit of Mercury.

F. Repeat step E for the remaining 12 elongation dates for Mercury. Make sure you measure the elongation angle to the left of the reference line to the Sun if it is an east elongation and to the right of the reference line if it is a west elongation angle.

G. Draw a smooth curve to connect the 13 positions for Mercury to trace out the planet's orbit. A drawing compass may help you connect the points. Because of slight errors in plotting points on the Earth's orbit and measuring angles, you may find that some positions do not seem to fit. If there are only one or two "bad" positions, you can ignore them in tracing the orbit. If there are more than two "bad" points, you should check the Earth positions and angle measurements for those points and make any necessary corrections. After you have checked the points, you can erase the sight and reference lines. The orbit of Mercury should look like a slightly lopsided circle with the Sun off center.

H. Repeat steps C–G for the elongation angles for Venus and trace out the planet's orbit. There are 10 positions for Venus. Venus's orbit should be a nearly perfect circle to be in agreement with the more accurate measurements made by astronomers.

DISCUSSION QUESTIONS

Refer to Table 8.1.

1. Mercury had 13 elongations in 2 years, while Venus had only 10 elongations in 7 years. Why do you think Mercury had more elongations than Venus?

2. The elongation angles for Mercury varied from 18° to 27°, while the angles for Venus varied only from 45° to 47°. Why do you think Mercury's elongation angles varied more than those of Venus?

3. What is the average distance from the Sun to Mercury, as a fraction of the average distance from the Sun to the Earth? Show how you arrived at your answer.

4. What is the average distance from the Sun to Venus, as a fraction of the average distance from the Sun to the Earth? Show how you arrived at your answer.

Table 8.1 Greatest Elongations of Mercury and Venus

Mercury: 1989–1990		
Date	East	West
8 Jan 89	19°	
18 Feb 89		26°
30 Apr 89	21°	
18 Jun 89		23°
28 Aug 89	27°	
10 Oct 89		18°
22 Dec 89	20°	
1 Feb 90		25°
13 Apr 90	20°	
31 May 90		25°
11 Aug 90	27°	
24 Sep 90		18°
5 Dec 90	21°	

Venus: 1983–1990		
Date	East	West
15 Jun 83	45°	
4 Nov 83		47°
21 Jan 85	47°	
12 Jun 85		46°
26 Aug 86	46°	
15 Jan 87		47°
2 Apr 88	46°	
22 Aug 88		46°
8 Nov 89	47°	
30 Mar 90		46°

Data obtained from *Sky & Telescope* magazine.

ACTIVITY 8.2

MAKING A SCALE MODEL OF THE SOLAR SYSTEM

PURPOSE

To build scale models of the size and distance relations in the solar system.

WHAT DO YOU THINK?

P1. *It took the Apollo astronauts about 3 days to get from the Earth to the Moon. If a spacecraft were to travel to Mars at the same average speed as the Apollo craft, how long would it take to get from the Earth to Mars?*

P2. *How long do you think it took the Voyager 2 spacecraft to get from the Earth to Neptune?*

MATERIALS

Per team of two students
1 meterstick
1 roll of heavy string
1 pair scissors
masking tape
planetary data tables
modeling clay
an assortment of different size spheres

PROCEDURE

A. Your teacher will provide you with tables of planetary data. Follow the instructions at the top of the tables indicated by your teacher and complete columns (3) and (4) with the appropriate information. When you are done, you will have a set of scale distances and sizes for the major objects in the solar system. Copies of these tables are also provided at the end of this activity.

B. Find the scale distance from the Sun to Pluto on the chart of planetary data. Take a length of string and cut it so that it is about 30 cm (1 ft) longer than the Sun-Pluto scale distance.

C. Mark a point 5 cm (2 in.) from one end of the string with masking tape and leave a tag of tape sticking out from the edge of the string. Label the tag "Sun." Refer to the scale distances on your chart. Measure the proper scale distance along the string from the Sun marker to where each of the planets would be found.

D. Mark the position of each planet on the string, and attach a tag 10 cm long (made of masking tape) at the point labeled with the planet's name. On this tag, draw a line at a scale distance for the orbital path for the outermost moon of the planet (if it has one). See Figure 8.8.

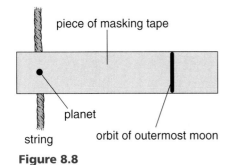

piece of masking tape

planet

string   orbit of outermost moon

Figure 8.8

E. When you have the positions of the Sun, Moon, and the nine planets located, refer again to the chart for the scale diameters of these objects. Use modeling clay to make spherical objects of the proper scale sizes and attach them with tape or pins to the labeled points. When finished, you will have a model of the solar system that shows the diameters and distances of its major objects to proper scale. (The moons' scaled sizes will usually be too small for models.)

> **The model you have built may leave you with the impression that the planets "line up" in a row on one side of the Sun. Such an alignment can never happen! Moreover, the orbits of the planets are not even all in the same plane.**

HEADS UP!

To answer the following questions, walk at a regular pace and time yourself using a sweep secondhand or a digital watch. The scaled comparisons you make with actual spacecraft times of flight will not be very accurate because we ignore here the important facts that spacecraft do not travel in straight lines between planets and do not travel at constant speeds.

1. *Walk from the Earth to the Moon. How long did it take you to get there? (Recall from question P1 that it took the Apollo astronauts about 3 days to travel to the Moon.)*

2. *Walk from the Earth to Mars. How long did it take you to get there? (It took the Viking spacecraft about 1 year.)*

3. *Walk from the Earth to Jupiter. How long did it take you to get there? (It took the Voyager spacecraft about 2 years.)*

4. a) *Predict how long it will take you to get from the Earth to Saturn.*

   b) *How long do you think it took Voyager 2 to get there?*

5. *Walk from the Earth to Pluto. How long did it take you to get there? Calculate approximately how long it would take a spacecraft to travel from the Earth to Pluto.*

6. *The nearest star to our solar system is Alpha Centauri. It is more than 7,000 times farther from the Earth than is Pluto. How long would it take you to walk to Alpha Centauri using this scale model?*

HOMEWORK

Refer to the tables for data on the planets and their moons. *Ignore the scale factors provided on the charts;* you will be inventing your own scales with their own scale diameters and distances.

1. Choose a spherical household object to represent the planet Jupiter. Use this object as a scale and find objects from around your home that would represent the four largest moons of Jupiter. These moons are often called the "Galilean" moons in honor of their discoverer, the 17th century Italian astronomer Galileo. List the objects you used, their diameters, and the distances you placed the moons from Jupiter.

2. Answer question 1 for Saturn. Choose a spherical object to represent Saturn. Choose objects to be scale models of a few of Saturn's moons. Use string to outline the boundaries of Saturn's rings. List the objects you used, their diameters, and the distances you placed the moons and rings from Saturn.

3. What specific features (lakes, islands, oceans) on the Earth's surface are similar in width to Cassini's Division and Encke's Division in the rings of Saturn? Cassini's Division is about 3,000 km (1,800 mi) wide and Encke's Division is about 875 km (550 mi) wide.

4. If we built a large scale model of the solar system in which the Sun was 1.4 km in diameter, then the Earth would be located 150 km from the Sun. In the model, each km represents 1,000,000 km in the real world. Using the planetary data tables, list the distances that the other planets would be from the Sun on this model scale.

   Mercury   Venus   Earth   Mars   Jupiter
   Saturn   Uranus   Neptune   Pluto

5. Using a large map of the United States and another one of the world, locate cities whose actual distances from your own are about the same as the scale distances you calculated in answering question 4. Remember that the planets go around the Sun and the Sun is in your town, so you can measure the distance in any direction from your town; the planets are not lined up in a nice, neat row out from the Sun.

SOLAR SYSTEM SCALE MODELS (KILOMETERS)

Use a scale factor of 1 cm equals 1,000,000 km. Convert the actual distances and diameters in columns (1) and (2) to scale sizes in centimeters by dividing the values in (1) and (2) by the scale factor 1,000,000 km/cm. Record the converted values from column (1) into column (3) and the converted values from column (2) into column (4).

Follow these directions for making scale models of each planetary system using the information on the next page.

OBJECT	(1) MEAN DISTANCE FROM THE SUN (km)	(2) EQUATORIAL DIAMETER (km)	(3) SCALED DISTANCE (cm)	(4) SCALED DIAMETER (cm)
SUN	—	1,390,000		
MERCURY	58,000,000	4,880		
VENUS	108,000,000	12,100		
EARTH	150,000,000	12,800		
MARS	228,000,000	6,800		
CERES	420,000,000	1,000		
JUPITER	780,000,000	142,800		
outer ring diameter	—	261,000		
SATURN	1,430,000,000	120,000		
outer ring diameter	—	272,700		
URANUS	2,870,000,000	51,200		
outer ring diameter	—	99,800		
NEPTUNE	4,500,000,000	48,600		
outer ring diameter	—	106,000		
PLUTO	5,900,000,000	2,300(?)		

PLANETARY SYSTEM SCALE MODELS

PLANET / Moon	(1) MEAN DISTANCE FROM PLANET (km)	(2) EQUATORIAL DIAMETER (km)	(3) SCALED DISTANCE (cm)	(4) SCALED DIAMETER (cm)
EARTH	—	12,800		
Moon	400,000	3,480		
MARS	—	6,800		
Phobos	9,400	21		
Deimos	23,500	12		
JUPITER	—	142,800		
outer ring	130,400	—		
Amalthea	180,000	170		
Io	422,000	3,630		
Europa	671,000	3,140		
Ganymede	1,070,000	5,260		
Callisto	1,885,000	4,800		
SATURN	—	120,000		
A ring	121,900 to 136,300	—		
B ring	91,700 to 117,600	—		
Mimas	187,000	390		
Enceladus	238,000	500		
Tethys	295,000	1,060		
Dione	378,000	1,120		
Rhea	526,000	1,530		
Titan	1,221,000	5,150		
Hyperion	1,481,000	255		
Iapetus	3,561,000	1,460		
URANUS	—	51,200		
outer ring	49,900	—		
Miranda	130,000	485		
Ariel	190,000	1,160		
Umbriel	266,000	1,190		
Titania	436,000	1,610		
Oberon	583,000	1,550		
NEPTUNE	—	48,600		
outer ring	53,000	—		
Triton	354,000	2,785		
Nereid	5,600,000	300		
PLUTO	—	2,300 (?)		
Charon	20,000 (?)	1,200 (?)		

SOLAR SYSTEM SCALE MODELS (MILES)

Use a scale factor of 1 in. equals 1,000,000 mi. Convert the actual distances and diameters in columns (1) and (2) to scale sizes in inches by dividing the values in (1) and (2) by the scale factor 1,000,000 mi/in. Record the converted values from column (1) into column (3) and the converted values from column (2) into column (4).

Follow these directions for making scale models of each planetary system using the information on the next page.

OBJECT	(1) MEAN DISTANCE FROM THE SUN (mi)	(2) EQUATORIAL DIAMETER (mi)	(3) SCALED DISTANCE (in.)	(4) SCALED DIAMETER (in.)
SUN	—	865,000		
MERCURY	36,000,000	3,030		
VENUS	67,000,000	7,520		
EARTH	93,000,000	7,930		
MARS	142,000,000	4,220		
CERES	257,000,000	620		
JUPITER	484,000,000	88,700		
outer ring diameter	—	162,000		
SATURN	887,000,000	75,600		
outer ring diameter	—	169,000		
URANUS	1,780,000,000	31,800		
outer ring diameter	—	62,000		
NEPTUNE	2,790,000,000	30,200		
outer ring diameter	—	66,000		
PLUTO	3,670,000,000	1,400(?)		

PLANETARY SYSTEM SCALE MODELS

PLANET Moon	(1) MEAN DISTANCE FROM PLANET (mi)	(2) EQUATORIAL DIAMETER (mi)	(3) SCALED DISTANCE (in.)	(4) SCALED DIAMETER (in.)
EARTH	—	7,930		
Moon	240,000	2,160		
MARS	—	4,220		
Phobos	5,840	13		
Deimos	14,600	7.5		
JUPITER	—	88,700		
outer ring	81,000	—		
Amalthea	112,000	110		
Io	260,000	2,260		
Europa	420,000	1,950		
Ganymede	665,000	3,270		
Callisto	1,170,000	2,980		
SATURN	—	74,600		
A ring	75,700 to 84,700	—		
B ring	57,000 to 73,100	—		
Mimas	116,000	240		
Enceladus	148,000	310		
Tethys	183,000	660		
Dione	235,000	700		
Rhea	327,000	950		
Titan	759,000	3,200		
Hyperion	920,000	160		
Iapetus	2,213,000	910		
URANUS	—	31,800		
outer ring	31,000	—		
Miranda	81,000	300		
Ariel	120,000	720		
Umbriel	165,000	740		
Titania	270,000	1,000		
Oberon	360,000	960		
NEPTUNE	—	30,200		
outer ring	33,000	—		
Triton	220,000	1,740		
Nereid	3,480,000	190		
PLUTO	—	1,400 (?)		
Charon	12,000 (?)	750 (?)		

Figure 8.9
Looking from left to right, this photograph shows Jupiter, Mars, and Venus very early in the morning, before sunrise.

The Paths of the Planets ✳ **189**

CHAPTER 9

Keeping It All Together: Gravity

GRAVITY AND MOTION—WHOM DO YOU BELIEVE?

Below is a list of ideas that famous scientists and philosophers have had concerning gravity and motion. While some of these ideas have been proven wrong, others are still thought to be true. Which ideas do you believe?

1. If two stones of different weights are dropped from the same height above the ground, the heavier stone will hit the ground first. (Aristotle)

2. All the planets orbit the Sun in circular paths. (Copernicus)

3. You are exerting a very small pull on all the objects in the room around you. These objects are also exerting a small pull on you. (Newton)

4. Gravity can bend a beam of light. (Einstein)

5. The farther away a planet is from the Sun, the slower it moves in its orbit around the Sun. (Kepler)

HOW MUCH WILL KATE WEIGH?

Kate is an astronaut who weighs 70 kg (150 lb) when on the surface of the Earth. If Kate were placed in the situations described at right, would she weigh more, less, or the same as she does on the Earth?

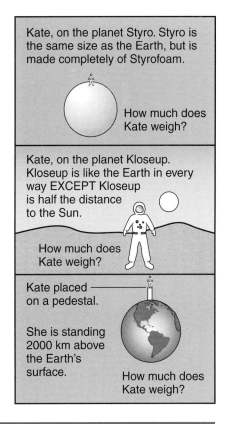

Kate, on the planet Styro. Styro is the same size as the Earth, but is made completely of Styrofoam.

How much does Kate weigh?

Kate, on the planet Kloseup. Kloseup is like the Earth in every way EXCEPT Kloseup is half the distance to the Sun.

How much does Kate weigh?

Kate placed on a pedestal.

She is standing 2000 km above the Earth's surface.

How much does Kate weigh?

Preview: In this chapter you will learn more about (1) the paths the planets follow and (2) how the model of gravity explains these paths.

How the Planets Behave

You have built a scale model of the solar system and you know that the planets move in paths around the Sun. How long does it take each planet to complete a circuit of the Sun? Table 9.1 shows the distance of each planet from the Sun and the time it takes in Earth-years for each planet to complete one circuit around the Sun—its orbital period. Can you figure out how astronomers determined these orbital periods?

Table 9.1

	Average distance from Sun in units of 10^6 km	Average distance from Sun in units in which the distance from Earth to Sun = 1	Orbital period in years
Mercury	57.9	0.387	0.241
Venus	108.	0.723	0.615
Earth	150.	1.00	1.00
Mars	228.	1.52	1.88
Jupiter	778.	5.20	11.9
Saturn	1,430	9.54	29.5
Uranus	2,870	19.2	84.0
Neptune	4,500	30.1	165.
Pluto	5,900	39.4	248.

EXERCISE: Make a graph comparing the distance of each planet from the Sun with the planet's average speed in its orbit. (Hint: You can determine the approximate circumference of each planet's orbit by using the formula for the circumference of a circle: $2 \times \pi \times$ radius. [The fractional errors you make by considering the orbits of most planets to be circular are small, that is, a few percent; for only two of the planets are these errors significantly larger.] If you divide this number by the time it takes the corresponding planet to make one circuit, what do you get?)

Looking at either the table or your graph, you can tell at once that the farther a planet is from the Sun, the longer it takes to make a circuit of the Sun. Can you tell more? For example, if you only knew the average distance of a planet from the Sun, could you figure out how long it would take the planet to make one trip around the Sun? Or, if you knew how long a planet takes to make one trip around the Sun, could you tell how far on average the planet is from the Sun?

The answer to those questions is "yes," and the relation between the planet's average distance from the Sun and the time it takes the planet to make one trip around the Sun was discovered by Johannes Kepler almost 400 years ago. (In Chapter 8 you learned that Kepler also discovered that the planets move in elliptical orbits.) Kepler did not know the distance from the Sun to each planet in terms of measures of distance used on the Earth, such as the kilometer. But he was able to determine the distance from each planet to the Sun in terms of the distance from the Earth to the Sun, now called the astronomical unit or a.u. for short. You learned how to find these distances for Mercury and Venus in Activity 8.1.

Kepler was working with hundreds of observations of the planets made by Tycho Brahe. The process of converting these observations to positions of each planet with respect to the Sun is very complicated and you will not be asked to duplicate Kepler's efforts. Kepler worked for many years, for example, trying to discover a simple pattern in the positions and motions of Mars, which at times moves "backwards" in the sky as we see it from the Earth. He believed the solar system was built according to a harmonious scheme and this conviction inspired his devotion to the task. Kepler eventually found a key relation that, along with other mathematical tools, allowed him to determine the positions and motions he sought. Table 9.2, based on more recent observations and analyses, lets you see the relation he discovered.

Table 9.2				
	Average distance from Sun in a.u. (distance from Earth to Sun = 1)	Cube of the average distance (a.u.^{3})	Orbital period in years	Square of the orbital period (yr^2)
Mercury	3.9×10^{-1}	5.8×10^{-2}	2.4×10^{-1}	5.8×10^{-2}
Venus	7.2×10^{-1}	3.8×10^{-1}	6.2×10^{-1}	3.8×10^{-1}
Earth	1.0×10^{0}	1.0×10^{0}	1.0×10^{0}	1.0×10^{0}
Mars	1.5×10^{0}	3.5×10^{0}	1.9×10^{0}	3.5×10^{0}
Jupiter	5.2×10^{0}	1.4×10^{2}	1.2×10^{1}	1.4×10^{2}
Saturn	9.5×10^{0}	8.7×10^{2}	2.9×10^{1}	8.7×10^{2}

EXERCISE: Draw a graph in which you plot the second column of numbers in Table 9.2 on the "y" axis and the fourth column of numbers on the "x" axis.

You can see at once that the numbers in column 2 (a.u.^{3}) and column 4 (year^2) are the same. The relation Kepler found can be written

(period in years)^2 = (average distance of planet from the Sun in a.u.)^3

Three planets were discovered after Kepler uncovered this relation; Table 9.3 shows that the relation holds for them as well. It was very comforting to astronomers to find that new data followed the same relation. If the data departed from the original relation, it might have been necessary to develop a new model.

Table 9.3				
	Average distance from Sun in a.u. (distance from Earth to Sun = 1)	Cube of the average distance (a.u.^{3})	Orbital period in years	Square of the orbital period (yr^2)
Uranus	1.9×10^{1}	7.1×10^{3}	8.4×10^{1}	7.1×10^{3}
Neptune	3.0×10^{1}	2.7×10^{4}	1.7×10^{2}	2.7×10^{4}
Pluto	3.9×10^{1}	6.1×10^{4}	2.5×10^{2}	6.1×10^{4}

PLANETS AND PENDULUMS

As surprising as it might be, the behavior of a planet is similar to that of a pendulum—both have periods that are related to a distance. In a planet's case, the time it takes to return to a point in its path around the Sun is related to its average distance from the Sun. In the pendulum's case, the time it takes to return to a point in its path is related to the length of its "arm." The Italian physicist Galileo Galilei (Gal-i-LAY-oh Gal-i-LAY-ee) (1564–1642) was the first person to discover the relationship between the period of a pendulum and the length of its arm.

The first person to guess that there might be a connection between the period of a pendulum and the period of a planet was the English scientist Isaac Newton (1642–1727). You may have heard the story of the apple hitting Newton on the head and giving him the idea of his model of gravity. Newton guessed that the bob of a pendulum is attracted toward the Earth in the same way the apple is. Newton's leap of imagination was to reason that the Moon can be said to be pulled toward the Earth in the same way that an apple or a pendulum bob can be said to be pulled toward the Earth. In the same way, he also argued that the planets can be thought of as being pulled toward the Sun.

When you whirl a weight, tied to a string, around your head, you can feel the string pulling on your hand. Newton said that your hand must be pulling back on the string to keep the weight from flying off as it would if you let go of the string. (The best place to test this prediction is outside, far from anybody or anything that could be damaged when you release the string.) There is no string connecting the Earth to the Moon, but Newton invented a model in which an invisible pull called gravity does the work of the string and can never break or be released.

In this model, gravity is a pull exerted by every body in the universe on every other body. You can think of Newton's model of the gravitational pull between the Earth and the Moon in terms of an invisible rope connecting the centers of the two objects. The pull exerted by this imaginary rope, Newton said, is simply proportional to the amount of matter in the Earth and

Galileo's Surprising Demonstration

Before Galileo, many people thought it was "obvious" that heavy objects fall faster than light objects. Galileo performed experiments that convinced him that all objects fall at the same rate. In a famous demonstration, whose historical accuracy has, however, often been questioned, Galileo dropped a heavy cannon ball and a light cannon ball from the "leaning tower" in Pisa, Italy. Both balls struck the ground at almost the same time.

Why is Galileo's demonstration, that all objects dropped at the same time from the same height reach the ground at the same time, so surprising? Suppose you start to pull a stationary 100-kg object and keep pulling it until it reaches a speed of 30 km per hour. You would have to exert yourself much more than if you were pulling a 10-kg object. Yet, when an object is "pulled" by gravity, gravity somehow manages to tailor its exertion so that all objects dropped from the same height at the same time—independent of how massive they are—all reach the ground at the same time. How can gravity be so clever? Why do objects fall at the same increasing rate no matter how massive they are? Isaac Newton knew that any theory of gravity must be consistent with this remarkable fact.

also to the amount in the Moon. The amount of matter in an object is called its mass. One measure of the mass of an object is the effort required to put the object in motion or to stop it: The harder you have to push or pull, the more massive is the object you're pushing or pulling—all other things being the same. If you wish to think in terms of an invisible rope connecting the Earth and Moon, you must assume that the rope has no mass.

In Newton's model the pull of gravity between the Earth and the Moon depends on how far apart they are. This pull diminishes as the inverse square of the distance between the centers of the two bodies increases: The pull is proportional to $(1/\text{distance})^2$, just as apparent brightness diminishes as the inverse square of the distance between the source and the observer increases. For example, moving an object twice as far away from another object results in a pull between them that is one-fourth as great.

In Newton's model there is a gravitational "rope" between you and the Earth and between you and every other body in the universe. The rope connecting you to the Earth is pulling the hardest on you, however, because the Earth is a massive body that is closer to you than any other very massive body. That is how Newton's model explains the fact that you fall to the Earth whenever you are unsupported. How should you measure the distance between you and the Earth? You are very close to the part of the Earth you are standing on, but thousands of kilometers from other parts of the Earth. Newton was able to show that in his model the pull depends on the distance between the centers of the two spherical bodies. You are approximately 6,400 km from the center of the Earth.

Gravity was more than "a good idea" for Newton—he developed a formula that allowed him to calculate the strength of the pull exerted by a body on an object at any distance from the body. For example, he was able to calculate how much gravitational pull the Earth exerts on an object at the distance of the Moon. In this way, Newton was able to figure out how far the Moon should "fall" from the path it would take were it not for the pull of the Earth (see Figure 9.1).

Figure 9.1
The Moon's orbit, showing the distance the Moon falls toward the Earth every second (not to scale).

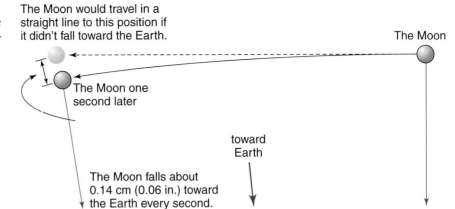

The Moon would travel in a straight line to this position if it didn't fall toward the Earth.

The Moon

The Moon one second later

The Moon falls about 0.14 cm (0.06 in.) toward the Earth every second.

toward Earth

When Newton compared his calculation with the distance the Moon deviates from a straight path, as inferred from measurements, he found the two numbers did not agree. Newton believed his model was inadequate and put it aside. Most models fail at some point to agree with observations; such a failure is an incentive to develop new models. But it turned out that there was nothing dramatically wrong with Newton's model, only with the data he was using. The value he had been using for the diameter of the Earth was wrong by almost 900 km; it was, in fact, not easy to determine an accurate value for the Earth's diameter with the techniques then available. Twenty years later Newton learned of a new determination of the value for the diameter of the Earth. When he used this new value in his equations to calculate the pull the Earth exerts on the Moon, he found the calculated path of the Moon agreed with the observed path.

Newton's model of gravity is one of the most successful scientific models ever invented. As you will see, it applies just as well to distant stars and to even more distant galaxies.

Newton's Formula

Newton's formula for calculating the gravitational pull one body exerts on another is worth knowing. It can be written as

pull exerted by one body on another body =

$$\frac{\text{Newton's Constant} \times \text{mass of first body} \times \text{mass of second body}}{(\text{distance between the centers of the two bodies})^2}$$

Newton's Constant is a number that depends on the system of units you are using. Notice that Newton's formula describes the pull one body exerts on another in terms of the masses of the two objects, but makes no distinction between which object is doing the pulling. The pull the Earth exerts on you is identical to the pull you exert on the Earth. Think about that for a while.

Testing Newton's Model of Gravity

Newton used the distance between the centers of two bodies to calculate the strength of the pull exerted by one body on the other. The distance from the center of the Earth to the center of an apple is approximately the radius of the Earth, 6.4×10^3 km. The average distance from the center of the Earth to the center of the Moon is approximately 3.8×10^5 km. Newton divided these two numbers to find the ratio between the two distances.

$$\frac{3.8 \times 10^5 \text{ km}}{6.4 \times 10^3 \text{ km}} = 5.9 \times 10^1$$

The center of the Moon is thus approximately 60 times farther from the center of the Earth than is the apple. There-fore, since the pull of gravity is an inverse square relation, the gravitational pull exerted by the Earth at the distance of the Moon is $(1/60)^2 = (1/60) \times (1/60) = 1/3{,}600$ times as strong as the pull it exerts on the apple. This difference in the strength of the pull exerted by the Earth is reflected in the rate at which the Moon falls in comparison with the rate at which an apple falls. In 1 sec an apple falls 500 cm. According to Newton's calculation, in 1 sec the Moon must fall 500 cm / 3,600 = 0.14 cm. Amazingly, this is just the departure from a straight path that the Moon actually undergoes according to measurements (see Figure 9.1).

Mass and Weight

You can think of mass as a measure of how hard it is to get a stationary object into motion. It takes more effort from you to move a 100-kg object than to move a 10-kg object, as stated in the box on page 194. This difference in effort you need to expend to move different objects is a measure of the masses of these objects. All objects have mass. But an object has weight only when there is something to resist its falling toward some other object. You don't normally think of the floor as resisting your falling toward the center of the Earth, but what would happen if the floor suddenly gave way beneath you? Suppose you were standing on a scale when the floor disappeared. What do you think the scale would read as both you and the scale fell?

The mass of an object does not depend on where the object is located. The mass of an object is the same whether it is on the Earth or on the Moon or anywhere else. But when an object is on the Moon, for example, it weighs only one-sixth of what it weighs when on the Earth. See Figure 9.2. Objects in the vicinity of the Moon "want" to fall toward the center of the Moon. If something prevents this fall, such as the sur-face of the Moon, the object will have a weight as well as a mass.

Some people think that objects in orbit around the Earth are outside the Earth's gravity and so are weightless. Objects in orbit around the Earth are weightless (see Figure 9.3), but not because they are beyond the Earth's gravity; they are weightless because they are falling freely and all freely falling objects are weightless. A freely falling object is one that is not restrained in any way.

Strictly speaking, there is no "beyond the Earth's gravity"—in Newton's model every object in the universe is subject to

Figure 9.2
Astronauts on the Moon can jump over a meter up from the lunar surface because they weigh only one-sixth of their weight on the Earth.

the Earth's gravitational force and, for another example, to yours. When an object, such as a spacecraft, approaches the Moon, the gravitational force exerted by the Moon on the spacecraft becomes greater than the gravitational force exerted on the spacecraft by the Earth, but the force exerted by the Earth never vanishes. In fact, as Newton showed, the force exerted by the Earth is what keeps the Moon in orbit around the Earth. Furthermore, nothing can shield an object from the gravitational force exerted by the Earth. There are no "anti-gravity" devices or gravity screens.

Figure 9.3
Because the space shuttle and the astronauts inside are freely falling when the shuttle rockets are not firing, the shuttle and the astronauts are "weightless" (except for their **very** small effect on each other).

EXERCISE: Refer to Table 9.4. Draw a graph showing the speed with which an object above, but close to, the surface of the Earth is falling after it has been dropping for 1, 2, 3, 4, and 5 sec. Can you extend the graph beyond 5 sec?

Table 9.4 Objects falling near the Earth's surface.		
Time elapsed in seconds	**Total distance fallen in meters at end of time elapsed**	**Speed in meters per second at end of time elapsed**
1	5	10
2	20	20
3	45	30
4	80	40
5	125	50

QUESTION: How much bigger is the mass of the Sun (2×10^{30} kg) than the mass of Jupiter (2×10^{27} kg)? Do you see why you would not make a large fractional error in using Newton's relation if you replaced 2.002×10^{30} with 2×10^{30}?

Now that you know something about Newton's model, turn back to the questions about Kate at the beginning of this chapter. Would you answer any of them differently now?

Newton and Kepler

The gravitational force exerted by the Earth on the Moon is largely responsible for the path followed by the Moon (the Sun plays a role, too). Newton argued that the gravitational force exerted by the Sun on the planets determines the paths followed by the planets. Newton was able to derive an expression that revealed this dependency of the orbit of a planet on the mass of the Sun and the planet (the derivation, however, is too difficult for this course). If we define our units properly, we can write

$$(\text{period of planet around the Sun})^2 = \frac{(\text{average distance of planet from the Sun})^3}{(\text{mass of the Sun} + \text{mass of the planet})}$$

Just as you can define a unit of distance (1 a.u.) equal to the average distance between the Earth and the Sun, you can define a unit of mass equal to the mass of the Sun. Setting some large number such as the mass of the Sun, approximately 2×10^{30} kg, equal to 1, may seem like magic. However, this process is no different from the one involved in setting 10^3 m equal to 1 km, or 5,280 ft equal to 1 mi. The fact that units can be created so easily for any occasion is one reason why it is important to keep track of the units you are using. Since the mass of the Sun is so much bigger than the mass of any planet, the mass of the Sun + the mass of any planet is approximately equal to the mass of the Sun.

Newton's relation can thus be written

$$(\text{period of planet around the Sun})^2 = \frac{(\text{average distance of planet from the Sun})^3}{1}$$

This expression may look familiar. It is Kepler's relation. Newton's formula displays the importance of the mass of the Sun; Kepler's relation does not make the importance of the mass of the Sun obvious. As you will see later, Newton's relation applies to stars and galaxies as well as to planets.

Newton and Einstein

As useful as Newton's model is, it does not always lead to accurate predictions. In some situations another model of gravity is used—the model developed by Albert Einstein (1879–1955). These situations include places where a great deal of matter is contained in a limited space—a black hole; calculations where the behavior of the entire universe is involved; or circumstances in which the motions of planets are studied very precisely. Einstein's model treats gravity in a very different way than does Newton's model. In Newton's model, gravity is a pull exerted by one body on another body. In Einstein's model, gravity is treated as a property of the geometry of space and time. This geometry, in turn, is determined by the amounts of matter and energy that are in space and by where they are. (This concept is rarely treated in physics courses before college—often not even then.) In Einstein's model, gravity bends the paths of photons by twice as much as in Newton's model. The bending, however, is by a very tiny amount; even by a body as massive as the Sun, the bending is less than an angle of 5 ten-thousandths

(0.0005) of a degree. Measurements have confirmed these and some other predictions from Einstein's model.

Escape Speed

Imagine that many rockets traveling at different starting speeds were launched from the surface of the Earth. Further imagine that each rocket burns all its fuel in the first few seconds of flight. Some rockets might fall back to the Earth. Others, moving more rapidly, might escape into space. There would be some lowest speed at which a rocket would just barely be able to overcome the continuous gravitational pull of the Earth and travel into space far beyond the Earth. This speed is called the escape speed for the Earth. Notice that to escape from the Earth is not to escape from the Earth's gravitational pull. According to Newton's model, no matter how far away a rocket was from the Earth, the Earth would exert a gravitational pull on the rocket. To escape from the Earth, a rocket must be moving fast enough so that the ever-weakening pull of the Earth with increasing distance is unable to stop the rocket's progress.

This argument applies to the pull exerted by any object. Not only is there an escape speed associated with the Earth, but there is an escape speed associated with every body, including yours (see Figure 9.4). The speed needed to escape from the surface of a body depends on both the mass and the size of the body. The bigger the mass, the higher the escape speed. The

Figure 9.4
An Atlas booster rocket on the Earth (left) and the lunar module from Apollo 11 on the Moon (right). What can you conclude about the escape speed for the Moon relative to the escape speed for the Earth by looking at these two spacecraft? Notice the people in both photographs to get a sense of the size of each spacecraft. Both spacecraft were designed to escape from the surface of the body on which they are pictured.

bigger the size the lower the escape speed. In Newton's model, the following relation holds for escape speed:

$$(\text{escape speed from a body})^2 = 121 \times \frac{\text{mass of the body}}{\text{radius of the body}}$$

where the escape speed is measured in km/sec when the mass and radius of the body are respectively measured in units of the Earth's mass and radius. One way to find the mass of an object in units of the Earth's mass is to divide the mass of the object in kilograms by the mass of the Earth in kilograms—if you knew these values! (How could you determine them?) A similar calculation yields the radius of an object in units of the Earth's radius.

QUESTION: In Table 9.5 you can see that Uranus has a radius of 3.73 Earth radii. What is the radius of Uranus in kilometers?

A rocket must travel at approximately 11 km/sec to escape from the Earth. Table 9.5 gives the escape speeds for some of the other bodies in the solar system.

Table 9.5			
	Mass divided by mass of Earth	**Radius divided by radius of Earth**	**Escape speed in km/sec**
Sun	333,000.	109.	618.
Mercury	0.054	0.38	4.2
Venus	0.82	0.96	10.
Earth	1.0	1.0	11.
Moon	0.012	0.27	2.4
Mars	0.1	0.53	5.0
Jupiter	318.	11.2	59.6
Saturn	95.2	9.47	35.5
Uranus	14.5	3.73	22.
Neptune	17.2	3.49	25.
Pluto	0.0017	0.18	1.1

Black Holes

Imagine placing the Earth in a giant vise and squeezing it down to a quarter its size. Its escape speed would double (why?), increasing to 22 km per second. Now an object would need a speed of 22 km per second to escape from the Earth. If you were to continue squeezing the Earth to a smaller and smaller size, the escape speed would get larger and larger. When the Earth had been squeezed down to a radius of 0.9 cm, about a third of an inch, the escape speed would have increased to 300,000 km per second—the speed of light. Now, not even light could escape the gravity of the Earth. The Earth would be invisible from the outside—it would be a black hole.

SUMMARY

Four hundred years ago Johannes Kepler discovered that if you measure the period of a planet in Earth-years and its distance from the Sun in a.u., the square of the time it takes the planet to complete one circuit of the Sun is equal to the cube of the average distance of the planet from the Sun.

Newton developed a model in which every body in the universe exerts a pull on every other body. The strength of this pull increases as the mass of either of the two bodies increases, and the strength decreases as the inverse square of the distance separating them increases. In Newton's model every body in the universe has an escape speed associated with it—the minimum speed an object must have to be able to leave the surface of the body and travel into space. The escape speed associated with a body is directly proportional to the body's mass and inversely proportional to the body's radius.

HOMEWORK

1. Assume that in Activity 9.1 you made a simple pendulum out of a piece of light thread and a 15-g fishing sinker. Assume also that the pendulum is 0.50 m long.

   a) When you double the length of the pendulum to 1.00 m, what happens to its period? Does it increase, decrease, or stay the same?

   b) With the pendulum length still 0.50 m, and with a 30-g mass, what happens to its period? Does it increase, decrease, or stay the same?

   c) If you took the pendulum (still 0.50 m long and with a 15-g mass) to the height of a geosynchronous satellite, what would happen to the period of the pendulum? Assume that the pendulum is not on the satellite or in orbit by itself; rather, assume that the pendulum is (somehow!) fixed in space above the Earth, about 3.5×10^4 km (nearly 22,000 mi) from the surface of the Earth.

2. If the Sun suddenly were to cease to exist, what would happen to the motion of the planets? Create a diagram with three concentric circles for the approximate orbits of three planets. Draw a planet on each orbit, but draw each planet in a different position with respect to the Sun, that is, do not line the planets up with the Sun. Then draw an arrow with a dark line showing what path each planet would take just after the Sun had ceased to exist. Explain why you drew the paths as you did.

3. Ronnie uses a spring balance to weigh a fish she has just caught (the fish's weight is measured by measuring the pull of its mass on a spring). How would the weight indicated by the balance change (increase, decrease, or remain the same) after Ronnie and her catch were suddenly transported to

   a) the top of Mt. Everest (about 9,000 m above sea level)?

   b) the Space Shuttle, 300 km above the Earth's surface?

   c) the surface of the Moon?

4. The mass of Halley's comet is approximately 10^{14} kg (about 10^{-11} of the mass of the Earth). The comet has an average radius of 5 km (about 10^{-3} of the radius of the Earth). What is the escape speed from Halley's comet? Could you reach that speed by jumping?

1. How do the "swing" periods of a 50-cm-long (20-in.) pendulum differ from those of a 70-cm-long (28-in.) pendulum? Do they have the same period, or is one period longer?

2. How does the orbital period of a planet 4×10^8 km (about 2.5×10^8 mi) from the Sun differ from that of a planet 8×10^8 km (about 5.0×10^8 mi) from the Sun?

3. If you weigh 55 kg (120 lb) when you are standing on the surface of the Earth about 6,400 km (4,000 mi) from its center, what would your weight be if the Earth suddenly expanded and you were then 1.3×10^4 km (8,000 mi) from its center?

4. Suppose you were standing on the Earth's surface, as in the previous problem, and it suddenly shrank so that you were then 3,200 km (about 2,000 mi) from its center, what would your weight be?

What Is a Nomogram?

A nomogram is a computer. It is not the kind you are familiar with; rather, it is designed to provide some special information—different information for different nomograms. Each nomogram is drawn to allow you to "read" the content of a specific, relatively simple mathematical equation that relates three different quantities. A typical example would be, say, a "rate times time equals distance" equation. The simple illustration on this page is a nomogram that allows you to read the result of multiplying any one number between 1 and 10 by any other number between 1 and 10. Here is how the nomogram works: You place a straightedge on the nomogram and slide it so you could draw a straight line from a number on the left scale to a number on the right scale. (*But don't actually write in the book!*) Now read the number that this line would pass through on the middle scale. That's your answer. Simple, isn't it? For example, say you want to multiply 5 by 9. This line is already drawn on the nomogram. Notice that it crosses the middle line at 45. You have just calculated that $5 \times 9 = 45$. Try a few problems yourself. Can you verify that $4 \times 4 = 16$ and that $9 \times 8 = 72$ using the nomogram?

Are nomograms magic? Not really. The "secret" is in the way the nomogram is drawn. The lines are placed so that the number lines represent mathematical expressions, in this case multiplication. You will see nomograms that will help you to calculate numbers with more complicated mathematical relationships. By the way, there's more to this "multiplication" nomogram. Do you see how you can use it to calculate the square root of any number from 1 to 100? Line up your straightedge with the tickmark next to a number on the middle number line and perpendicular to it. The number your straightedge crosses on both the left and right number lines is

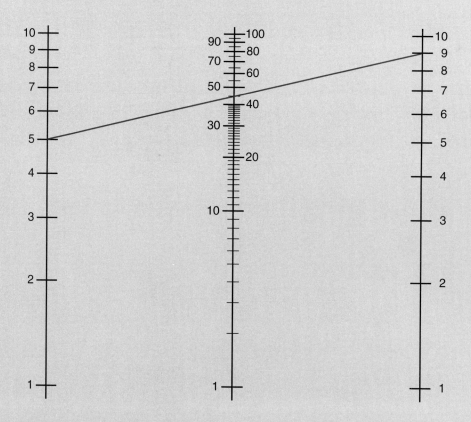

Nomogram for Escape Speed

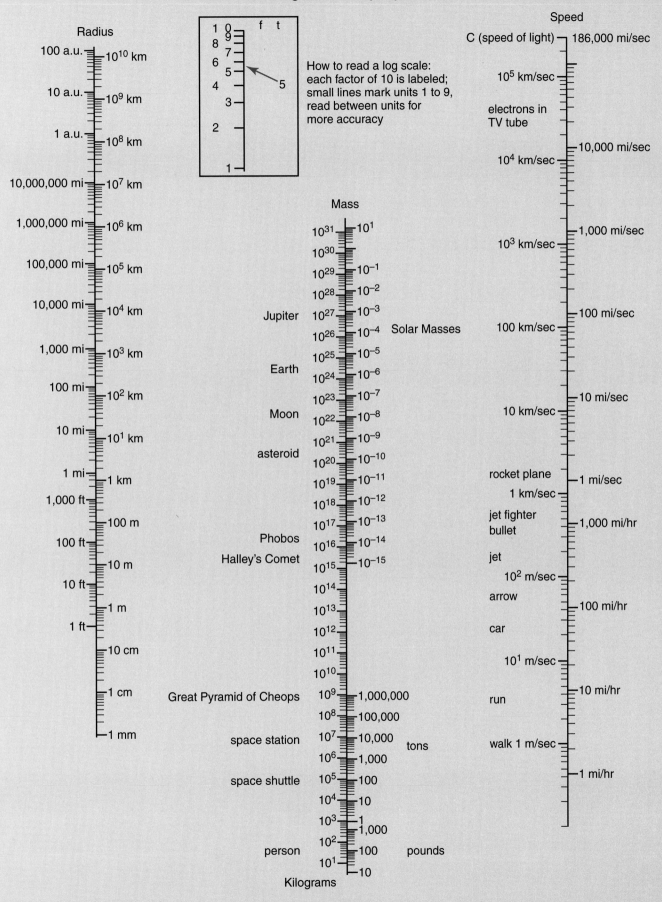

How to read a log scale:
each factor of 10 is labeled;
small lines mark units 1 to 9,
read between units for
more accuracy

the square root. If your straightedge crosses a number line *between* two tick-marks then the answer is some number between the numbers next to the tickmarks. More accuracy can be obtained if you place more tickmarks on the line; to know where to place the tickmarks requires knowledge of a mathematical notion called logarithms (often abbreviated "log").

Escape Speed Nomogram Problems

1. What speed did the Apollo astronauts have to reach to escape from the Earth? (mass $= 6 \times 10^{24}$ kg; radius $= 6,400$ km)

2. What speed did the Lunar Excursion Module (LEM) have to reach when blasting off from the Moon? (The LEM transported two astronauts to and from the Moon's surface.) (mass $= 7 \times 10^{22}$ kg; radius $= 1,750$ km)

3. The *Voyager* spacecraft attained escape speed from the Sun (mass $= 2 \times 10^{30}$ kg) at a distance of about 1 a.u. from the Sun. How many times faster is that speed than the escape speed from the Earth?

4. If you pushed yourself off from the proposed Space Station (mass $= 10^6$ kg; radius $= 6$ m), would its gravity be able to pull you back?

5. What would happen to a baseball thrown by a major league pitcher on Mars's moon, Phobos (mass $= 2 \times 10^{16}$ kg; radius $= 10$ km)? (A professional pitcher can throw a baseball with a speed of about 40 m/sec.)

6. How fast must a particle be going to reach escape speed from the surface of the Sun (mass $= 2 \times 10^{30}$ kg; radius $= 7 \times 10^5$ km)? Do you know of anything that can move at that speed?

7. Light would not be able to leave from an object that has an escape speed of the speed of light. For an object the mass of the Sun, how small would it have to become, without losing any mass, to turn into a black hole?

ACTIVITY 9.1   HOW DOES A PENDULUM SWING?

PURPOSE

To determine which features of a pendulum affect its period.

WHAT DO YOU THINK?

Your teacher will show you a simple pendulum. When the bob is released without being pushed or pulled, it takes a certain amount of time for the bob to complete one full swing (swing through one arc, then swing back to near its release point). The time for one full swing, or one cycle, is called the period of the pendulum. See Figure 9.5.

P1. *What change(s) could you make in a pendulum that would increase or decrease its period? List the changes in a table (we will refer to this table as Table 9.6), indicating whether the period would be increased or decreased.*

NOTE: You will use Table 9.6 as the guide for this activity.

Table 9.6 Pendulum Prediction			
Change	**Increase**	**Decrease**	**No Effect**
1.			
2.			
3.			
4.			
5.			
6.			

MATERIALS

Per team of two students

    1 balance
    1 meterstick
    1 2-m (7-ft) length of strong string, nylon cord, or fishing line
    a selection of objects to use as bobs, with hooks for string attachment
    1 stopwatch, digital watch with timer function, or watch with second
       hand

PROCEDURE

A. Tie one end of the string to the fixture ("pivot point") indicated by your teacher. (The string must be attached to a structure that will not move when the pendulum swings.)

B. Tie a small loop in the other end of the string. Slip the hook of a bob (mass) through the loop. Lower the bob with your hand until the string is tight. Do not let go of the bob until the string is tight; the string may break if the bob is allowed to fall.

C. Pull the bob back from its vertical resting position no more than 45° and then release the bob without pushing or pulling it. Your partner should start timing the swings as soon as the bob is released. Try a few practice releases first. Because timing one cycle may be difficult, time 10 cycles, then divide the total time by 10 to get the average, which is your estimate of the period for one cycle.

EXAMPLE

If it takes 26 sec for 10 cycles, then it takes 26 sec/10 cycles = 2.6 sec for one cycle (2.6 sec/cycle). The period is 2.6 sec.

Figure 9.5

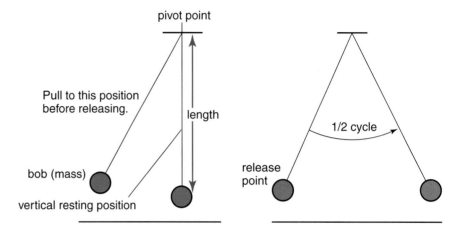

D. Select a feature of the pendulum to test from Table 9.6. (You and your partner should compare tables first and decide between yourselves which features to test.) Test only one feature at a time; if you change more than one feature, you will not know which feature affected the period or if changes in different features canceled each other out. Test each feature in several ways. For example, if you think the color of the bob affects the period, determine the period using three bobs of different colors without changing any other feature. Record the feature, its variations (such as the bob colors), and the period in a table like Table 9.7.

1. *Did the period of the pendulum change when you changed this feature? If so, by what percent did it change?*

E. Repeat step D for all other features you and your partner decided to test. Make your own copies of Table 9.7 for recording your data.

2. *Did the period of the pendulum change when you changed this feature? If so, by what percent did it change? (Answer separately for each feature tested.)*

Table 9.7

Feature variation	Period (seconds)

F. Observe the overall pattern of motion of the bob. Put any bob on the string and release the bob from any reasonable angle. Watch the bob swing back and forth (you are getting sleepy...).

3. *Write a description of the bob's motion, including any changes in its speed and the maximum angle of its swing from the vertical resting position. Is there any pattern to the bob's motion (besides swinging back and forth)?*

4. *In all trials, you released the pendulum bob without pushing or pulling it. However, a motionless object, such as the bob held by your hand, will not move without being pushed or pulled. Why did the bob move when it was released? (The cause of this motion is another factor controlling the period of the pendulum.)*

CHAPTER 10

Stars

HOW FAR AWAY ARE THE STARS?

Find five students in your school who are not taking this class and ask them the following questions. (Make sure that these students haven't already been asked by someone else in your class.)

Which object is farther from the Earth:

the nearest star visible in the night sky or

1. clouds?

2. the Moon?

3. the Sun?

4. Pluto?

Write down their beliefs and be prepared to discuss them at the next class meeting.

WHAT DO YOU THINK?

In the constellation of Perseus, there is a star that the Arabs named Algol ("The Demon"). Algol noticeably changes its apparent brightness every 3 days. Describe what you believe might cause Algol's apparent brightness to change.

Preview: You will learn (1) how to determine distances to stars and (2) how to estimate the sizes and masses of some stars.

How Far Away Are Stars?

Stars appear to be faint points of light sprinkled across an otherwise black sky. Even in the largest telescopes stars appear to be only points of light. What could these mysterious lights be? Some American Indian tribes believed that stars were campfires of their brothers and sisters in the sky. Other people thought stars were holes in the dome of the sky—holes through which they could see a light coming from beyond.

Perhaps the boldest guess of all was that stars were distant Suns. At first this notion seems pretty weird, because the Sun seems so much larger and brighter than the stars. If stars are Suns, how far away are they? Very far! Yes, but how very far? How could you measure this distance? One approach is to ask how far away the Sun would have to be, to appear to be as faint as the brightest appearing star.

NOTE: When we refer to bright or faint stars, we mean that the stars *appear* to be bright or *appear* to be faint to an observer on the Earth.

On a dark night when there are not too many bright lights around, you can see stars that range from very bright to very faint. If you measure the photons arriving from these stars, you would find that about 10^{-3} (1/1,000) times as many photons arrive each second from the faintest stars as from those that appear brightest. If all stars emitted the same number of photons each second, how much farther away would the faintest stars be than the brightest stars?

The faintest stars that can be detected in a large telescope are only about 10^{-10} (1/10,000,000,000) times as bright as the brightest stars you can see without a telescope. How much farther away are the faintest stars than the brightest stars? One way to answer those questions is to compare the apparent brightness of a star with the apparent brightness of the Sun, because you have measured the apparent brightness of the Sun and computed its distance from the Earth (Activity 10.1).

First, you will have to make an assumption. The assumption is that if all the stars were as close to the Earth as is the Sun, they all would appear to be as bright as the Sun. (Instead of talking about something "appearing to be as bright as the Sun, if it were at the same distance as the Sun," replace these words with a simpler expression—"the same wattage as the Sun." You will learn later in this chapter (see, also, Chapter 5) what "wattage" means. Here consider it to be the "amount" of light emitted by a star.)

Why do you have to make any assumption at all? Since you don't know either the wattage of a star or how far away it is from the Earth, its apparent brightness doesn't tell you very much about its distance. *Why not?*

Do all stars really have the same wattage as the Sun? You don't know. Scientists often make simple assumptions in tackling problems. Assumptions are guesses and must be checked whenever possible. Thus, scientists always try to check their assumptions. You will have a chance to check the assumption that all stars have the same wattage as the Sun.

In Chapter 5 you learned about the apparent brightness-distance relation and used it to determine how apparent brightness changes with distance. For example, suppose you were looking at the same lightbulb first from one distance, and then from a second distance. Suppose that from the second distance the bulb appeared to you to be 1/16 as bright as from the first distance. How much farther away from you was the bulb when it appeared to be 1/16 as bright? If the bulb appeared to be 1/16 as bright, you know that the area of a sphere centered on the bulb over which the photons spread each second must have been 16 times larger. You also know that the area over which the photons spread changes with the square of the distance from you to the source. So if the area were 16 times greater, the distance must have been the square root of 16, or 4 times, greater.

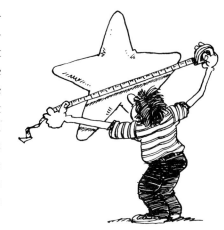

Apparent brightness depends on two things: (1) the number of photons a source emits each second (this number is proportional to the wattage of the source); and (2) the surface area of an imaginary sphere, centered on the source, that these photons pass through (this number depends on the *square* of the *distance* the photons must travel to reach the surface of the sphere). You can write this relation as a fraction. (As the top of a fraction gets larger, the fraction gets larger. As the bottom of a fraction gets larger [say going from 2 to 4], the fraction gets smaller [going, for example, from 1/2 to 1/4].) If two objects are at the same distance from you, the object with the greater wattage will appear brighter to you. Thus, wattage must be on the top (numerator) of the fraction. The farther an object is from you, the dimmer the object will appear to be. Thus, the distance squared (distance^2) must be on the bottom (denominator) of the fraction. You can write this relation in the following way:

apparent brightness = wattage / (distance)^2

where we must describe quantities in consistent units, for example apparent brightness in watts per meter squared, wattage in watts, and distance in meters.

In Activity 10.2 you made your first estimate of the distance to a star. How good an estimate is it? To check, look first at the assumption that all stars have the same wattage.

Do All Stars Have the Same Wattage?

On a clear evening in the Northern Hemisphere in October or November, if you are not too close to city lights, you can often see a very small group of stars above the eastern horizon. Most people can see six stars in this prominent group, which seems to many people to resemble a tiny dipper—so they sometimes think it must be the "Little Dipper." The Little Dipper, however, is much larger (and much harder for most people to find in the sky!). The smaller group of stars is called the Pleiades (PLEE-yuh-deez). Without binoculars or a telescope most people can see six stars in the Pleiades (see Figure 10.1). With a pair of binoculars, you can see several dozen stars (see Figure 10.2). With a telescope, several hundred stars can be photographed in the Pleiades (see Figure 10.3).

All the stars in the Pleiades are relatively close together in the sky. Are they also close together in space? (That is, are they all also at nearly the same distance from us?) Let's make the assumption that they are and see what follows.

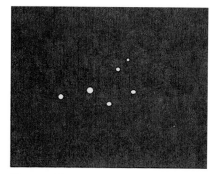

Figure 10.1
The Pleiades as seen by the naked eye.

Figure 10.2
The Pleiades as they might appear
through a pair of binoculars.

Figure 10.3
The Pleiades as photographed through
a telescope.

The first conclusion is that, contrary to the assumption you were asked to make, all stars would not have the same wattage as the Sun. It is not difficult to understand why. Imagine that two stars were the same distance from you, and that one star appeared to you to be twice as bright as the other star. Suppose the stars were moved until they were twice as far away from you. How would their apparent brightnesses compare? You know that if the stars were twice as far away from you the surface area of an imaginary sphere, centered on each star and filling the space between you and the star, would have to be 4 times as great—so the photons each star emits each second would be spread over 4 times as much area by the time they reach you. Thus, each star would appear to be one-fourth as bright, but one star would still appear to be twice as bright as the other. (*Check this result by using the expression for apparent brightness.*)

Similarly, if two sources that are close together in space appear equally bright to you, they will appear equally bright at *any* distance from you, no matter how far away they are as long as they are both at the *same* distance from you.

Now let's return to the Pleiades. Remember that you are assuming stars in the Pleiades are relatively close to each other. Therefore they would all be at approximately the same distance from the Earth. Since they have different apparent brightnesses, all the stars in the Pleiades could not have the same wattage. (If the stars in the Pleiades appeared equally bright, a telescope would not be needed to see any of them—or one would be needed to see all of them.)

You have used the ideas of apparent brightness and wattage, but you have not yet been given a definition for either. Something should first be added to the description of the photon model. So far you have treated photons as if they were all identical. In Chapter 11 you will find one of the ways in which one photon can be different from another—in the amount of energy it has. Energy is a very important concept, but difficult to describe accurately; but for now you need to know about only one aspect of energy. Energy is the ability to do work—for example, you can do work. Every photon has energy, but different photons can have different amounts of energy: One type of photon can do a different amount of work than another type of photon. In Chapter 11 you will see how the energy associated with a photon is related to color.

DEFINITION: The "wattage" of an object is the total energy of all the photons emitted every second by the object. Wattage therefore does not depend on the distance between you and the source (a 100-watt lightbulb is a 100-watt lightbulb even if you are a kilometer away from it). You can conveniently measure the wattage of stars in units of the Sun's wattage—part of a system of units in which the wattage of the Sun is set equal to one (just as astronomical units are part of a system in which the distance from the Earth to the Sun is defined to be one).

DEFINITION: The "apparent brightness" of a source is a measure of the total amount of energy carried by the photons reaching your eye each second from the source. More precisely, the apparent brightness of a source is a measure of the total amount of energy carried by the photons reaching a unit of area on the surface of an imaginary sphere that is centered on the source and that has a radius equal to the distance between you and the source. (The area of the surface of this sphere is proportional to the square of the distance from the source to you, who are located at the surface of the sphere.) Apparent brightness is related to how a source appears to you, so apparent brightness depends on how far you are from the source. Astronomers often measure apparent brightness in magnitudes (see Activity 10.2). Apparent brightness can also be described in watts per square meter. You can often tell which of two sources appears brighter simply by looking at them. In this book, however, you will use apparent brightness in a special way that allows you to describe apparent brightness accurately.

Here again is the expression for apparent brightness:

apparent brightness = wattage / (distance)^2

Notice that wattage is on top of the fraction, so that the *larger* the *wattage* the *larger* the *apparent brightness;* distance is on the bottom of the fraction so that the *larger* the *distance* the *smaller* the *apparent brightness.*

QUESTION: Suppose you forgot the expression for the apparent brightness of a source and thought that it might be

apparent brightness = distance/wattage

How could you check your guess to see if it might be right? (Hint: See what happens as the distance gets larger and smaller; repeat the process for wattage.)

By continuing to assume that the Pleiades are all almost the same distance from the Earth, and by measuring the apparent brightnesses of the stars in the Pleiades, you can get some idea of the range of wattages of the stars (see Figure 10.4). How much more wattage does the star in the Pleiades with the greatest wattage have than the star with the least wattage? If the Sun has as much wattage as the star marked "1" on the graph, how many stars in the Pleiades plotted in Figure 10.4 have a greater wattage than the Sun? How many stars in the Pleiades have a lesser wattage than the Sun?

At the beginning of this chapter, you estimated that the faintest stars you could see with the unaided eye were 30 times farther away than the brightest stars, because they appear to be 1,000 times fainter. Now that you have reason to believe that all stars do not have the same wattage, what does this conclusion suggest about the distances between the stars?

Figure 10.4
Stars in the Pleiades arranged by apparent brightness.

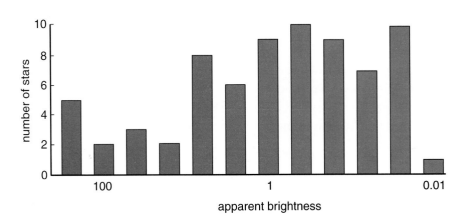

✳   The Universe in Your Hands

Some of the brightest stars in the sky are very far away; what does this fact tell you about their wattages?

Some stars appear bright because they are close. But some stars appear bright even though they are very far away. These latter stars appear bright because they have much greater wattages than the average star.

Another Way to Measure the Distance to a Star

To compare the wattages of stars you must know how bright they appear to be and you must also know how far away they are. If all stars do not have the same wattage as the Sun, how can you tell how far away a star is?

You make use of a similar principle to judge how far away a car is on a dark road at night. The apparent brightness of the car's headlights provides one clue—the brighter the lights appear to be, the closer the car is to you. The angular separation between the headlights provides another clue—the closer the headlights appear to be to each other, the farther away the car is from you. (Think of a triangle formed by an imaginary line between the headlights and two imaginary lines, one from each headlight to your eye.)

QUESTION: If the two headlights of a car appear to be one finger width apart when your arm is fully extended, how far away is the car? (Assume the headlights are 2 m apart.)

By thinking about this triangle method in another way, you can tell how far away a star is. Imagine that a star is observed from the Earth at opposite points in the Earth's orbit and that these two points are connected by an imaginary line that makes approximately a right angle with the direction to the star (see Figure 10.5). The two apparent positions of the star will be separated by a small angle. This angular separation is analogous to the angular separation between the headlights of a distant car. The smaller this angle, the farther away the star is from the Earth. Using the triangle method, astronomers have been able to measure the distances to the nearest stars. They found that the nearest star is approximately 2.8×10^5 (280,000) times as far away as the Sun.

The triangle method (often called the parallax method; see Chapter 7) is the most direct way known to measure large distances, but from the surface of the Earth it only works for the nearest stars. Why? Because astronomers must look at the stars through the Earth's atmosphere and the molecules in the atmosphere move as if it were boiling. This motion alters the paths of photons randomly, making it hard for astronomers to measure very small angles. Telescopes above the atmosphere can measure smaller angles more accurately and astronomers are now able to use the triangle method to measure the distance to many more stars (see Figure 10.6).

Before you made the comparison between the apparent brightness of a star and that of the Sun, you had some idea of how far away the stars are, because they only appear to be dim points of light. However, stars could have been 10,000 times as far away as the Sun, or a million times, or a hundred million times as far away. The nearest stars are of the order of 3×10^5 (300,000) times as far away as the Sun. This kind of approximate measurement is very important in science. Before scientists carry out detailed calculations, they often make estimates to see if a detailed calculation is worth

Figure. 10.5

Top: a star viewed from the Earth on two different occasions, separated by 6 months. Bottom: the Earth and the Sun as seen from the star in the top pictures of this figure.

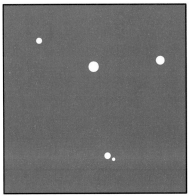

telescopic view of a nearby star as seen from Earth on Jan 1

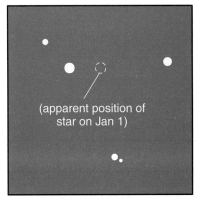

(apparent position of star on Jan 1)

telescopic view of a nearby star as seen from Earth on July 1

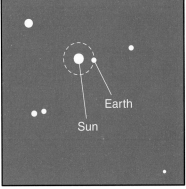

Earth

Sun

telescopic view of Earth (&Sun) as seen from the nearby star on Jan 1

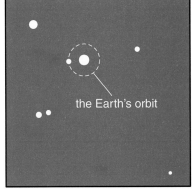

the Earth's orbit

telescopic view of Earth (&Sun) as seen from the nearby star on July 1

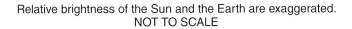

Relative brightness of the Sun and the Earth are exaggerated.
NOT TO SCALE

Figure 10.6

The same region of the sky photographed by a 2.2-m (86-in.) telescope on Earth (left) and by the Hubble Space Telescope (right). Because the Hubble Space Telescope is above the Earth's atmosphere, images taken with its cameras are sharper than those taken from the ground.

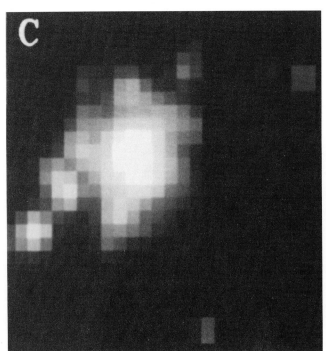

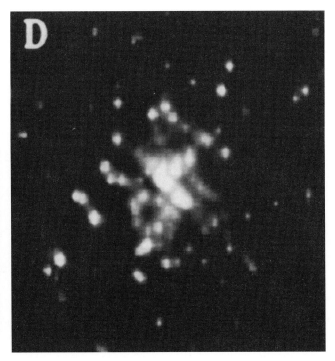

undertaking. Such estimates are also a good way to check the validity of a detailed calculation. (If an answer should be approximately 10^5, you know something is wrong if the number you calculate is 300.)

The Doppler Effect—A Story about Photons

When an object moves toward or away from you, the energy of the photons you receive from it changes. (This effect is discussed in many high school physics courses. In this course, accept that this energy shift is observed by astronomers and do not try to understand how the photon model accounts for it.) If an object is moving *away* from you, the photons it emits appear to you to have *lower* energies. If an object is moving *toward* you, the photons it emits appear to you to have *higher* energies. This "Doppler effect," or "Doppler shift," is named after the man who first explained a similar effect with sound, the Austrian physicist Christian Doppler (1803–1853). By measuring the energies of the photons received from a star, astronomers can tell how fast it is moving toward or away from the Earth.

Why is the Doppler effect important? Think about a distant car moving along a road at a right angle to your line of sight (see Figure 10.7). The farther away the car is, the longer it takes for you to be sure that the car is moving. A similar problem concerns astronomers: The farther away a star is, the longer it takes them to determine (by making observations over periods of months or years) that the star is moving. It takes longer for the motions of distant stars to be observable than the time in which astronomers have had telescopes to make such observations. For even more distant objects (such as some of those you will meet in Chapter 14), it would take hundreds or even hundreds of thousands of years to observe such motion!

The energy effect associated with motion toward or away from the observer has no such limitations. As long as an object can be observed, the energy shift of photons emitted by the source tells an astronomer the speed the object is moving toward or away from the Earth. You will see in Chapter 14 that this important fact is used to determine which observable objects are the most distant from us.

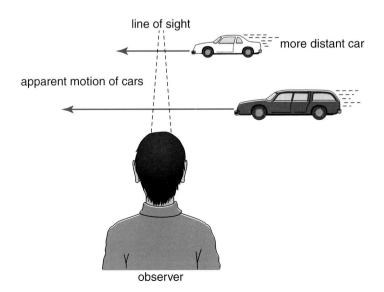

line of sight

more distant car

apparent motion of cars

observer

Figure 10.7
Distant cars moving at right angles to the observer's line of sight.

Figure 10.8
Motion of a star with respect to an observer.

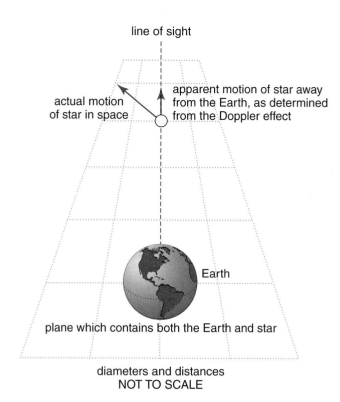

To summarize: The energy shift produced by motion toward or away from the observer *does not* depend on the distance to the star, unlike angular separation produced by motion at right angles to the observer, which *does* depend on the distance to the star (see Figure 10.8). For that reason astronomers can measure one aspect of the motion of stars no matter how far away the stars are—provided the stars appear bright enough for astronomers to observe them.

How Big Are Some Stars?

If you watch very carefully you will find that in the constellation of Perseus there is a star that noticeably changes its apparent brightness every 3 days. The Arabs called this star Algol, or "the demon." In 1783 Richard Goode figured out a way to explain this behavior. He reasoned that Algol is not the single star astronomers see through even the largest telescopes. Rather, it must be two stars moving around each other, but too close to be seen as separate objects. If the first star passed between you and the second star every 3 days, the light of the second star would be at least partially cut off and you would see a dimming—just as with Algol (see Figure 10.9).

Suppose each time the larger of the two stars passed in front of the smaller star, the light from the smaller one was completely blocked from your view. Suppose, further, that you could infer from measurments how fast each star was moving across your line of sight (see Figure 10.7). You could then determine the diameter of the smaller star by using relatively simple mathematics.

How could you tell whether the light from the smaller star was being completely shielded from reaching the Earth? You can only observe the apparent brightness of the combined light from both stars. You cannot dis-

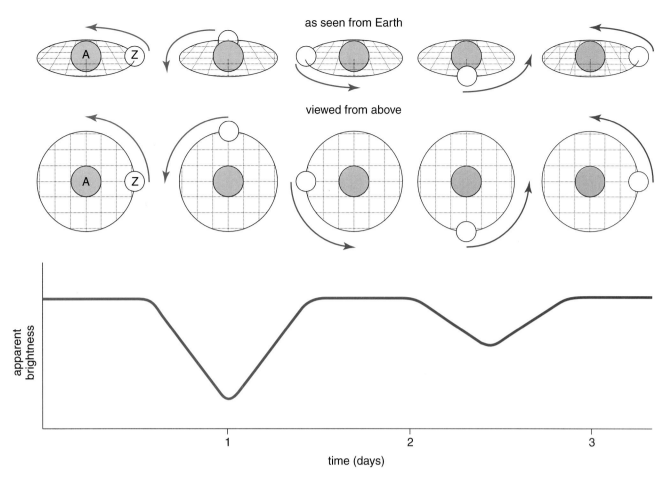

as seen from Earth

viewed from above

Figure 10.9
A two-star system (also called a binary system) in which a larger, apparently dimmer star regularly blocks part of the light of a smaller, apparently brighter star.

tinguish the light from the individual stars. When the combined light appears dimmest, you can infer that the larger star is passing between you and the smaller star. If the interval for which the light appears dimmest (and constant) is "reasonably" long, then you can conclude that the larger star is completely shielding the smaller star during this time.

How can you estimate the speed at which the stars are moving? Here the Doppler effect comes in handy. Some of the photons emitted by a star have characteristic energies, determined by the atoms in the star; the energies of these photons, as measured on the Earth, are different and depend on the apparent motion of the star away from the Earth (as shown in Figure 10.8) or toward the Earth. Using measurements of these photon energies made at different times as the stars move around each other, astronomers can infer their speeds, including their speeds across the line of sight. By combining this information with that obtained from monitoring the apparent brightness, astronomers can then determine the size of the smaller star. In a system of stars like Algol, astronomers can use the changing pattern of apparent brightness and the speed of the stars determined by the energy shift of the photons to make a scale model of the system (see Figure 10.10).

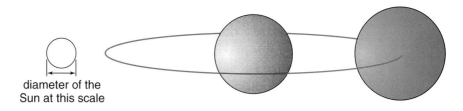

diameter of the
Sun at this scale

Determining the Masses of Stars

When two stars are in orbit about one another, it is sometimes possible to determine the sum of their masses from measuring the time it takes them to orbit each other and the speed with which they orbit each other. Another relation is also needed. Recall the relation Kepler discovered between the average distance of a planet from the Sun and the time it takes the planet to complete one trip around the Sun. Newton showed that this relation depends on the mass of the Sun and the mass of the planet. However, the mass of the Sun is so much larger than the mass of the planet that when using Kepler's relation for objects in our solar system, you can ignore the mass of the planet (see Chapter 9):

$$(\text{period of planet})^2 = \frac{(\text{average distance of planet from the Sun})^3}{(\text{mass of the Sun})}$$

This equation, or relation, is correct as long as you do all your calculations using bodies in orbit around the Sun and use distances measured in a.u. and orbital periods measured in Earth-years, with the mass of the Sun taken to be 1. For example, in the case of the Earth, Kepler's relation becomes:

$$(1 \text{ year})^2 = (1 \text{ a.u.})^3/1 \text{ solar mass}$$

or

$$1 \times 1 = 1/1$$

that is

$$1 = 1$$

You can also use Kepler's relation to describe the motion of two stars in orbit about each other, but you can no longer assume that the mass of the system is equal to 1 solar mass. Furthermore, you have to include the masses of both stars. It turns out that the expression for Kepler's relation then becomes

$$(\text{orbital period})^2 = \frac{(\text{average distance between two stars})^3}{(\text{sum of the masses of the two stars})}$$

How can you use this relation to determine the sum of the masses of the two stars? Measuring the period of the variations in the Doppler shift of the light gives you the orbital period directly. But how can you determine the average distance between the two stars? If the orbit is oriented so that you view it nearly edge-on, you can find this distance. You know you are viewing the system edge-on when the apparent brightness varies as shown in Figure 10.9: Eclipses of one star by the other can only occur in this orientation. Measurements of the Doppler shift then give you the average speeds of the stars in their orbits. Dividing the orbital period by the average speed

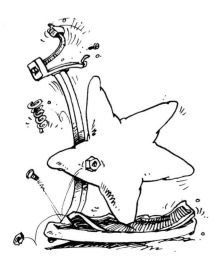

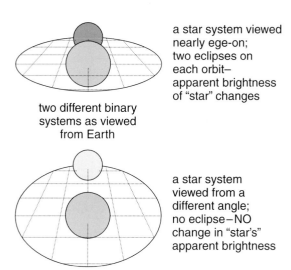

a star system viewed nearly ege-on; two eclipses on each orbit– apparent brightness of "star" changes

two different binary systems as viewed from Earth

a star system viewed from a different angle; no eclipse–NO change in "star's" apparent brightness

Figure 10.11
Two different binary star systems; both would appear to be only one "star" when seen from the Earth through a telescope. (A binary system is a system with two stars orbiting each other.)

gives you the circumference of the equivalent circle. The radius, *r*, of the circle, which is the average distance you want, then follows from the formula $2\pi r$ for the circumference of a circle. Suppose, as an example, you found this average distance between two stars to be twice the average distance between the Earth and the Sun, and the orbital period to be one year:

$$(\text{orbital period})^2 = \frac{(\text{distance between two stars})^3}{(\text{sum of the masses of the two stars})}$$

$$1^2 = \frac{2^3}{(\text{sum of the masses of the two stars})}$$

Multiply both sides of the equation by the sum of the masses of the two stars:

$$1^2 \times (\text{sum of the masses of the two stars}) = 2^3$$

$$(\text{sum of the masses of the two stars}) = 8$$

The two stars therefore have a combined mass of 8 times the mass of the Sun.

Most multiple-star systems are not so conveniently lined up so that they produce eclipses (see Figure 10.11). But it is still possible to get some idea of the masses of the stars involved, although you are less certain about the values of these masses. You can use the nomogram for Kepler's relation on the next page to explore possible varieties of masses and periods of two stars orbiting each other.

SUMMARY

The distances to stars can be determined by two methods. Knowing the wattage of a star and its apparent brightness, you can determine its distance from you by using the apparent brightness-distance relation. For stars that are closer than 100 light-years, the distances can also be measured by observing the apparent shifts in the locations of the stars in the sky due to the motion of the Earth around the Sun. The closer the star to the Earth, the greater this shift. However, this shift is very small even when observed through the longest focal length telescopes.

By observing two stars orbiting each other, you can sometimes determine the masses and diameters of the stars.

HOMEWORK

Use the apparent brightness-distance nomogram and the Kepler's relation nomogram when applicable.

1. The star Alpha Centauri is 275,000 times farther from the Sun than is the Earth. How would the apparent brightness of the Sun as seen from Alpha Centauri compare to the Sun's apparent brightness as seen from the Earth?

2. The distance from the Earth to the star Procyon is about 11 l.y. What is the wattage of Procyon? Does it have more or less wattage than the Sun?

3. The distance from the Earth to the star Aldebaran is about 70 l.y. What is the wattage of Aldebaran? Does it have more or less wattage than the Sun?

4. The distance from the Earth to Barnard's star is about 6 l.y. What is the wattage of Barnard's star? Does it have more or less wattage than the Sun?

5. The wattage of each of the stars below was estimated by studying its light; they are some of the brightest appearing stars in the sky. Determine the distance to each using the apparent brightness-distance nomogram. The wattage is given in units of the wattage of the Sun—for example, Altair's wattage is equal to the wattage of 15 Suns, that is, $15 \times 4 \times 10^{26} = 6 \times 10^{27}$ watts. "V" indicates that the apparent brightness of the star varies; the apparent magnitude given is the average value.

STAR	APP MAG	WATTAGE (Suns)	DISTANCE (l.y.)
Deneb	1.3	60,000	
Antares	0.9v	6,000	
Spica	0.9v	2,500	
Capella	0.0	200	
Regulus	1.4	170	
Pollux	1.2	50	
Castor	1.6	40	
Altair	0.8	15	

6. On the next page is a curve of apparent brightness for the Algol system, which contains two stars that orbit each other *and* undergo eclipses.

   a) How long does it take the stars to orbit each other?

   b) What is the combined mass of the stars in this system? (Use your answer for question 6a as well as Figure 10.10 to answer this question.)

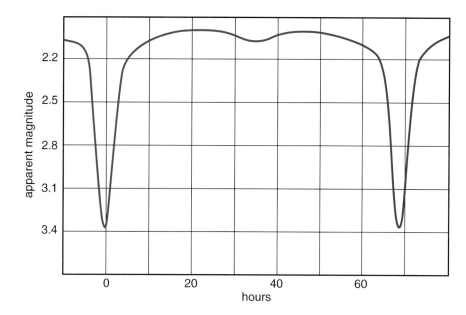

7. The bright appearing star at the bend of the handle of the Big Dipper (Ursa Major) is named Mizar. Through a telescope, this star appears as two unrelated stars. The brighter appearing one is actually two stars orbiting one another, a binary star system. By studying the light from this binary system, astronomers estimate that its two stars are really 30 million km (about 18 million mi) apart and take 20.5 days to make one orbit of each other. What is the combined mass of the stars in this binary system in kilograms and in units of the Sun's mass?

8. Appropriately, the star Castor, in Gemini the twins, appears as a binary system. The two stars are about 13.5 billion km apart and take 400 years to complete one orbit around each other. What is the total mass of the system in kilograms and in units of the Sun's mass?

SELF-TEST

1. If you see a star as a single point of light, does that mean there is only one star there? Explain.

2. If you were out in the Oort cloud (the region around the Sun where comets are thought to originate, about 50,000 times farther from the Sun than is the Earth), how would the apparent brightness of the Sun compare to its apparent brightness as seen from the Earth? What would its apparent magnitude be? What star would then have an apparent brightness closest to the Sun's?

3. The distances between the stars in each of the binary systems of Sirius and Alpha Centauri are nearly the same, about 20 times the average Earth-Sun distance. The stars in the Sirius system take about 50 years to orbit each other; the stars in the Alpha Centauri system orbit in 80 years. Which system has the greater mass? Explain.

4. The wattage of Alpha Centauri is about 7×10^{26} watts. How far would you have to be from this star so that it would appear as bright as the Sun does to us?

5. The star Sirius has a wattage of 1.4×10^{29} watts. At what distance from us would Sirius appear as bright as the Sun appears from the Earth?

6. Consider the stars described in homework question 5. What is the worst percentage error you would make in computing their distances from their apparent brightnesses if you assumed each had the same wattage as the Sun?

7. Discuss the accuracy of the following statements:

   a) The wattage of a star decreases as one gets farther away from it.

   b) The brighter appearing stars in the sky are the closer stars.

   c) There is no way to show that the Earth orbits around the Sun.

8. In two eclipsing binary systems, the members of each pair are separated by the same distance. System L takes 10 years for one revolution, while system M takes 100 years. Which system has the greater total mass? Explain your answer.

9. In each of two eclipsing binary systems, the stars orbit each other with a period of 90 days. In system A the stars are separated by a distance of 10 a.u. and in system B the stars are separated by a distance of 50 a.u. Which system has the greater total mass?

Questions to Answer with Nomogram of Kepler's Relation

1. The Moon orbits the Earth in a month. What is the Earth's mass compared to the Sun's?

2. Geosynchronous satellites have to stay fixed above a certain spot on the Earth, so they must orbit in exactly 1 day. How far are they from the Earth's center? How far from the Earth's surface?

3. The space shuttle orbits the Earth at about 200 km above its surface or about 6,600 km from the Earth's center. What is the period of its orbit?

4. Pluto's distance from the Sun is about 40 a.u. What is the period of its orbit?

5. Find Jupiter's mass from the radius and orbital period of each of four of its moons (the masses of the moons are negligible compared to Jupiter's mass):

Moon	Orbital Period	Radius of Orbit
Io	1.8 days	422,000 km
Callisto	16.7 days	1,883,000 km
Himalia	251.0 days	11,480,000 km
Ananke	631.0 days	21,200,000 km

6. A comet is circling the Sun at a distance from it of 10,000 a.u. What is the comet's orbital period?

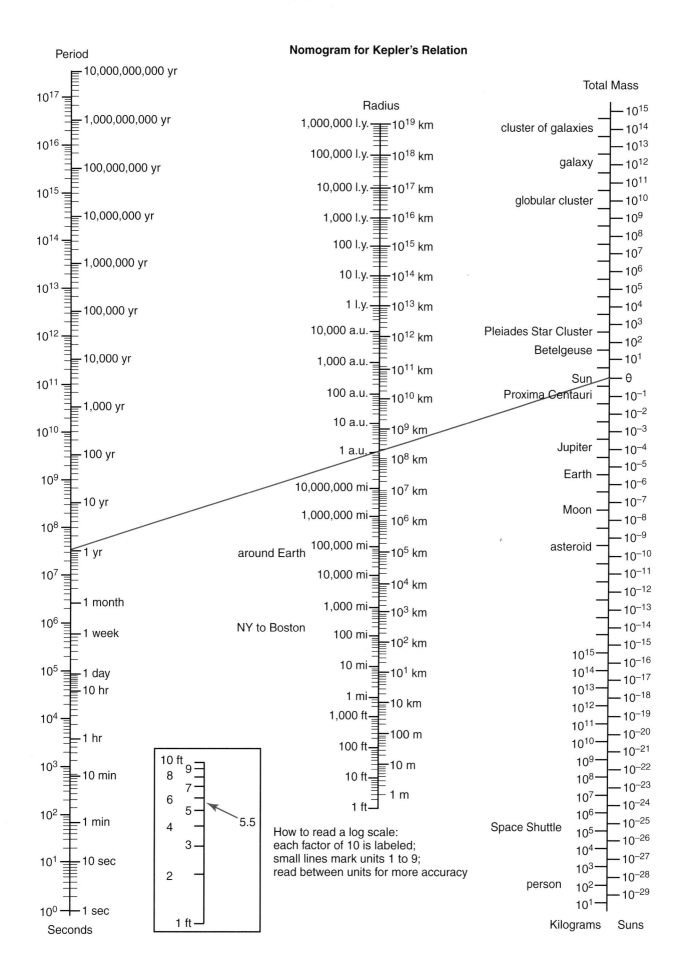

Nomogram for Kepler's Relation

Period

10,000,000,000 yr
10^{17}
1,000,000,000 yr
10^{16}
100,000,000 yr
10^{15}
10,000,000 yr
10^{14}
1,000,000 yr
10^{13}
100,000 yr
10^{12}
10,000 yr
10^{11}
1,000 yr
10^{10}
100 yr
10^9
10 yr
10^8
1 yr
10^7
1 month
10^6
1 week
10^5
1 day
10 hr
10^4
1 hr
10^3
10 min
10^2
1 min
10^1
10 sec
10^0
1 sec

Seconds

Radius

1,000,000 l.y. — 10^{19} km
100,000 l.y. — 10^{18} km
10,000 l.y. — 10^{17} km
1,000 l.y. — 10^{16} km
100 l.y. — 10^{15} km
10 l.y. — 10^{14} km
1 l.y. — 10^{13} km
10,000 a.u. — 10^{12} km
1,000 a.u. — 10^{11} km
100 a.u. — 10^{10} km
10 a.u. — 10^9 km
1 a.u. — 10^8 km
10,000,000 mi — 10^7 km
1,000,000 mi — 10^6 km
100,000 mi — 10^5 km
around Earth
10,000 mi — 10^4 km
1,000 mi — 10^3 km
NY to Boston
100 mi — 10^2 km
10 mi — 10^1 km
1 mi — 10 km
1,000 ft — 100 m
100 ft —
100 m — 10 m
10 ft —
1 ft — 1 m

How to read a log scale:
each factor of 10 is labeled;
small lines mark units 1 to 9;
read between units for more accuracy

10 ft
9
8
7
6
5.5
5
4
3
2
1 ft

Total Mass

10^{15}
cluster of galaxies — 10^{14}
10^{13}
galaxy — 10^{12}
10^{11}
globular cluster — 10^{10}
10^9
10^8
10^7
10^6
10^5
10^4
Pleiades Star Cluster — 10^3
10^2
Betelgeuse — 10^1
Sun — θ
Proxima Centauri — 10^{-1}
10^{-2}
10^{-3}
Jupiter — 10^{-4}
Earth — 10^{-5}
10^{-6}
Moon — 10^{-7}
10^{-8}
asteroid — 10^{-9}
10^{-10}
10^{-11}
10^{-12}
10^{-13}
10^{-14}
10^{15} — 10^{-15}
10^{14} — 10^{-16}
10^{13} — 10^{-17}
10^{12} — 10^{-18}
10^{11} — 10^{-19}
10^{10} — 10^{-20}
10^9 — 10^{-21}
10^8 — 10^{-22}
10^7 — 10^{-23}
10^6 — 10^{-24}
Space Shuttle
10^5 — 10^{-25}
10^4 — 10^{-26}
10^3 — 10^{-27}
person — 10^2 — 10^{-28}
10^1 — 10^{-29}

Kilograms   Suns

7. What orbital period would a satellite close to the Moon's surface have? The Moon has a mass of 4×10^{-8} solar masses (M_S).

8. The asteroid Juno has a mass of 10^{-11} M_S and a radius of 110 km. What would be the orbital period of a satellite moving just above its surface? What would be the orbital period of a spaceship moving 100 km above Juno's surface?

9. Sirius has a dim companion, Sirius B, separated from Sirius by 20 a.u. Its orbital period is 50 years. What is the total mass of the two stars?

How Bright Is Bright?

How bright does the Sun appear to be? A scientist can give you a specific number that describes its apparent brightness. The average five-year-old will tell you the Sun appears *really* bright. Neither answer may tell you what you want to know. You might have a better understanding by comparing to each other the apparent brightnesses of several different kinds of lights, when each is viewed from the same distance. Then comparisons of apparent brightness will be equivalent to comparisons of wattage. The chart below is therefore set up with units of watts.

The chart is set up on a logarithmic, or "log," scale, as are nomograms (see the nomogram box in Chapter 9). On most other graphs you have probably seen, the lines are evenly spaced and evenly numbered. The first line may represent 1, the second represent 2, the third 3, and so forth. On a log scale, lines marking powers of 10 are evenly spaced. The first line may represent 10, the second 100, the third 1,000, etc. Each line is marked by a number 10 times bigger than the number marking the line before it. This kind of graph helps you to look at both big and small numbers at the same time. It is helpful in this case because you can then compare lights of vastly different apparent brightnesses.

Reading lamps usually have 60-watt lightbulbs, so the line on the graph for a reading lamp points between the graph lines indicating 10^1 watts and 10^2 watts. How many times brighter do the stadium lights appear to be than the lights in your kitchen when you view them both from the same distance? How many times brighter would the Sun appear to be than a reading lamp at the same viewing distance? Do these comparisons help you to understand better how much light the Sun emits?

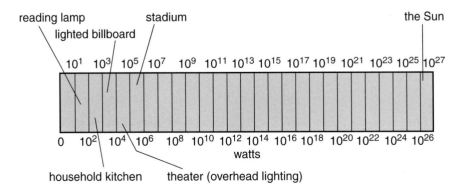

Reading lamp	60 watts
Household kitchen lights	480 watts
Billboard lights	1,300 watts
Theater lights	16,000 watts
Stadium lights	240,000 watts

ACTIVITY 10.1   ESTIMATING HOW MANY 200-WATT BULBS "EQUAL" THE SUN

PURPOSE

To estimate the number of 200-watt lightbulbs required to equal the wattage of the Sun.

WHAT DO YOU THINK?

P1. *How far would you have to stand from a 200-watt lightbulb for it to have the same apparent brightness as the Sun?*

P2. *If you could collect a large number of 200-watt lightbulbs and place them in the sky at a distance of 150,000,000 km from you (approximately the average Earth-Sun distance), how many bulbs do you think it would take to equal the apparent brightness of the Sun if all were lit?*

PART A   CONSTRUCTING A SIMPLE PHOTOMETER

PURPOSE

To assemble and test a paraffin block photometer.

MATERIALS

1 paraffin block, about 6 cm × 12 cm (2.5 in. × 5 in.)
1 meterstick
1 piece of aluminum foil, about 6 cm × 12 cm (2.5 in. × 5 in.)
2 rubber bands
1 200-watt unfrosted lightbulb, with clamp socket
1 pair of scissors or 1 nail
1 100-watt unfrosted lightbulb, with clamp socket

PROCEDURE

A. Refer to Figure 10.12. Split the paraffin block in half so you have two equal-sized pieces, each about 6 cm × 6 cm. To split the block smoothly, use the point of a scissors or the tip of a nail to make a deep

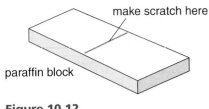

make scratch here

paraffin block

Figure 10.12

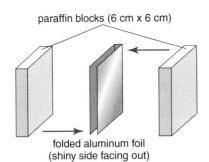

paraffin blocks (6 cm x 6 cm)

folded aluminum foil
(shiny side facing out)

Figure 10.13

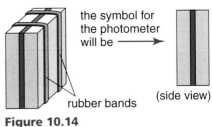

the symbol for
the photometer
will be ——→

rubber bands

(side view)

Figure 10.14

scratch across the center of the block. Place the block on a hard, stable surface, such as a lab table or sturdy desk, with the scratch line facing up, parallel to and slightly beyond the table edge. With one hand, press down on the block to hold it on the table and with your other hand grasp the end of the block extending beyond the table edge and pull down firmly. The block should split along the scratch line. *Do not* hit the block; the blow may break the block unevenly.

CAUTION **BE CAREFUL NOT TO CUT YOURSELF WITH ANY SHARP INSTRUMENT!**

B. Fold the piece of aluminum foil into a square 6 cm x 6 cm with the shiny side facing out on both sides. Place the folded foil between the paraffin blocks. See Figure 10.13.

C. Secure the two pieces of paraffin and the foil by wrapping them with two rubber bands. See Figure 10.14.

D. Turn on the 200-watt lightbulb. Darken the room as much as possible. Stand within 3 m of the light. Hold the photometer in one hand so that one side of the photometer faces the lightbulb, as shown in Figure 10.15. Look at the side of the photometer, as you do by looking at Figure 10.15. Slowly move the photometer toward the light and then away.

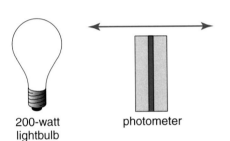

200-watt
lightbulb

photometer

Figure 10.15

CAUTION **DO NOT TOUCH THE BULB WHEN IT IS ON! YOU MAY BE BURNED! ALSO BE CAREFUL WHEN HANDLING THE BULB AFTER SHUTTING IT OFF, AS IT WILL REMAIN HOT FOR SEVERAL MINUTES!**

1. *Compare the apparent brightness of the side of the photometer facing the light and the side of the photometer that is not facing the light.*

E. Place the 100-watt bulb at a distance of 1 m from one side of the photometer. Place the 200-watt bulb on the other side of the photometer 1 m away. Move the 200-watt bulb closer to and then farther from the photometer. By looking at the two sides of the photometer (as in step D), you will be able to determine which side appears to be brighter.

2. *Describe what happens to the apparent brightness of the side of the photometer facing the 200-watt bulb as you change the bulb's distance from the photometer.*

F. Leave the 100-watt bulb at a distance of 1 m from one side of the photometer. Change the distance of the 200-watt bulb from the other side of the photometer until both sides have the same apparent brightness. Measure the distance from the 200-watt bulb to the photometer.

CAUTION: DO NOT TOUCH THE BULBS. THEY ARE VERY HOT!

3. *Is the distance from the 200-watt bulb to the photometer greater than or less than the 1-m distance to the 100-watt bulb?*

4. *In general terms, how would you describe what a photometer does?*

PART B   MEASURING THE SUN'S WATTAGE

PURPOSE

To determine how many 200-watt lightbulbs are needed to equal the wattage of the Sun.

MATERIALS

For each team of two students

    1 photometer
    1 meterstick
    1 extension cord
    1 200-watt unfrosted bulb with clamp socket

DO NOT TOUCH THE BULB WHEN IT IS ON! YOU MAY BE BURNED! BE CAREFUL WHEN HANDLING THE BULB AFTER SHUTTING IT OFF, AS IT WILL REMAIN HOT FOR SEVERAL MINUTES!

PROCEDURE

A. On a bright, sunny day, take the 200-watt bulb with socket and extension cord, the photometer, and a meterstick outside or remain inside if the Sun shines directly into the room. Clamp the socket to a stable object. Plug the cord into an outdoor socket or run the cord from inside the school. Turn on the bulb.

B. Hold the photometer between the Sun and the bulb with the bulb's filament parallel to the face of the photometer. Hold the other face of the photometer toward the Sun. See Figure 10.16. Move the photometer toward and away from the bulb, stopping when the two sides have the same apparent brightness. Hold the photometer steady while your partner measures the distance from the filament in the bulb to the wax surface of the photometer.

1. *Describe the colors you noticed on the side of the photometer facing the lightbulb and on the side facing the Sun.*

Figure 10.16

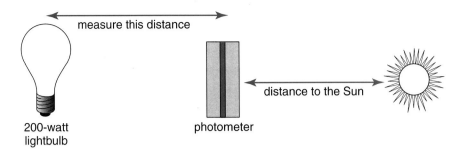

This color difference will make it difficult to compare the apparent brightnesses of the sides. Make observations as carefully as you can.

C. Repeat step B 3 times, exchanging positions with your partner each time. (The four measurements may vary.)

D. Record your measurements in a table. Add your four measurements and then divide by four. The resulting number will be the average of your measurements of the distance between the filament and the photometer surface. Record this number as the answer to question 2.

2. *What is the distance between the 200-watt bulb and the photometer in centimeters?*

3. *The Sun is about 150,000,000 km from the Earth. How many centimeters is the Sun from the Earth?*

4. *How many lightbulb-photometer distances is it from the Sun to the Earth?*

5. *Using the same reasoning as you used in Activity 5.1 (refer to questions 10 through 14 in that activity), calculate how many 200-watt lightbulbs are needed to equal the wattage of the Sun.*

6. *What is the wattage of the Sun? (Hint: How many 1-watt lightbulbs are required to equal the wattage of the Sun?)*

HOMEWORK

1. Mars is 1.5 times farther from the Sun than is the Earth. If you repeated this experiment on Mars, how far would you have to hold the photometer from the 200-watt lightbulb for the two sides of the photometer to have the same apparent brightness?

2. Venus is 0.7 times the distance of the Earth from the Sun. If you repeated this experiment on Venus, how far would you have to hold the photometer from the 200-watt lightbulb for the two sides of the photometer to have the same apparent brightness?

ACTIVITY 10.2

USING A FLASHLIGHT TO ESTIMATE DISTANCES TO STARS

PURPOSE

To construct an artificial star and, by comparing its apparent brightness to that of a bright star, to estimate the distance to the bright star.

MATERIALS

1 30-cm length of optical fiber
5 5-cm pieces of transparent tape
1 flashlight (with 2 D-cell batteries)
1 sheet of aluminum foil, 12 cm × 12 cm (5 in. × 5 in.)
1 yardstick or a measuring tape (Use a meterstick or a measuring tape with centimeter markings if one is available.)

PROCEDURE

You will receive the materials for building the artificial star in class and then complete the activity at home. Steps F and G will require the help of two friends or family members (partners).

The only light that you should be able to see from your flashlight is the light from the end of the optical fiber. This is your artificial star. Your artificial star has a wattage of approximately 1 millionth (0.000001) of a watt.

An optical fiber is a thin thread of plastic that allows most of the light entering it to pass through its length with very little light escaping through its sides.

A. Tape the fiber across the face of the flashlight with about 5 cm of transparent tape (Figure 10.17).

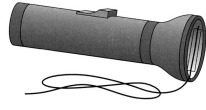

Figure 10.17

B. Cover the face of the flashlight with aluminum foil so that no light escapes. Tape the foil to the body of the flashlight (Figure 10.18).

C. Tape the fiber to the flashlight so that the light-emitting end points to the back (Figure 10.18). (Use less fiber than is shown in the figures and do not fold it tightly; resulting small holes will allow light to leak.)

D. Take your artificial star outside on a clear night. Locate a bright star such as Sirius in Canis Major or Procyon in Canis Minor. You may wish to use the star finder you constructed in Activity 2.2 or the information in Appendix 1 to help you locate one of these stars. NOTE: Take some extra foil and tape with you for repairs in case you have a "light leak."

Figure 10.18

1. *Record the name of the star you are using to make the apparent brightness comparisons.*

E. Turn on the flashlight. Repair any light leaks around the aluminum foil. Hold the free end of the fiber optic directly toward your eye so you can see the glow of the light from it.

Figure 10.19

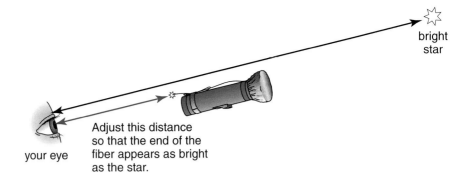

bright
star

Adjust this distance
so that the end of the
fiber appears as bright
as the star.

your eye

F. Give the "artificial star" to one of your partners. Have that partner move the fiber toward and away from your eye holding the end of the fiber optic up so you can see both it and the sky clearly. Have your partner move the fiber until the apparent brightness of the fiber end matches the apparent brightness of the star in the sky. Refer to Figure 10.19.

G. Have your second partner measure the distance from your eye to the end of the fiber. Look at the same star again, or take turns with your partners, and again measure the distance from your eye to the end of the fiber. Repeat the observation and measurement a third time. Record the values.

2. a) *1st measurement = ? m*
   2nd measurement = ? m
   3rd measurement = ? m

   b) *What is the average of the three measurements in m?*

H. To determine the distance to the star, you need to know its wattage. Because you do not know this quantity for this star, assume that it has the same wattage as the Sun.

3. *What is the wattage of the Sun?*

I. You know the wattage of the star (i.e., you have assumed it equals the Sun's), you know the wattage of a standard source (the artificial star = one-millionth of a watt), and you know the distance to that standard source (answer to question 2, b). Using similar reasoning as you used to determine the wattage of the Sun, calculate how far away the star is. (Hints: How many of your standard sources are needed to equal the wattage of the Sun? You may have to find a square root instead of squaring as you did earlier.)

4. *What is the distance to the star in kilometers?*

5. *What is the distance to this star in light-years?*

ACTIVITY 10.3   USING APPARENT BRIGHTNESS TO ESTIMATE STELLAR DISTANCES

PURPOSE

To use data from Activities 10.1 and 10.2 and a nomogram to find the distances to some stars that appear to be very bright.

WHAT DO YOU THINK?

P1. *How do the wattages of the stars that are visible in the nighttime sky compare to that of the Sun?*

P2. *How many light-years away from us would the Sun have to be to have the same apparent brightness as the brightest appearing star in the nighttime sky?*

MATERIALS

a ruler or other straightedge
a list of wattages (Table 10.3)
data from Activities 10.1 and 10.2
apparent brightness-distance nomogram
a fine-point pen or sharpened pencil
a list of apparent magnitudes (Table 10.1)

PROCEDURE

Astronomers classify the apparent brightness of stars, planets, and other celestial objects by a number called "apparent magnitude." This system was introduced about 2,000 years ago when the astronomer Hipparchus gave the brightest appearing stars a value of 1. In his system, stars such as Sirius (in Canis Major), Vega (in Lyra), and Rigel (in Orion) were all given this number. Dimmer stars were assigned apparent magnitude values of 2. Stars that were even dimmer were assigned apparent magnitudes of 3, 4, 5 or 6. Stars of apparent magnitude 6 are about the dimmest that can be seen with the unaided eye. This numbering system may seem odd, with dimmer stars getting higher numbers. But it is similar to awarding prizes in a race: the fastest runner (brightest star) gets 1st place (apparent magnitude 1); the others are runners-up, placing 2nd, 3rd, 4th, etc. (apparent magnitudes 2, 3, 4, and so on).

After astronomers began using telescopes, a far larger number of even dimmer stars were observed and the apparent magnitude scale was extended to larger numbers. In the middle of the 19th century, the scale was revised on a more systematic basis. As a result, we now have apparent magnitude values of zero and even negative values. In the new system, Sirius (the brightest appearing nighttime star) has an apparent magnitude of −1.5. Vega is assigned an apparent magnitude of +0.0, and Rigel a value of +0.1.

Table 10.1

APPARENT MAGNITUDE	OBJECT
−26.7	Sun
−12.5	Full Moon
−4.0	Venus (at its brightest)
−2.5	Jupiter (at its brightest)
−1.5	Sirius (brightest star)
0.0	Alpha Centauri, Vega
0.4	Betelgeuse, Procyon
0.7	Altair
0.9	Aldebaran
2.0	Polaris (North Star)
6.5	Limit with unaided eye on darkest night
9.0	Limit with 7 × 50 binoculars
10.0	Barnard's star
13.0	Limit with 20.5-cm (8-in.) telescope (visually)
24.0	Limit with 5-m (200-in.) telescope (photographic)
28.0	Limit with the Hubble Space Telescope

These values are measures of the apparent brightness of a star (or other object) as seen by an observer on Earth.

The apparent brightness of a star depends on its distance from us as well as on its wattage. You experimented with this principle in Activity 10.2. When an astronomer knows the distance to a star and its apparent magnitude, she or he is able to estimate its wattage.

A. Your teacher will give you a copy of the nomogram; you can also see it in the homework section of this activity. Write the name of the object from Table 10.1 next to its corresponding apparent magnitude on your copy of the nomogram (*not* in the book, please!). Table 10.1 is a list of apparent magnitudes for some astronomical objects.

Table 10.2 lists some distances that will be used in the problems. "A.u." is an abbreviation for "astronomical unit," which equals the average distance from the Earth to the Sun, about 1.5×10^8 km (9.3×10^7 mi). Larger celestial distances are often measured in "light-years" (or l.y.); a light-year is equal to the distance light travels in 1 year, about 10^{13} km (about 6×10^{12} mi).

Table 10.2

METRIC UNITS	ENGLISH UNITS	DISTANCE REFERENCE
1.3×10^4 km	8.0×10^3 mi	diameter of the Earth
4.0×10^5 km	2.4×10^5 mi	distance from the Earth to the Moon
1.4×10^6 km	8.7×10^5 mi	diameter of the Sun
1.5×10^8 km	9.3×10^7 mi	distance from the Earth to the Sun
6.0×10^9 km	3.7×10^9 mi	distance from the Sun to Pluto (average)

B. Write the distance references from the right-hand column of Table 10.2 next to the corresponding distances on the nomogram.

C. By connecting the distance and apparent magnitude on the nomogram, you can find the wattage of an object. For example, the apparent magnitude of the Sun is –26.5. The Sun is 1 a.u. from the Earth. By drawing a line with a straightedge from –26.5 on the apparent magnitude scale through 1 a.u. on the distance scale, and continuing the line, it will pass through the value for the Sun's wattage in the third column. Refer to Figure 10.20.

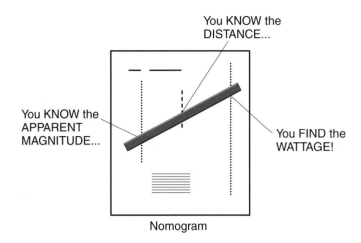

You KNOW the DISTANCE...

You KNOW the APPARENT MAGNITUDE...

You FIND the WATTAGE!

Nomogram

Figure 10.20

1. *What is the wattage of the Sun?*

2. *In answering question 6 in Activity 10.1, Part B, what did you find for the wattage of the Sun?*

The wattages of various objects are listed in Table 10.3.

Table 10.3	
WATTAGE	**OBJECT**
1.4×10^{26} watts	Sun
10^{16} watts	Trinity atom bomb test (1945)
200 watts	lightbulb
1.0 watts	candle
1.0×10^{-3} watts	firefly (lightning bug)
1.0×10^{-6} watts	artificial star (Activity 10.2)

D. Write the name of each object in Table 10.3 next to its wattage on the nomogram.

E. Refer to Figure 10.21 to see how apparent magnitude is read from the nomogram.

3. *What would be the apparent magnitude of a 200-watt lightbulb if it were 100 m from you?*

4. *With what astronomical object does that apparent brightness correspond?*

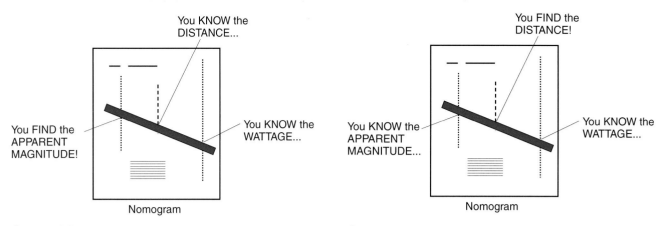

Figure 10.21

Figure 10.22

F. Refer to Figure 10.22 to see how distance is read from the nomogram.

5. *At what distance would you have to view the "artificial star" (from Activity 10.2) for it to have the same apparent brightness as the star Sirius?*

Use the nomogram to answer the following questions:

6. *How far would you have to be from a burning candle for it to be barely visible to the unaided eye?*

7. *How far away would the burning candle have to be in order to be barely visible through the 5-m (200-in.) telescope?*

8. *How far away would a firefly have to be to have the same apparent brightness as the planet Venus at its brightest?*

9. *How far away would the firefly have to be to appear as bright as the North Star (Polaris)?*

10. *How far would the Sun have to be from us to be barely visible to the unaided eye?*

11. *How far would you have had to have been from the Trinity atom bomb test for it to have had the same apparent brightness as the Sun?*

12. *How far away would a 200-watt bulb have to be for it to be barely visible through a pair of 7 × 50 binoculars?*

HOMEWORK

Refer to Tables 10.1–10.3 and the nomogram to answer the following questions.

1. The distance from the Earth to Sirius is about 9 l.y. What is the wattage of Sirius?

2. Does Sirius have a larger or a smaller wattage than the Sun?

3. How far would you have to be from Sirius for it to appear as bright as the Sun?

4. The distance from the Earth to Alpha Centauri is about 4 l.y. What is the wattage of Alpha Centauri?

Apparent Brightness-Distance Nomogram

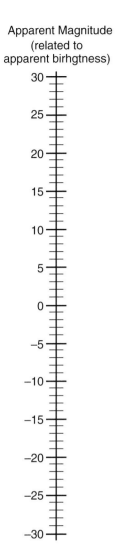

Apparent Magnitude
(related to
apparent birhgtness)

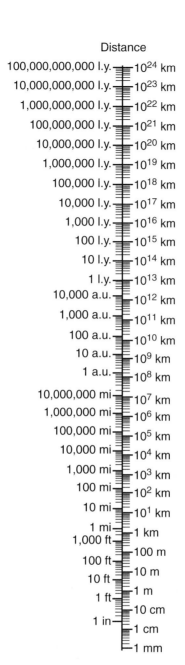

Distance

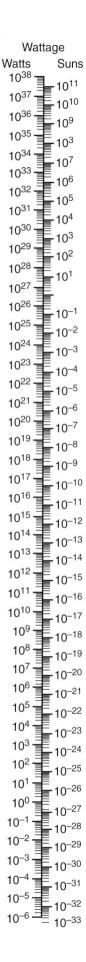

Wattage

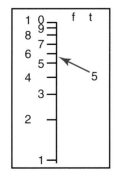

How to read a log scale:
each factor of 10 is labeled;
small lines mark units 1 to 9;
read between units for more accuracy

5. Does Alpha Centauri have a larger or a smaller wattage than the Sun?

6. How far would you have to be from Alpha Centauri for it to appear as bright as the Sun?

7. By analyzing its light with an instrument called a spectroscope, and using other information, astronomers can estimate the wattage of a star. With this method, astronomers determined the wattage of Betelgeuse to be about 5×10^{30} watts. How many light-years is Betelgeuse from us?

8. How far would you have to be from Betelgeuse for it to appear as bright as the Sun?

9. Using the method mentioned above, astronomers also found the wattage of the North Star (Polaris) to be that of about 10^4 Suns. How many light-years is it away from us?

10. How far would you have to be from the North Star for it to appear as bright as the Sun?

11. Another apparently bright star in the constellation of Orion is Rigel (see Appendix 1). Its apparent magnitude is 0.1 and its wattage is estimated to be nearly 5×10^4 Suns. How many light-years is Rigel from us?

12. How far would you have to be from Rigel for it to appear as bright as the Sun?

13. The star Deneb is the apparently very bright star that marks the tail of Cygnus, the swan (or the top of the Northern Cross) and is one of the stars in the Summer Triangle (see Appendix 1). Its apparent magnitude is 0.1 and its wattage is estimated to be 2.5×10^{31} watts. How many light-years is Deneb from us?

14. How far would you have to be from Deneb for it to appear as bright as the Sun?

ACTIVITY 10.4   BUILDING THREE-DIMENSIONAL MODELS OF CONSTELLATIONS

PURPOSE

To build three-dimensional models of constellations.

WHAT DO YOU THINK?

P1. *All the stars in the Big Dipper appear almost equally bright to us. Do you think all the stars that you see in the Big Dipper are almost the same distance from the Earth? Discuss your answer.*

P2. *Imagine you could observe the Big Dipper from a planet orbiting the star at the end of the Dipper's handle. Do you think the Big Dipper would look the same from that planet as it does when you observe the Dipper from the Earth? Why or why not?*

MATERIALS

constellation photograph
1 steel washer
1 meterstick
1 ballpoint pen (with long, exposed writing point)
transparent tape
1 piece of box cardboard, about 30 cm × 30 cm (1 ft × 1 ft)
constellation chart
glass beads (number equal to number of stars in constellation)
1-m-long pieces of black thread (number of pieces equal to number of beads)

PROCEDURE

A. Choose one of the constellation photographs your teacher will give you. Carefully tape this photo to a piece of cardboard. Cut pieces of thread about 1 m (40 in.) long. You will need one piece of thread for each star marked with an arrow on the constellation chart.

B. Place a bead on each string by first passing the thread through it, then around and through it again. By stringing the bead this way, you will be able to slide the bead along the length of the string but it will stay in place when you let go.

C. Refer to Figure 10.23. Using a ballpoint pen, punch holes through the photo and cardboard at the position of each star that has a distance written next to it on the corresponding chart. Slide a piece of thread through each hole leaving about 2–3 cm (1 in.) at the back and the rest on the front. (The front side is the side with the constellation photo.) Tape the 2–3 cm (1 in.) length of thread to the back of the cardboard to hold it in place.

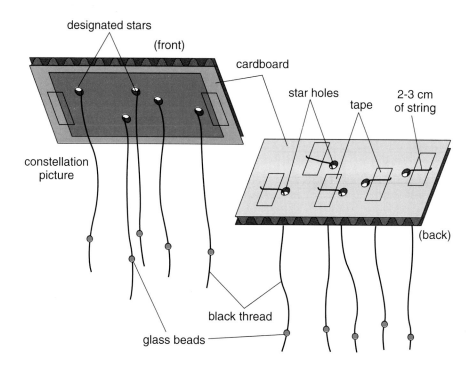

Figure 10.23

designated stars

(front)

cardboard

star holes

tape

2-3 cm of string

constellation picture

(back)

black thread

glass beads

D. Bring the ends of all the threads on the star side of the cardboard together and tie them into a tight knot around a steel washer about 56 cm (22 in.) from the sheet of cardboard. Cut off the excess string.

This thread length of 56 cm is used here because the camera that took the pictures of these constellations had a focal length of 56 cm. If you hold the picture at a distance of 56 cm from your eyes, the constellation will appear the same size as it does in the sky.

E. The distance to the stars on your photo is indicated on the consellation charts your teacher will give you. A star labeled "75 l.y." is 75 light-years from the Earth. (As noted in Activity 10.3, a light-year is the distance that light travels in 1 year, about 10^{13} km.)

1. *What is the name of your constellation?*

2. *What is the distance to the farthest star in your constellation?*

3. *What is the distance to the closest star in your constellation?*

F. To make a three-dimensional model of your constellation, you must slide the beads along the string until they are the correct scale distance from Earth. You will use a scale of 2.5 cm = 100 l.y. For example, if a star is 100 l.y. away, slide the bead representing that star to 2.5 cm (1 in.) from the washer. If you have a star that is 830 l.y. away, slide that bead out 21 cm (8.3 in.). Use your meter stick or ruler to position the beads at their approximate scaled distances. *Remember to measure star distances from the washer toward the photograph!*

G. When you have finished positioning the beads, hold the washer with one hand and the photo upright with the other hand. Stretch the strings and hold the washer next to your eye. Look at the photo through the hole in the washer. You should be able to see the beads outlining the shape of the constellation. As we mentioned above, the scale of the photo is such that if you hold the cardboard at 56 cm from your eye, your view of the constellation is the same as you would have at night looking at the constellation with your naked eye. (You may wish to have a partner hold up your cardboard so that it is easier to view the constellation. In turn, you can hold up your partner's cardboard.)

H. Hold the model so that you are looking at the constellation from the side. This is how the constellation would appear if you traveled many light-years out into space and looked at it from the "side."

4. *Draw the constellation the way it would appear in a "side view." Indicate the direction toward the Earth with an arrow. Write down the name of your constellation.*

I. Exchange your model for that of another student in your class who has a model of a different constellation. Examine your new model by looking at it first through the washer and then from the side.

5. *In what ways does the side view of this model look different from the side view of your original model?*

J. The star or stars (as seen from the Earth) that appear brightest are marked with an asterisk (*) on the constellation charts.

6. *What is the distance to your apparently brightest star(s)?*

7. *What is the distance to your closest star(s)?*

8. *Is your closest star the one with the greatest apparent brightness?*

9. *Compare your answer to question 8 with that of someone with a different constellation. In general, are the stars that appear brightest the closest stars?*

CHAPTER 11

More about Light

WHAT DO YOU THINK WILL HAPPEN?

Look at the drawing below. When the flashlight is on, a white spot appears on the movie screen.

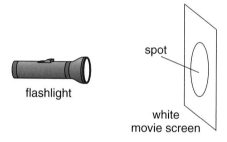

A) Look at the next drawing. If a piece of blue glass is placed between the movie screen and the flashlight, what will appear on the movie screen?

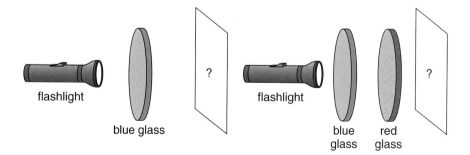

B) Look at the last drawing (on the right). If red glass is placed between the blue glass and the movie screen, what will appear on the movie screen?

C) Describe as best you can why you answered Parts A and B the way you did.

WHAT DO ADULTS THINK?

Before the next class meeting, interview one or two adults (parents, teachers, older relatives, family friends, etc.). Ask them the following questions, making sure that you write down their responses as completely as possible. Provide them with paper so that they can make sketches if they want to. Bring the answers and drawings to the next class meeting and be prepared to talk about them.

1. You are in charge of the stage lights for a dance company. All the dancers wear red leotards. The choreographer asks you what color the leotards would appear to be *if you shined only a blue spotlight on the dancers.* How would you respond?

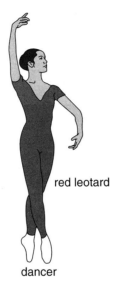

red leotard

dancer

blue
spot light

2. What colors are visible in a rainbow? Draw a sketch of what you think a rainbow looks like and label the position of each color.

3. Imagine seeing the rainbow that you drew in response to question 2. Draw what you think the rainbow would look like if you viewed the rainbow through a piece of red glass.

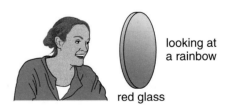

looking at
a rainbow

red glass

Preview: In this chapter you will learn something about color. You will also learn how the photon model describes colors and the way it helps you to understand how filters work.

Anyone with an electric stove knows that after it has been turned on for a while, the coils begin to glow. First the coils glow a dull red. Then a more intense red. If the coils get hotter, in addition to melting any pots that happen to be on them, the coils would seem to glow orange or yellow. The photon model explains this behavior in terms of the energy associated with individual photons.

The photon model was invented by Einstein to explain the strange fact that electric current sometimes flows when blue light shines on a metal, but no current ever flows when red light shines on the same metal. Einstein built this model around the idea that (1) light consists of individual photons, (2) each photon has energy; and (3) the amount of energy each photon has determines the color of the light. Einstein inferred that photons associated with red light have a lower energy than photons associated with blue light, and that photons associated with blue light have enough energy to cause a current to flow, whereas photons of red light do not. Einstein was also able to explain why there is such a threshold, but we leave that explanation, along with a more complete discussion of energy, for a physics course.

Let's return to the electric stove. What relation is there between the temperature of the stove and the photons it emits? According to Einstein's photon model, the higher the temperature of the stove or any object, the more photons of higher energy the object emits. Figure 11.1 shows a plot of the relative numbers of photons of different energies emitted by objects at

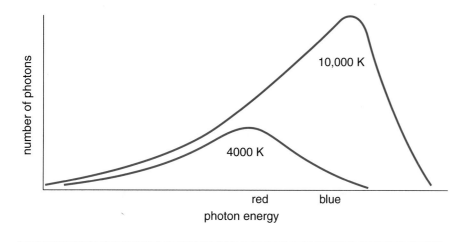

Figure 11.1
Photon energy versus number of photons from two hot objects.

Photon Energies

How much energy does a typical photon have? A 100-watt lightbulb gives off a lot of photons each second—approximately 10^{21} (1,000,000,000,000,000,000,000). This number is so huge because the amount of energy in a typical photon is so tiny. You need a convenient unit to describe the small amount of energy carried by each photon. Such a unit is an "electron volt" (e.v.). (If one e.v. of energy were emitted each second by a lightbulb, it would be a 1.6×10^{-19} [0.00000000000000000016] watt bulb.) The origin of this unit is described in many physics courses.

Table 11.1 Relation between the energies of photons and their colors.	
Energy in e.v.	**Color**
1.8	Red
2.0	Orange
2.1	Yellow
2.4	Green
2.6	Blue
3.2	Violet

two different temperatures. The values plotted were calculated using the photon model and agree with laboratory measurements. Notice that the cooler body emits more photons with energies associated with red light than with other colors. The hotter body, on the other hand, emits more photons with energies associated with blue light than with other colors. Thus, the color of the light emitted by an object depends on the energy of the photons making up the light, which in turn depends on the temperature of the object. Table 11.1 shows the energies of photons associated with light of different colors. (See also Color Plate 1.)

How does this model relate to what your eyes "see"? When a photon strikes your eye (more accurately when many photons with similar energies strike your eye), you see a corresponding color, but you do not see photons. Suppose you are looking at a green light that appears very bright. According to the photon model, many photons, each with an energy of approximately 2.4 e.v., are reaching your eyes. If you see a green light that appears very faint, on the other hand, the photon model says that fewer photons, each also with an energy of approximately 2.4 e.v., are reaching your eyes. Some objects, such as the filament of a lightbulb or the Sun (Color Plate 2), have a sufficiently high temperature that the photons they emit have energies associated with visible light—you can see these objects. Most objects do not emit visible light—if they did, you would likely never be in the dark because you could see a glow from most objects. How then does the model explain your ability to see objects that do *not* emit enough photons with the energies associated with visible light? You see most objects because they reflect or scatter photons that came originally from an object at a high enough temperature to emit visible light, light that you can see. (See Color Plate 3.)

Why, then, is a red sweater red? In the photon model, a sweater is red *not* because it is hot enough to emit photons associated with red light. A sweater is red because it scatters photons of red light emitted by a source that is hot enough to emit "red" photons, along with photons of other colors. Because the sweater absorbs most of the photons of the other colors that struck it, primarily the red photons from the sweater reach your eyes. So the sweater appears red to you. If the idea of photon scattering and absorption isn't clear to you, look at Chapter 5 again—it *might* help!

All red sweaters appear red for primarily the same reason: They scatter red photons and absorb most of the photons of other colors. However, if light with only blue photons were to shine on the red sweater, the sweater would appear "black" to you. There would be no red photons for the sweater to scatter. By contrast, a solid object like a stove glows red only because of its high temperature: The stove is *emitting* red photons, not scattering them. Any solid object at a high enough temperature has a color determined *only* by its temperature, *not* by the composition of the object. All glowing red coals appear red for the same reason, their temperature.

The Photon Model and the Temperature of the Surface of the Earth

In the photon model, when an object emits a photon the object cools slightly: the photon takes energy away from the object, leaving the object slightly cooler. Correspondingly, when an object absorbs a photon, the object is heated ever so slightly. According to the photon model, the surface of the Earth is warm largely because it absorbs vast numbers of photons emitted by the Sun. Each photon of visible light that reaches the surface of the Earth from the Sun has an energy in the range from about 1.8 to 3.2 e.v.

What prevents the surface of the Earth from getting warmer and warmer if it keeps on absorbing all of these photons from the Sun? In the photon model, the Earth also emits photons into space. Each emitted photon carries energy away from the Earth. If the surface of the Earth is not getting hotter or cooler, on average—this is the key, the photon model predicts that the Earth must lose the same amount of energy into space that it receives from the Sun. What would happen if the Earth continued to lose more energy than it received? What would happen if the Earth continued to gain more energy from the Sun than it lost into space?

What about the "greenhouse" effect? You probably have heard that the greenhouse effect may be causing the entire Earth to get warmer. Why? Since you can see through glass, photons associated with visible light must be able to pass through glass. When such photons from the Sun strike the plants in a greenhouse, or the seats in a car with its window closed, or the floor and furniture in a house that is "solar heated," some of the photons are absorbed by the materials, thus warming them. In the photon model, as material is warmed it emits more photons. The energies of these emitted photons depend on how hot the material is. Since the contents of the greenhouse do not become as hot as the Sun (fortunately), the photons emitted by the plants, soil, floors, etc., have energies associated with infrared (see box "Photographing the Invisible," in this chapter) rather than with visible light. So what happens?

When glass is placed between a source of infrared photons and a detector of infrared radiation, the rate at which photons arrive at the detector diminishes. This observation is explained in terms of the photon model by saying that glass absorbs infrared photons. Therefore the infrared photons emitted by the objects in the greenhouse cannot escape from the greenhouse, but instead are absorbed by, and therefore heat, the objects in the greenhouse.

Laboratory measurements show that, like glass, carbon dioxide and other gases in the Earth's atmosphere absorb infrared photons in the same way that greenhouse glass does. Human activities such as burning gasoline and coal produce carbon dioxide and other gases in excess of that produced "naturally" by plants, animals, and volcanoes. These additional gases appear to be accumulating in the atmosphere. If their effect is not offset by other effects, which tend to cool the Earth, the Earth's climate might get warmer and warmer. The Earth's climate changes a great deal over periods of tens of thousands of years. Over the past several million years, much of the Northern Hemisphere was covered with ice most of the time. Many millions of years ago, even the poles were not covered with ice. The reasons for these climate changes are only partially understood. Since we can only predict how human activities will affect the rates of increase of carbon dioxide and other gases in the atmosphere, it is difficult to be certain how these activities might change the future climate of the Earth.

Photographing the Invisible

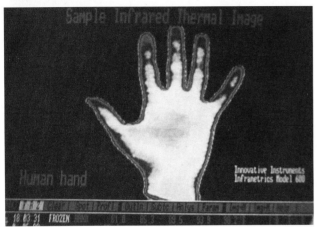

Figure 11.2
A picture of a cup of coffee and a hand made with infrared "light."

Most objects in a typical room only emit light that you cannot see, but which can be recorded by certain kinds of film and other detectors. Each of the photons making up this light has a lower energy than a red photon and is called an infrared photon. An infrared photon has an energy between 0.01 and 1.0 e.v. Infrared films can detect objects, such as those in a typical room, even though the photons emitted by these objects do not have enough energy to register in your eyes (see Figure 11.2). X rays used to make images of your bones, internal organs, and teeth (Figure 11.3) are made up of photons with energies of several thousand electron volts, much higher than the energies associated with visible light. These X-ray photons, emitted by the X-ray machines such as those found in hospitals, are able to pass through flesh and other objects that absorb photons associated with visible light. The X-ray photons in turn are absorbed by bone, thus casting shadows on the film used to record their presence and allowing your dentist to determine whether you have any cavities in your teeth.

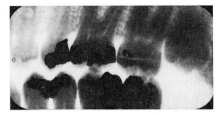

Figure 11.3
A dental X-ray photograph. (The black areas in some of the teeth are metal fillings.)

Filters

In Activity 11.3 you discovered some of the properties of filters. How are these properties explained in terms of the photon model? Why does the world look red when you look at it through a piece of red transparent plastic?

In the photon model, a filter is a device that discriminates on the basis of the energy of photons and hence on the color of the light that strikes it. A filter absorbs most photons of some energies and allows most photons of other energies to pass through. A red filter lets a larger fraction of the photons associated with red light through and a smaller fraction of the photons associated with other colors such as blue light. (See Color Plate 4.)

SUMMARY

In the photon model, light is considered to be made up of particle-like objects—photons—with differing energies. The energies of the photons making up light determine the color of the light. Photons associated with blue light have more energy than photons associated with red light. Accord-

Why Is the Sky Blue and Why Are Some Sunsets Red?

Experiments show that particles as small as the individual molecules of oxygen and nitrogen that make up most of the air can scatter light, and therefore according to the photon model, can change the directions in which photons move. Experiments also show that blue light is more likely to be scattered than red light. Using these results and the photon model, we can explain the color of the sky and the appearance of sunsets.

As sunlight passes through the atmosphere, most of the photons of yellow and red light are not scattered. The photons of blue light, on the other hand, are more likely to be scattered by the molecules in the air before they reach our eyes (Figure 11.4).

The photon model says that the color you see in a direction away from the Sun is produced by photons from the Sun that were scattered by the molecules in the air. The model explains the blue color of the sky in terms of the larger fraction of photons of blue light that were scattered by the air. Because more of the photons of blue light are scattered, they arrive on the ground from all directions in the sky. Photons of yellow and red light, on the other hand, for the most part reach your eyes directly from the Sun.

At sunset the light from the Sun travels through more of the atmosphere than at noon (Figure 11.5). The additional path through the atmosphere is sufficient to scatter even photons of yellow light, but still leaves the photons of orange and red light virtually unscattered. Thus, the Sun often seems orange or red at sunset, according to the photon model, because photons of yellow light reach your eyes from all directions, but photons of red light primarily come to your eyes directly from the Sun.

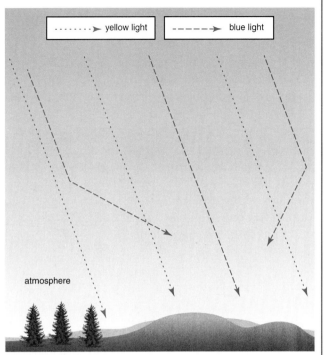

Figure 11.4
Photon scattering in the atmosphere.

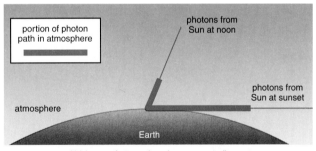

(thickness of atmosphere is exaggerated)

Figure 11.5
Path lengths through the atmosphere at noon and at sunset.

ing to the photon model, all objects emit photons. The higher the temperature of an object, the relatively more photons of higher energies the object emits. If the object has a sufficiently high temperature, most of the photons it emits will be of visible light; examples are the Sun, a lightbulb, and a candle. An object that is too cool for a large fraction of its emitted photons to be of visible light emits mostly photons of infrared light.

Most objects do not emit photons of visible light, but are visible only because they scatter photons of visible light. The apparent color of such objects depends on the energies of the photons the objects scatter, the rest of the photons striking them being absorbed. For example, a sweater appears red because it scatters most of the photons of red light that strike it and absorbs most of the photons associated with other colors.

Telescopes in Space

Why do astronomers need telescopes in space? One reason is that the Earth's atmosphere absorbs photons. Just as infrared photons cannot escape from the Earth through the atmosphere, they cannot reach the Earth from space because of the atmosphere. In addition, ultraviolet photons (photons with energies above 3.2 e.v., but less than the energies of X-ray photons) are mostly absorbed by the atmosphere. So if astronomers want to study objects that emit predominantly photons associated with infrared or ultraviolet radiation, they must place telescopes above the atmosphere (Figures 11.6 and 11.7).

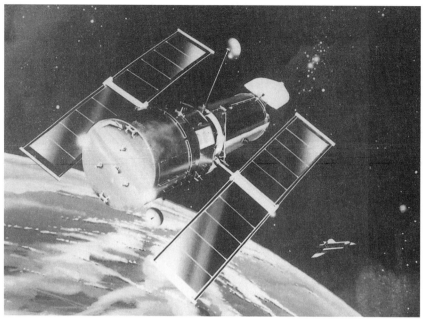

Figure 11.6
Hubble Space Telescope.

Another advantage of telescopes in space is that they are above the "boiling" atmosphere. Motions in the atmosphere smear images of objects—the way hot air rising above a road can blur the image of distant objects. Telescopes above the atmosphere thus have a clearer view of the universe (see Figure 10.6).

Figure 11.7
Artist's conception of the Space Infrared Telescope Facility (SIRTF), a space observatory that studies the heavens by detecting infrared photons.

HOMEWORK

1. A red flag, illuminated by a white light, is viewed through a blue filter. What color will the flag appear to be?

2. A blue shirt is viewed under a red light. What color will it appear to be?

3. A blue shirt is illuminated by a white light. You look at the shirt through a red filter. What color will the shirt appear to be?

4. A fluorescent light (Color Plate 7) is viewed through a green filter. What color will the light appear to be?

5. A beam of photons, each with an energy of 1.8 e.v., strikes your eyes. Another beam of photons, identical to the first, except that each photon has an energy of 2.4 e.v., then strikes your eyes.

   a) Which beam appears the brightest?

   b) Which beam contains the most energy?

   c) Which beam would appear redder?

6. An object emits photons, each with an energy of 1.0 e.v. Describe how these photons could be detected. What "color" might this light appear to be? What kind of object could be emitting this light?

7. An object emits photons, each with an energy of 5.0 e.v. Describe how these photons could be detected. What "color" might this light appear to be? What kind of object could be emitting this light?

8. List some of the factors that would affect the color of a star seen from the Earth's surface. Explain how each factor would affect the star's apparent color.

9. Describe what would happen to the temperature of black and white pieces of similar material sitting under a white light for a few hours. Explain.

10. What would you see on a white screen when beams of red, blue, and green light are projected onto the same spot?

11. Examine Color Plates 4, 5, and 6. Plate 4 shows the spectrum passed by a red filter; plate 5 shows the spectrum of light emitted by a red LED (Light Emitting Diode); plate 6 displays the spectrum produced by a red laser, such as used as a handheld pointer. Compare these spectra to each other; what conclusions can you draw about the light source of each? Which light would appear "reddest" to your eye? Explain.

SELF-TEST

1. What is white light?

2. What is a photon?

3. Explain why the unit called an electron volt (e.v.) is convenient to use when describing photons of visible light.

4. What happens to white light when it passes through a diffraction grating?

5. What happens to red light when it passes through a diffraction grating?

6. What happens to white light when it passes through a blue filter?

7. Glowing object A emits most of its light in the red part of the spectrum. Glowing object B emits most of its light in the green part of the spectrum. Which object is at the lower temperature?

8. Most of the photons emitted by object X have individual energies of about 0.01 e.v. Most of the photons emitted by object Y have individual energies of about 2.0 e.v. Describe the color each object would appear to you to have.

9. If you wanted evidence that heat was escaping from a building, what photon energies would you attempt to observe ?

10. Compare the advantages and disadvantages of using a telescope on the Earth's surface to using one in orbit around the Earth.

ACTIVITY 11.1   INVESTIGATING COLORS OF THE SPECTRUM

PURPOSE

To learn what colors are produced when white light shines through a grating. To test if spectral colors are combinations of the primary colors (red, yellow, and blue). To learn how colors of light combine.

WHAT DO YOU THINK?

P1. *When the spectrum projector you or your teacher made is used to display the spectrum of the light inside the projector, how many colors will appear?*

P2. *If you see green in the spectrum, will it be a mixture of two or more other colors? If you think it will be a mixture, of what colors is it composed? If you think it is not a mixture, how would you describe it?*

PART A   CONSTRUCTING A "COLOROMETER"

PURPOSE

To construct a "colorometer," a device that will be used for observing colors of the spectrum.

MATERIALS

Per student group
    2 large rubber bands
    ruler
    1 metal nail
    1 pair of scissors

5 paraffin blocks, each block 6 cm × 12 cm (2.5 in. × 5 in.)
1 sheet of aluminum foil, approximately 30 cm × 30 cm
(12 in. × 12 in.)
1 piece of cardboard that can be cut into two 6-cm × 6-cm (2.5-in.
× 2.5-in.) squares (optional)

PROCEDURE

A. Use a sharp object, such as a metal nail or the tip of a pair of scissors, to make a deep scratch across the middle of each paraffin block, to divide it into two square pieces. Grasp each end of the block and pull down and towards the middle firmly to break the block in half, making two 6-cm × 6-cm (2.5-in. × 2.5-in.) squares. There will be 10 paraffin squares in all.

BE CAREFUL NOT TO CUT YOURSELF WITH ANY SHARP INSTRUMENT!

CAUTION

B. Cut nine pieces of aluminum foil, making each piece 6 cm × 12 cm (2.5 in. × 5 in.).

C. Fold the pieces of foil in half to make squares 6 cm × 6 cm, with the shiny side of the foil on the outside. Alternately place paraffin blocks and aluminum foil squares to make a stack. Refer to Figure 11.8. (Optional: To keep the rubber bands from cutting into the paraffin, cut two cardboard squares the size of the paraffin squares and put one on each end of the stack of paraffin and aluminum foil squares. See Figure 11.9.)

D. Wrap the rubber bands lengthwise around the stack to hold the squares in place. See Figures 11.8 and 11.9.

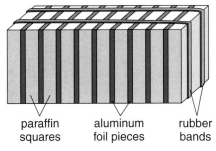

paraffin squares   aluminum foil pieces   rubber bands

Figure 11.8

PART B   WHAT COLORS DO YOU SEE?

PURPOSE

To use a colorometer to investigate how many colors are present in the "rainbow" spectrum.

colorometer with cardboard ends (top view)

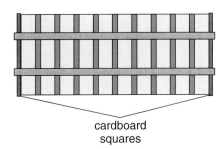

cardboard squares

Figure 11.9

MATERIALS

Per student group
1 mounted piece of diffraction grating
1 spectrum projector (see separate instructions or teacher will set up)
1 colorometer
2 pieces of cardboard, each approximately 10 cm × 15 cm
(4 in. × 6 in.)
1 metric ruler
2 pieces of white cardboard, each approximately 10 cm × 25 cm
(4 in. × 10 in.)
3 felt erasers
stack of books

PROCEDURE

A. Place the spectrum projector in the center of a large table and set up the spectrum projector and the colorometer as shown and described below. Put the white cardboard screen in the crease closest to one side of the felt eraser and place the screen and eraser unit close behind the colorometer. (Place the colorometer on the eraser if there is room.) Position the eraser and colorometer about 60 cm (2 ft) from the spectrum projector and to one side, with the colorometer facing toward the projector. Turn on the projector light. Focus the projector and move the two cardboard sheets on the projector "bed" toward or away from each other until you see two bright spectra, one on either side of the white light strip from the projector on a nearby wall or screen. Check to be sure the spectra are horizontal (that is, each color appears as a vertical "stripe"); move the colorometer so that one spectrum mostly covers it. Another team can use the other projected spectrum. You will need to use books to raise the colorometer to the appropriate height to "capture" the spectrum. Each block of the colorometer should glow a distinct color; the end blocks may appear dimmer than the center blocks. You can add extra paraffin blocks to the colorometer or move the whole setup toward or away from the spectrum projector until the entire (visible) spectrum is projected onto the colorometer. See Figure 11.10.

Figure 11.10

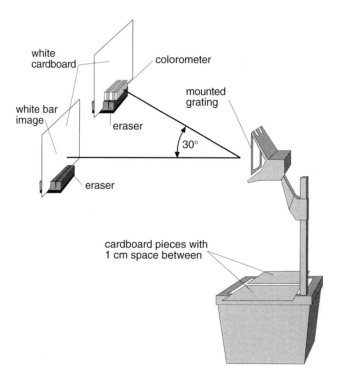

B. Look at the colorometer blocks from the spectrum projector. Number the blocks from left to right and list their colors in a table.

C. When facing the colorometer from the direction of the spectrum projector, move the colorometer 3 mm (about 1/8 in.) to the right.

1. *Has the color of any block changed? List any new colors of the blocks, with the numbers of the blocks, in a table.*

D. Move the paraffin colorometer another 3 mm to the right.

2. *Have any colors changed or are they all exactly the same colors as before?*

E. Pick up the colorometer and screen and move them about 3 m (10 ft) away from the spectrum projector.

3. *Describe what you see. How have the colors of the blocks changed? List their new colors in a table.*

F. Remove the colorometer from the setup. Take the white cardboard screen that was originally behind the colorometer and move it back at least 20 cm (8 in.) from its position in step A. At the original position of the white cardboard screen in step A, arrange a narrow cardboard slit that only lets one color through (for example, green). The slit can be made by placing two pieces of cardboard in a felt eraser so that there is a gap, or slit, about 1 cm (0.5 in.) wide between the adjacent edges of the pieces. Place a piece of mounted grating behind the slit so that the selected color of the spectrum passes through the grating. See Figure 11.11.

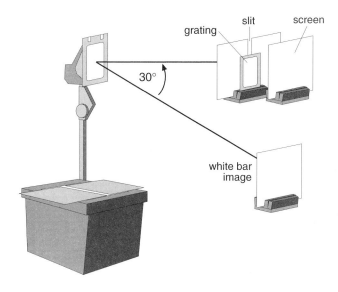

Figure 11.11

4. *What do you see on the screen now? What do you now conclude about the one color from the spectrum? (Is it really a single color?)*

G. Repeat step F using a different color.

5. *What do you see on the screen? In what ways is the appearance of the screen in step G different from its appearance in step F? In what ways is the appearance the same in the two steps?*

NOW WHAT DO YOU THINK?

6. *How many colors do you now think there are in the "rainbow" spectrum?*

7. *How would you describe the colors that appear in the spectrum? Are they mixtures of other colors? Explain your reasoning.*

PART C   ADDING COLORS OF LIGHT

PURPOSE

To investigate what happens when different colors of the spectrum are projected onto the same place on a white screen.

WHAT DO YOU THINK?

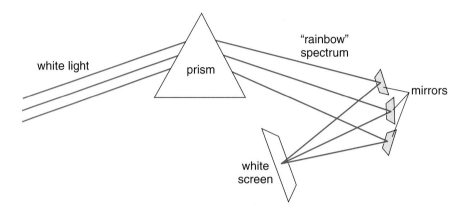

P1. *What do you predict will happen when red light and green light are projected onto the same place on a white screen?*

P2. *If several mirrors are placed in the "rainbow" spectrum created by a prism to intercept all of its light, what will you see when all the colors are reflected from the mirrors onto the same spot on a white screen? (See diagram.)*

MATERIALS

Per student group

    1 colorometer
    2 felt erasers
    1 spectrum projector setup
    1 piece of white paper or cardboard
    1 Fresnel lens, 20 cm × 25 cm (8 in. × 10 in.)
    7 2.5-cm (1-in.) square mirrors mounted on blocks
    2 pieces of white cardboard, about 10 cm × 25 cm (4 in. × 10 in.)
    tape
    stack of books

PROCEDURE

A. Place the spectrum projector in the center of a large table and turn on the light. Focus the projector and move the two cardboard sheets on the projector "bed" toward or away from each other until you see two bright spectra, one on either side of the white light strip from the projector on a nearby wall or screen. Check to be sure the spectra are hor-

INTRODUCTION TO COLOR PLATE SECTION

The color plates in this section show the spectra of the light emitted or scattered by various objects. Chapters 11 and 12 discuss what a spectrum is and why spectra may vary in appearance.

The spectra in Color Plates 1–11 are taken from simulations generated by VirtualSpectroscope, version 1.0. The upper, color portion of each plate shows how the light from an object appears when dispersed into its component colors (see Chapter 11). The graph accompanying each spectrum displays the intensity of the light vs. the energy of its photons: The locations of the peaks on each graph indicate where on the energy (color) scale an object is emitting or reflecting the most photons. Variations in the height of an intensity curve correspond to the apparent brightnesses of different parts of the spectrum; for example, a curve with a single, very high peak at 2.4 electron-volts would tell you that the object's light would look bright and green to your eye. (VirtualSpectroscope was developed with funding by National Science Foundation grant ESI-9553846, copyright 1998–2000 President and Fellows of Harvard College.)

Color Plates 12–14 are photographs of different light sources taken by a standard 35-mm camera that had a piece of diffraction grating placed over its lens. The activities in Chapter 11 will familiarize you with this grating.

Each plate can be compared to Color Plate 1, below, which illustrates the "rainbow" spectrum, the complete range of color visible to the human eye.

Note that along the bottom of each spectrum is a scale labeled from 350 to 850. These numbers refer to the wavelength of the colors measured in nanometers (nm), 1 nm being equal to 10^{-9} m (one billionth of a meter).

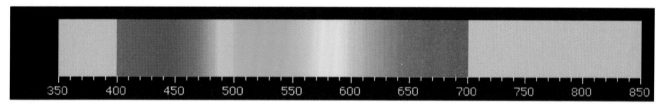

Color Plate 1

The "rainbow" spectrum, showing the continuous range of colors, which the eyes of most humans can see. Such a spectrum is produced by any source of white light.

Harvard College Observatory (HCO)

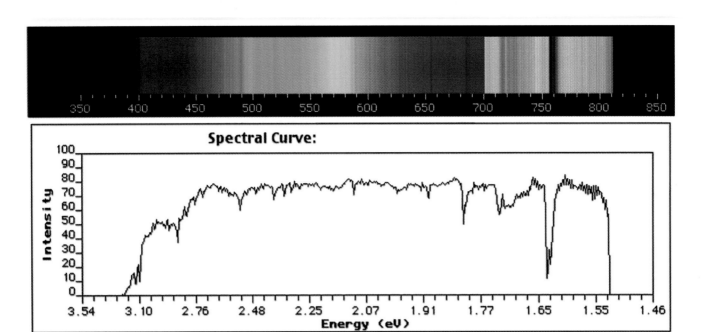

Harvard College Observatory (HCO)

Color Plate 2

The spectrum of light emitted by the Sun. The Sun is classified by astronomers as a yellow star; do you see any evidence for that classification in its spectrum? The dark lines are absorption lines; see Chapter 12 for a discussion of why such lines occur in a spectrum.

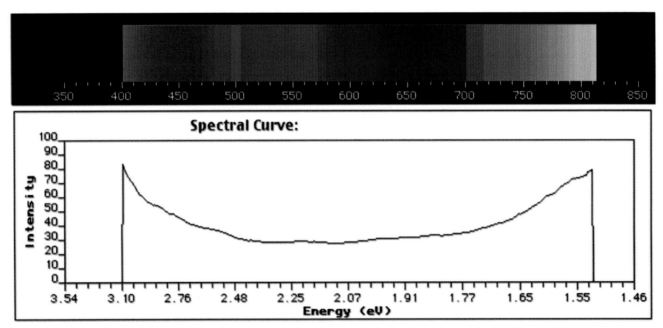

Harvard College Observatory (HCO)

Color Plate 3

Light reflected by clean, fresh snow. Compare this spectrum to plate 2. What conclusion can you make about the source of the light shining on the snow?

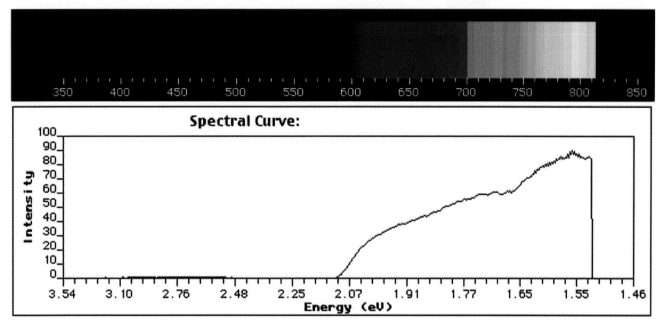

Harvard College Observatory (HCO)

Color Plate 4

White light as seen through one type of red filter. Try looking at plate 1 through a piece of clear, red plastic; compare what you see to plate 4. What do you think filters do to light?

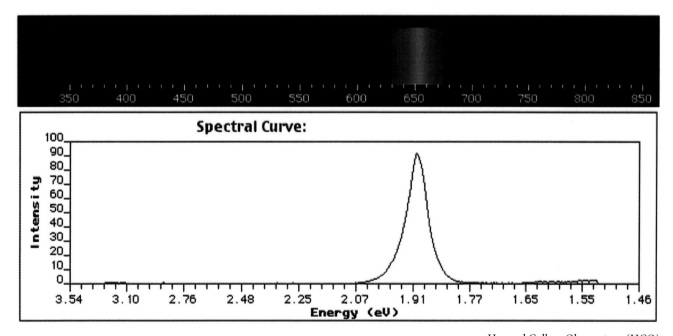

Harvard College Observatory (HCO)

Color Plate 5

This is what you would see if you looked through a spectroscope at a red LED light, such as those found on VCRs, alarm systems, and other electronic devices. Compare plate 5 to plate 4; which light do you think would look "redder" to your eye?

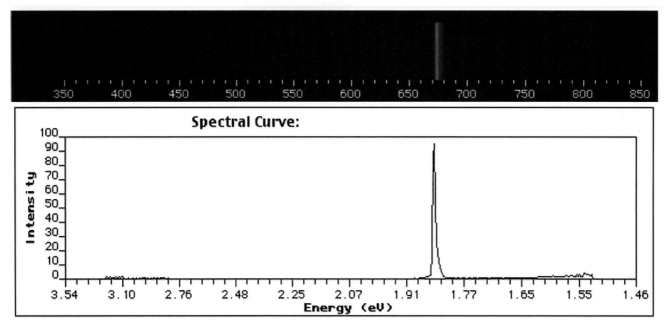

Harvard College Observatory (HCO)

Color Plate 6

The spectrum of light from a red laser, such as those used as handheld pointers.
Compare to plates 4 and 5. Which light would appear "reddest" to you? How do
you think a laser produces light with such a spectrum?

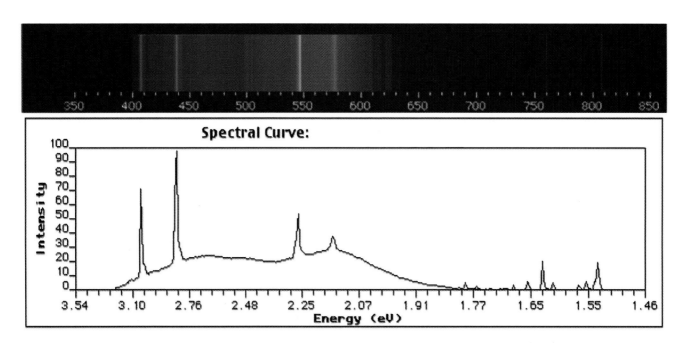

Harvard College Observatory (HCO)

Color Plate 7

The spectrum from a standard fluorescent light. Compare this spectrum to plates
1 and 2. What color would you predict a fluorescent light to be if you had never
seen one? Do you see any evidence for why many people who wear makeup are
careful about what type they put on?

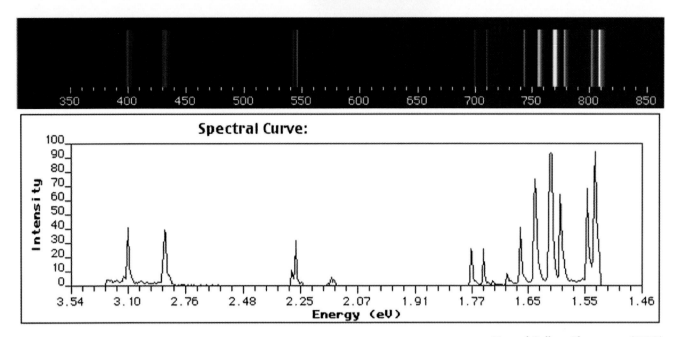

Color Plate 8

The spectrum from an electrified, sealed (emission) tube containing mercury.
What color is the glowing tube? Compare this spectrum to plate 7.

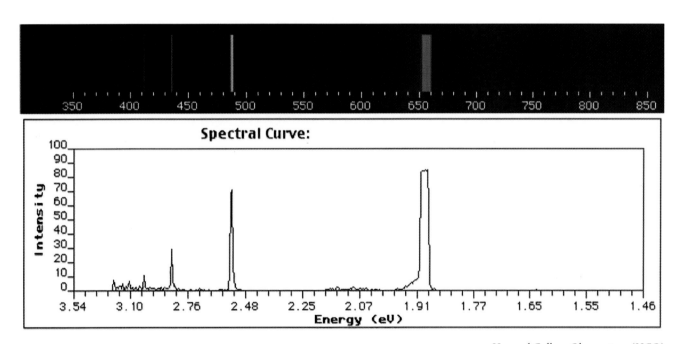

Color Plate 9

The spectrum from an electrified, sealed (emission) tube of hydrogen. What color
is the glowing tube?

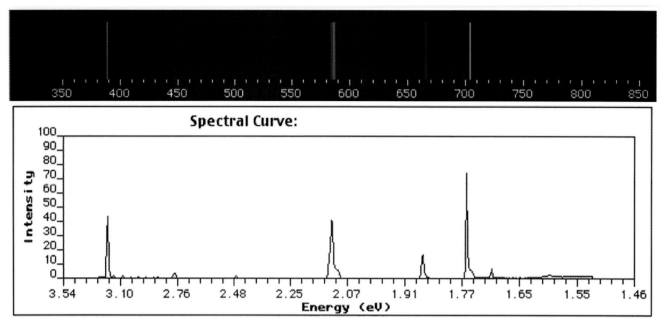

Color Plate 10

The spectrum from an electrified, sealed (emission) tube of helium. What color is the glowing tube?

Harvard College Observatory (HCO)

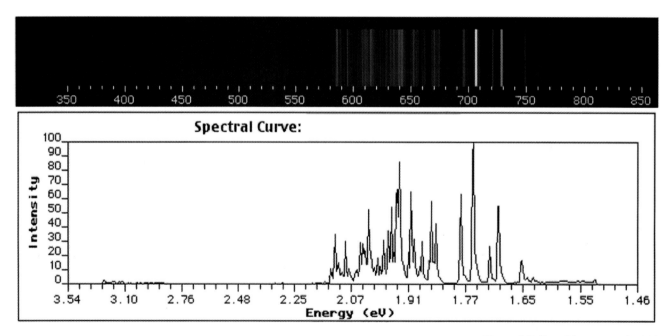

Color Plate 11

The spectrum from a neon light. What color is the light?

Harvard College Observatory (HCO)

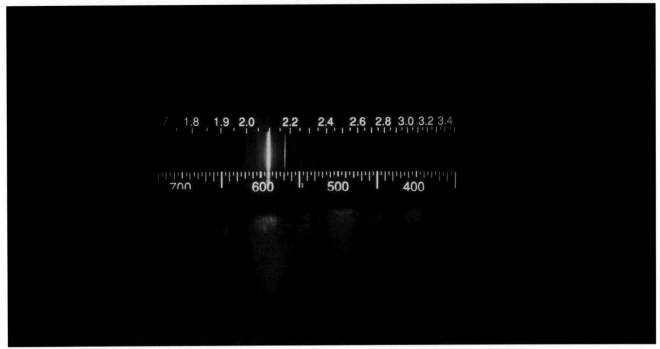

Photograph by Phil Sadler

Color Plate 12
A photograph of a sodium vapor lamp taken through a spectrometer (see Chapter 12).

Photograph by Phil Sadler

Color Plate 13
A photograph of the LED light on a window alarm system, taken through a piece of diffraction grating. Compare what you see to plate 5.

Color Plate 14

Photograph by Phil Sadler

A photograph of a city night scene taken through a piece of diffraction grating.
Can you tell what types of lights are in use?

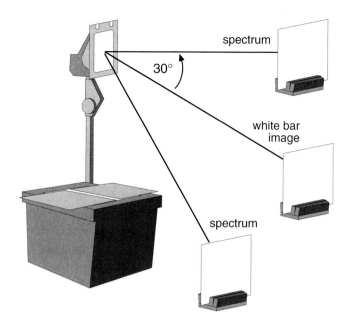

Figure 11.12

spectrum

30°

white bar
image

spectrum

izontal (that is, each color appears as a vertical "stripe"). Select one spectrum to use; another team can use the other projected spectrum. See Figure 11.12.

B. Place two of the mounted mirrors in the light of the spectrum. Put one mirror in one color region and place the other mirror in another color region. It will be necessary to put the mirror blocks on top of something (for example, a stack of books) to put them at a convenient height. Aim the colored light reflected from the mirrors onto a piece of white paper or cardboard taped to the side of the spectrum projector base facing the mirrors. (NOTE: If you cannot tape the paper to the projector base—some bases are too low—set up a white screen in an eraser and place it on some books.) Then turn the mirrors so that they reflect the two colors onto the same place on the white paper. Refer to Figure 11.13, which is an overhead view. What color is produced by the mixing? Repeat this step for different pairs of colors and make a table (call it Table 11.2) of the colors you mix and the colors that result.

C. Repeat step B, except use three mirrors to combine three colors. Make another table (Table 11.3) for the three "original" colors and the color that results.

D. Use as many mounted mirrors as necessary and try to recombine all the colors of the spectrum, adding one color at a time. What do you see?

1. *What happens as each color is added?*

2. *After you have added all the colors, what happens if you subtract a "dark" color (such as violet)? Try this subtraction and pay careful attention to the subtle change in color that results.*

3. *What happens if you take away a "light" color (such as yellow or orange)?*

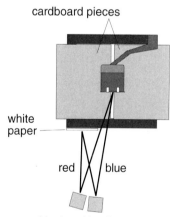

cardboard pieces

white
paper

red   blue

blocks with mirrors

Figure 11.13
Top view of setup described in step B.

E. Place the Fresnel (the "s" in Fresnel is silent) lens in the path of the spectrum and focus the image of the light that passes through it onto a screen. The screen should be about 1.2 m (4 ft) away from the spectrum projector. Move the lens toward or away from the screen so that the image of the light is as small and sharp as possible. Be certain that the lens intercepts all the colors of the spectrum.

4. *What do you see?*

NOW WHAT DO YOU THINK?

5. *What is white light?*

6. *Based on what you already know about mixing paints, do you think you can predict what you will see when two colors of light shine on the same part of a white screen? Explain the basis for your prediction.*

ACTIVITY 11.2   INVESTIGATING THE COLORS OF OBJECTS

PURPOSE

To learn how light travels; to observe objects of different colors through a variety of colored filters; and to observe how opaque materials of different colors reflect light of different colors.

PART A   WHERE IS THE LIGHT?

PURPOSE

To learn how light travels.

WHAT DO YOU THINK?

The spectrum projector is set up as shown below and a spectrum is projected onto the white cardboard screen.

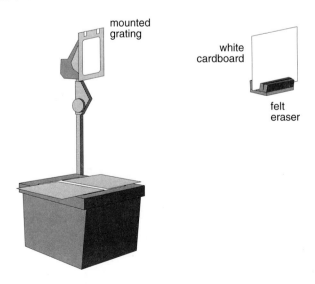

P1. *What happens to the light that comes from the lightbulb and goes through the lens and then the grating?*

P2. *When you see the spectrum on the screen, do you think there is light between the spectrum on the screen and you? Why or why not? If yes, describe the light. (Is it white? It it colored?)*

MATERIALS

Per student group

1 spectrum projector setup, with 2 white cardboard screens
assorted pieces of colored felt (including red, green, and blue)
1 large piece of black cloth or several black screens to block light
1 used chalkboard eraser or fine-mist water sprayer

PROCEDURE

A. Place the spectrum projector in the center of a large table and turn on the light. Focus the projector and move the two cardboard sheets on the projector "bed" toward or away from each other until you see two bright spectra, one on either side of the white light strip from the projector on a nearby wall or screen. Check to be sure the spectra are horizontal (that is, each color appears as a vertical "stripe"). Select one spectrum to use; another team can use the other projected spectrum. Place one eraser-mounted screen in the spectrum and the other mounted screen in the white light. See Figure 11.14.

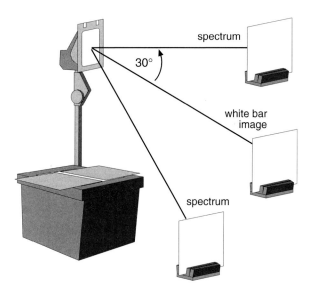

Figure 11.14
(same as Figure 11.12)

B. Sprinkle a little chalk dust in the air between the projector and the screen with spectrum by gently shaking a used chalkboard eraser over the space between the projector and the screen. (Or you can spray a little water from a spray bottle that sprays very small droplets [fine mist].) See Figure 11.15.

More about Light ✳

Figure 11.15

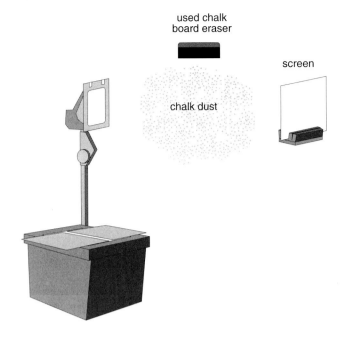

1. *Describe what you see.*

C. Replace the white screen with a piece of bright red cloth. Have your partner look at the red material. Use a dark screen to block your partner's face from the direct light from the projector. Refer to Figure 11.16 below.

Figure 11.16

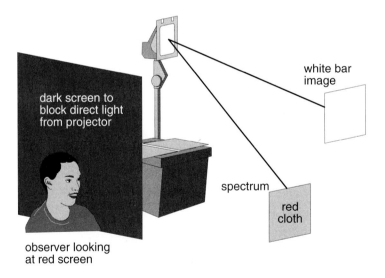

2. *What color does your partner's face appear to be? (Change places with your partner so both of you can make observations.)*

D. Replace the red cloth with a green one. Look at your partner's face, and then let your partner look at your face.

3. *What color does your partner's face appear to be?*

E. Repeat step C with any other colored materials that are available and make a table (Table 11.4) of the color of the material and the color of your partner's face.

NOW WHAT DO YOU THINK?

4. *What happens to the light between the spectrum projector and the screen?*

5. *Why does the red cloth look red?*

6. *In step B you observed all the colors of visible light traveling through space from the grating to the screen. What was there about the chalk dust (or the water) that allowed you to see the colors?*

PART B   WHY DO OBJECTS HAVE PARTICULAR COLORS?

PURPOSE

To observe objects of different colors through a variety of colored filters and to observe how opaque materials of different colors reflect or scatter light of different colors.

WHAT DO YOU THINK?

P1. *What colors do you think you will see when you look at a red shirt onto which all the colors of the spectrum are projected simultaneously?*

MATERIALS

Per student group

graph paper (1 piece per student)
2 colored pens or pencils, red and green
2 pieces of colored felt, red and green
1 spectrum projector setup, with 2 mounted white cardboard screens
1 red and 1 green colored filter, each about 15 cm × 15 cm
   (6 in. × 6 in.)
assorted pieces of colored patterned materials (for example, multi-colored plaid cloth)

PROCEDURE

A. Hold the pieces of colored felt so they cannot be seen by your partner. Have your partner hold the red filter in front of *both* eyes. Now show each piece of felt to your partner and ask what color each appears to be. Repeat this procedure using the green filter.

   Record your partner's answers in a table (Table 11.5). Trade places with your partner, and repeat.

1. *Discuss what connections exist among the color of the felt, the color of the filter, and the color observed by you and your partner.*

B. Observe some of the patterned materials through each of the filters.

2. *What happens to the patterns that you see on one piece of cloth when you change filters?*

C. Place the spectrum projector in the center of a large table and set it up as described in step A, Part A, except each team will use both projected spectra; cover one of the screens showing the spectrum with a piece of red felt.

D. *It is very important that one spectrum be projected onto a white screen and the other spectrum onto the screen with the red felt so that the two spectra can be compared.* Shine the spectra on the red felt and the white screen at the same time.

E. Judge the apparent brightness of each color of the spectrum on the white screen and on the red felt. Use the scale given below and record your data in a table (Table 11.6).

0 = no color at all; 1 = very faint color; 2 = moderate color; 3 = very bright color; 4 = brightest color

F. Label the horizontal axis of a graph (Graph 11.1) with the spectrum colors you wrote in Table 11.6. Label the vertical axis with the numbers from the apparent brightness-of-color scale above. Plot the data for the white screen from this table on your graph. Then, using a red pen or pencil, plot the data for the red felt on the same graph.

G. Repeat steps C, D, and E using green felt. Judge the apparent brightness of each color on the white screen and on the screen covered with the green felt. Use the scale from step E and record your data in another table (Table 11.7—see Table 11.6).

H. Plot the data for the green felt using a green pen or pencil on Graph 11.1 (see step F).

NOW WHAT DO YOU THINK?

3. *Why do you think the red object looks red? How would you explain this fact to a friend not in this class (or any other person who has **not** done this activity)?*

4. *Why do you think a white object looks white?*

5. *Why do you think a black object looks black?*

6. *Draw a sketch of what you think a graph like Graph 11.1 would look like if the white screen were replaced with a piece of magenta material. (Magenta is usually red plus blue/violet.) Label the horizontal axis with appropriate colors.*

EXTENSIONS

1. Repeat Part B using blue felt and then "Kodak" yellow paper (use part of any Kodak product box). What do you notice about the spectrum shining on objects that look blue compared to the spectrum shining on objects that look yellow?

ACTIVITY 11.3   WHAT DO FILTERS DO?

PURPOSE

To use a photometer, colored filters, and a colorometer to investigate what happens to light when it passes through a single filter and through combinations of filters.

WHAT DO YOU THINK?

P1. *Do you think that the light from a flashlight shining through a piece of green plastic would appear brighter or dimmer than the light from the flashlight without the plastic? Why do you think so?*

P2. *Do you think that the light from a flashlight shining through two pieces of green plastic would appear brighter or dimmer than the light from the flashlight shining through only one of these pieces of green plastic? Why do you think so?*

P3. *What do you think happens to light as it passes through a transparent piece of red plastic?*

P4. *What do you think you would see on the screen given the setup in the diagram to the right? Remember that the complete spectrum appears on the screen when the colored plastic is not there.*

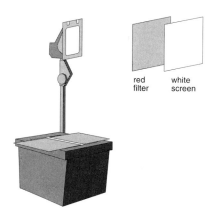

red filter   white screen

P5. *What do you think you would see on the screen given the setup in the diagram to the right?*

P6. *What do you think you would see on the screen given the setup in the diagram below?*

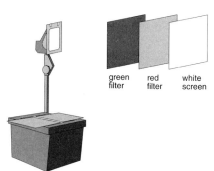

green filter   red filter   white screen

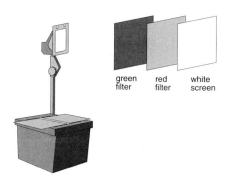

green filter   red filter   white screen

MATERIALS

Per student group

    1 colorometer

    1 meterstick

    1 paraffin photometer, from Activity 10.1, Part A

    1 spectrum projector setup, with mounted white cardboard screens

6 colored filters: 2 each of red, green, and blue, each filter about 15 cm × 15 cm (6 in. × 6 in.)

2 200-watt clear lightbulbs with mountings and extension cords, one equipped with a dimmer switch

PROCEDURE

A. Place the two lightbulbs 1 m apart on a flat surface. Put the photometer between the two bulbs, with the large sides of the photometer facing the bulbs. See Figure 11.17. Make the room as dark as possible, then turn on the 200-watt bulbs. Be sure the bulb with the dimmer switch appears as bright as the other bulb (with both bulbs viewed from the same distance away). Move the photometer until the two sides appear equally bright when viewed from the side.

Figure 11.17

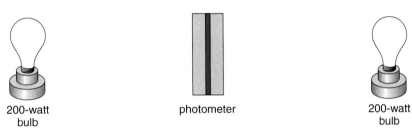

200-watt bulb   photometer   200-watt bulb

B. Look at the photometer from the side. Move the photometer slowly toward one bulb, then toward the other bulb.

1. *How do the two sides of the photometer compare in apparent brightness as the photometer is moved? Do the two sides always appear equally bright, or do they change in relative apparent brightness?*

C. Use the dimmer switch to make one bulb appear dimmer than the other. Move the photometer between the bulbs until the photometer sides appear equally bright.

2. *Did you move the photometer toward or away from the bulb that appears dimmer?*

D. Adjust the dimmed lightbulb to obtain the greatest apparent brightness. Position the photometer so that both sides appear equally bright. Place a red plastic sheet in front of one bulb. *Do not let the plastic touch the bulb as the plastic may melt or burn!* See Figure 11.18. Now move the photometer until both sides appear equally bright. *Always move the photometer toward the bulb with the filter until that side of the photometer appears much brighter than the other, then move the photometer in the other direction until the other side appears much brighter, and finally find the position where the two sides appear equally bright.* (This procedure will be difficult to carry out because the sides of the photometer are different colors. Have each person in your group try to position the photometer. Compare observations and decide on a common result. You may want to look through each filter or filter combination and comment on what you see when looking at a lightbulb; all the questions ask about what you see using the photometer.)

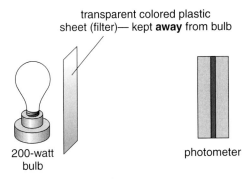

transparent colored plastic
sheet (filter)— kept **away** from bulb

Figure 11.18

200-watt
bulb

photometer

200-watt
bulb

3. *Did you move the photometer from its original position toward or away from the light with the red filter in front of it?*

4. *Does the light passing through the red filter appear dimmer, brighter, or about the same brightness as the light from the unfiltered bulb?*

E. Repeat step D, using two sheets of red plastic.

5. *Does the double-filtered red light appear dimmer, brighter, or about the same brightness as the single-filtered red light?*

F. Repeat step D, replacing the red plastic sheet with one green plastic sheet.

6. *Did you move the photometer from its original position toward or away from the light with the green filter in front of it?*

7. *Does the light passing through the green filter appear dimmer, brighter, or about the same brightness as the light from the bulb without the filter present? Does the light passing through the green filter appear dimmer, brighter, or about the same brightness as the light that passed through the red filter?*

G. Repeat step D, using two sheets of green plastic.

8. *Does the double-filtered green light appear dimmer, brighter, or about the same brightness as the single-filtered green light?*

H. Place a red filter and a green filter together in front of one light. Position the photometer so the sides appear equally bright.

9. *Does the light that is passed through two filters of different colors appear dimmer, brighter, or about the same brightness as the light passed through two filters of the same color?*

I. Repeat step H, adding a blue filter to the other two filters. Position the photometer so the sides appear equally bright.

10. *How does the apparent brightness of the light that has passed through the red, green, and blue filters compare to the apparent brightness of the light that has passed through only the red and green filters?*

11. *What do you think a colored filter does to the light passing through it?*

J. Look at the lightbulb through one or two filters. What do you see? Make a table (Table 11.8) of the numbers of filters, the colors of the filters, and the colors observed when looking at the bulb.

More about Light **267**

12. *What do you think happens to light as it passes through a transparent piece of red plastic?*

K. Place the spectrum projector in the center of a large table and turn on the light. Focus the projector and move the two cardboard sheets on the projector "bed" toward or away from each other until you see two bright spectra, one on either side of the white light strip from the projector on a nearby wall or screen. Check to be sure the spectra are horizontal (that is, each color appears as a vertical "stripe"). Select one spectrum to use; another team can use the other projected spectrum. See Figure 11.19. Put the white cardboard screen in the last crease of the felt eraser and put the colorometer in front of the cardboard on the eraser. Position the eraser and colorometer about 60 cm (2 ft) from the spectrum projector. Each block of the colorometer should glow a distinct color, except the end blocks, which should show almost no color. You can add extra paraffin blocks to the colorometer or move the whole setup toward or away from the spectrum projector until the entire spectrum is projected onto the colorometer.

Figure 11.19

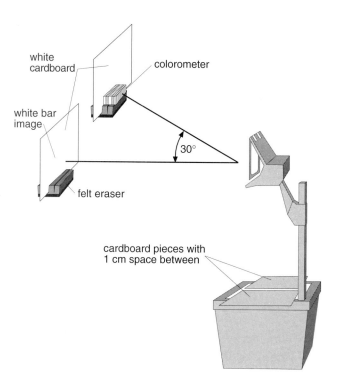

L. As you look at the colorometer from the position of the spectrum projector, number the blocks from left to right and list their colors in a table (Table 11.9).

M. Place a red filter in front of the grating. Which blocks remain "lighted"?

N. Place a green filter in front of the grating. Which blocks remain "lighted"?

O. Place a blue or cyan filter in front of the grating. Which blocks remain "lighted"?

P. Place both a red filter and a green filter in front of the grating. Which blocks remain "lighted"?

Q. Place both a blue filter and a green filter in front of the grating. Which blocks remain "lighted"?

NOW WHAT DO YOU THINK?

13. *What do you conclude that filters do to light?*

14. *What would you expect to happen if the filter allowed only one shade of green light to pass through? How many paraffin blocks would be illuminated?*

ACTIVITY 11.4 GRAPHING THE SPECTRUM

PURPOSE

To learn how to graph a spectrum and to graph the spectrum produced when light passes through various filters.

WHAT DO YOU THINK?

P1. *Do you think that all of the colors in the "rainbow" spectrum for a light-bulb appear equally bright?*

MATERIALS

1 transparency pen (washable)
1 piece of clear transparency plastic
graph paper
2 colored pencils or pens, red and green
1 colorometer
1 metric ruler
1 spectrum projector setup, with white cardboard screens
1 pair of scissors

PROCEDURE

A. Set up the spectrum projector and colorometer as shown in Figure 11.20 and explained in either Activity 11.1, Part B, step A or Activity 11.3, step K.

B. As you look at the colorometer from the position of the spectrum projector, number the colorometer blocks from left to right and list their colors in a table (Table 11.10); you will add to this table in step C.

Figure 11.20

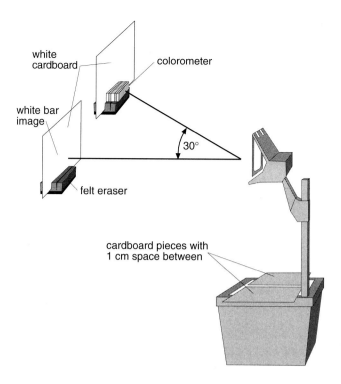

white cardboard — colorometer

white bar image

30°

felt eraser

cardboard pieces with 1 cm space between

C. Judge the apparent brightness of each block. Use the scale given below and record your data in Table 11.10.

0 = no color; 1 = very faint color; 2 = moderate color;
3 = very bright color; 4 = brightest color

D. Plot your points on a graph for the block number vs. apparent brightness (Graph 11.2). Connect your points with a smooth curved line.

E. Cut a piece of transparency plastic so that it is slightly larger than the top of the colorometer, about 8 cm × 25 cm (3 in. × 10 in.).

F. Turn the overhead classroom lights on and place the piece of transparent plastic over the top of the colorometer. Draw axes on the plastic overlay with the transparency pen. The horizontal axis is a line drawn along the edge of the blocks that is closest to the grating tube and the vertical axis is a line along the width of the blocks on either side (see Figure 11.21). As you look down on the blocks, place a point on the plastic over each block that corresponds to the apparent depth that the light has penetrated that paraffin block.

G. Connect your points with a smooth curve. Take the transparency and place it on top of Graph 11.2.

1. *In what ways are the two curves similar? In what ways are they different?*

H. Place a red filter in front of the grating on the spectrum projector and repeat the procedure in steps C and D. Begin by having your partner hold the filter in front of the grating and then remove the filter from in front of the grating. The colors of those blocks whose brightnesses do not change when the filter is removed are the colors not affected by the filter (that is, the filter passes those colors). In a table (Table 11.11), record the numbers of those blocks that appear unchanged; now also

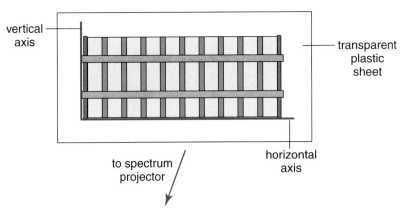

Colorometer: top view

Figure 11.21

vertical axis

transparent plastic sheet

to spectrum projector

horizontal axis

judge the apparent brightness of each of the blocks using the scale given in step C, and record your data in Table 11.11.

I. Using a red pen or pencil, plot the points from step H on Graph 11.2. Connect the points with a smooth curve.

2. *What has the red filter done to the spectrum?*

3. *What would you expect the graph to look like if the filter only allowed one shade of red light to pass through? Which paraffin block(s) would be illuminated?*

J. Now repeat steps H and I using a green filter and a green pen or pencil. Fill in the data in another table (Table 11.12) and plot the points on Graph 11.2.

4. *What has the green filter done to the spectrum?*

5. *What would you expect the graph to look like if the filter only allowed one shade of green light to pass through? Which paraffin block(s) would be illuminated?*

6. *Some people say that filters change the color of the light that goes through them. What would you say to them, or show them, to convince them of how filters really work?*

CHAPTER 12

More about Stars

How Did Astronomers Do It?

In 1868, astronomers discovered a gas in the Sun and named it helium (after Helios, the ancient Greek god of the Sun). Since these astronomers could not travel to the Sun to collect samples to analyze, how do you think they figured out that the Sun contains helium?

Preview: In this chapter you will learn (1) how astronomers take the temperatures of stars and (2) infer what they are made of.

The relative numbers of photons of different energies emitted by an object depend on its temperature—the hotter the object is, the more photons of higher energies it emits. (See Chapter 11 and Figure 12.1.) Temperature is discussed in most physics courses. Here you can imagine that the temperature of an object is simply the reading on a "super thermometer" placed in contact with the object. Scientists often measure temperature on a scale named after the English physicist Lord Kelvin. There are 100 Kelvins between the freezing and boiling points of water, just as there are 100 degrees Celsius. However, the zero point of the Kelvin scale is located at −273° C. Most physics and chemistry courses reveal the origin of this apparently unusual starting point called "absolute zero."

Astronomers reason that processes taking place in the laboratory are identical to similar processes taking place elsewhere in the universe. Since stars are very hot objects, astronomers believe that they behave very much like very hot objects in the laboratory. In fact, the photon model can be used to predict what would happen under conditions difficult to create in a laboratory. Let us consider temperatures of stars, an important example.

One way astronomers can take the temperature of a star is by observing the light emitted by the star and interpreting their observations in terms

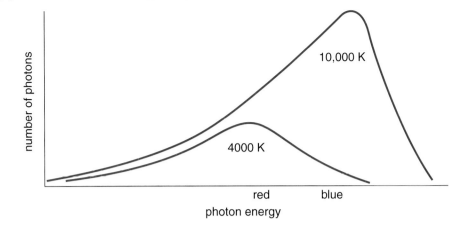

Figure 12.1
Photon energy vs. number of photons at that energy from two hot objects.

10,000 K

4000 K

red   blue

photon energy

number of photons

of the photon model. By measuring the relative numbers of photons of different energies coming from the star and comparing these observations with calculations made using the photon model, astronomers can infer the temperature of the star.

When astronomers observe the light emitted by a star, however, they often find that, rather than a smooth curve, such as those in Figure 12.1, they find "notches" in the curve (Figure 12.2). They interpret these notches as arising from elements such as hydrogen and calcium acting as filters (see Chapter 11) and absorbing some of the photons that would otherwise be present. Each element has its own "fingerprint" that depends on the amount of the element present and the temperature. Thus, astronomers can infer both the temperature and the composition of the surface of a star by studying the relative numbers of photons with different energies coming from the star.

The process of making such inferences of composition is more complicated than simply looking at the spectrum. Stars with identical compositions can have very different spectra if they have very different surface temperatures. Complicated mathematical models of a star's atmosphere must be constructed before the observations can be linked to specific compositions. Useful estimates of stellar temperatures can, however, be made relatively easily from the spectra of the stars.

Figure 12.2
Photon energy vs. number of photons at that energy detected in the light from a typical star.

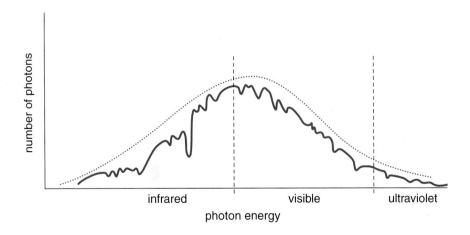

number of photons

infrared   visible   ultraviolet

photon energy

Figure 12.3
A busy street in a big city.

A Detective Story

When a detective gathers evidence, he or she is looking for more than random bits of information. A detective is looking for patterns that make sense out of a collection of otherwise apparently unrelated facts. Astronomers look for patterns for the same reason.

Imagine that an alien from another world were trying to understand what humans are like from a photograph taken on a busy street in any major city (Figure 12.3). The alien might arrive at the conclusion that humans come in a variety of sizes and shapes, and possibly that they come in two sexes. The alien would notice that humans seem always to have one head, and almost always to have two arms and two legs.

Suppose the alien decided to look for a pattern by categorizing the individuals in the photograph on the basis of their height and the length of their hair. If the alien put these data on a graph, the graph might look something like Figure 12.4. The alien would probably have trouble making sense out of this graph—the points seem to be nearly at random places. There is no apparent connection between length of hair and height. Knowing the length of hair of a person would not help you predict the person's height.

Suppose the alien were able to measure the height and weight of the people; it might try to find a pattern by studying a graph that looks like Figure 12.5. This graph looks more promising. Even though there is a lot of "scatter," it shows a pattern. For example, there appear to be no humans who are under 150 cm tall and weigh more than 80 kg. Nor are there any humans who are more than 150 cm tall and weigh less than 40 kg. Thus, a relation ("correlation") exists between the height and weight of humans.

QUESTION: Imagine a height-weight graph for a group of aliens (see Figure 12.6). How do the aliens differ from humans in the way their height and weight are related? Can you think of any explanation for the way the height and weight of the aliens are related?

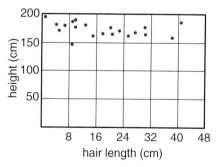

Figure 12.4
Graph of height vs. length of hair for people passing in the street.

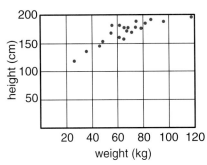

Figure 12.5
Graph of height vs. weight for a typical sample of humans.

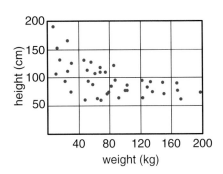

Figure 12.6
Graph of height vs. weight for hypothetical aliens.

Suppose an alien wanted to know more about humans and happened to come across a photograph of a fourth-grade homeroom. A graph of the height vs. weight of the students would not be so extreme in range as the graph for the people in the street. *Why?*

Typical aliens.

An Astronomical Story

Like aliens, astronomers often make plots to help them understand what they are observing. One such plot of the wattages and temperatures of stars in the neighborhood of the Sun is shown in Figure 12.7. Astronomers are always forward-looking, but sometimes backward-plotting: Notice that the temperature scale on Figure 12.7 runs "backward" with higher numbers to the left. Astronomers have a reason for using this procedure, but you don't have to worry about its purpose. We follow this way of plotting temperatures only so that you can look at other astronomy books and recognize what you are seeing. In any case, it pays to look carefully at the axes of any graph!

Figure 12.7 is analogous to the picture of the crowded street corner studied by the alien. Notice that not every possible combination of wattage and temperature is found in this sample of stars, just as every possible combination of height and weight is not found among humans. In fact, if you

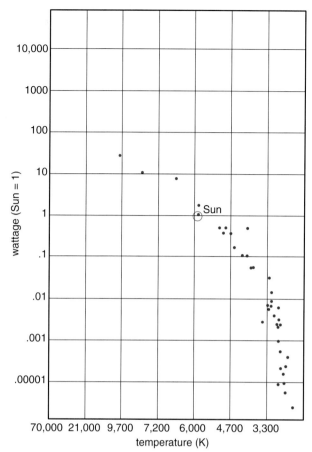

Figure 12.7

Graph of wattage vs. temperature for stars in the neighborhood of the Sun.

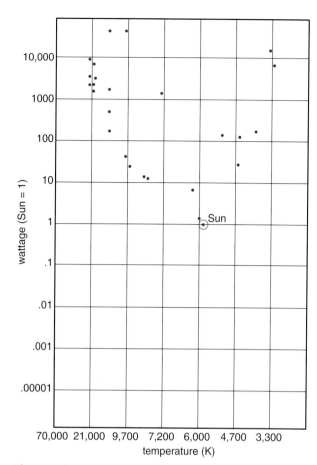

Figure 12.8

Graph of wattage vs. temperature for the 25 stars aside from the Sun with the greatest apparent brightness. (The Sun is included for reference.)

know the wattage of a star plotted in Figure 12.7, you can estimate its temperature with reasonable accuracy.

Figure 12.8 shows a plot of wattage vs. temperature of the 25 stars with the greatest apparent brightness. Notice how this plot differs from the plot for the stars nearest the Sun.

QUESTION: Why do you think the two plots look so different? (Hint: Which can the alien see at greater distances, very short people or very tall people?)

By studying wattage vs. temperature plots for many groups of stars and "building" mathematical models of stars, astronomers infer that stars, like living things, are born, grow older, and eventually die when they have used up all their sources of energy.

Astronomers infer that in Orion they can see stars being born from the dust and gas in space. Astronomers infer that all the stars in the Pleiades, like all the students in a fourth-grade class, are almost the same age. The wattage vs. temperature graph for some of stars in the Pleiades (see Figure 12.9) looks much the way astronomers expect such a graph to look for a group of stars that are about 10^8 years old. (How, you might ask, do astronomers know what to expect? In this case, they know by building mathematical

Figure 12.9
Graph of wattage vs. temperature
representative of some of the stars in
the Pleiades.

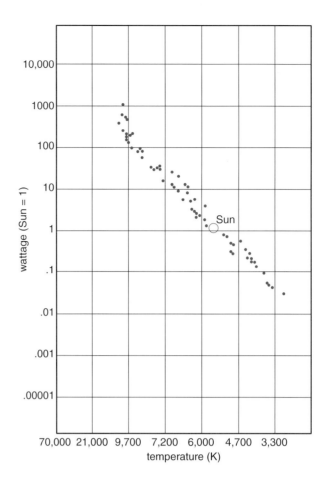

models of stars and determining how their wattages and temperatures change as the stars consume their nuclear fuel.)

M 13 and M 3 (see Figures 12.10 through 12.12) are two groups of stars that astronomers think are much older than the Pleiades, analogous to retirement homes. Notice that the stars with wattages greater than the Sun's wattage lie in different places on the graphs (Figures 12.13 and 12.14) than comparable stars in the Pleiades. Astronomers infer from this difference that the stars in M 13 and M 3 are of the order of 10^{10} years old: The "curve" in the wattage vs. temperature relation plays an important role in determining this age, based on mathematical models of the way stars age. One more

Figure 12.10
Two globular clusters, M 13 and M 3, can be seen in the summer sky from the Northern Hemisphere.

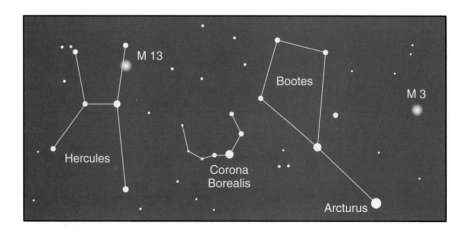

Figure 12.11
A closer look at M 13.

Figure 12.12
A closer look at M 3.

point: the absence of stars with wattages much less than the Sun's in M 3 and M 13 is probably not "real." There probably are such stars, but they are too faint to be observed.

Summary

A spectrometer of the type you used in Activity 12.2 is a device for separating photons according to their energies and therefore according to the colors with which they are associated. By measuring the relative numbers of photons with different energies emitted by an object, we can determine its temperature. In a graph of photon energy vs. number of photons emitted by a source of light, "missing" energies show up as "notches." These notches allow astronomers to determine the chemical elements that are in the source.

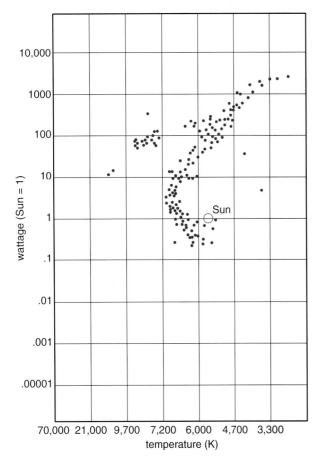

Figure 12.13
Graph of wattage vs. temperature representative of some of the stars in M 13. (The Sun is included for reference.)

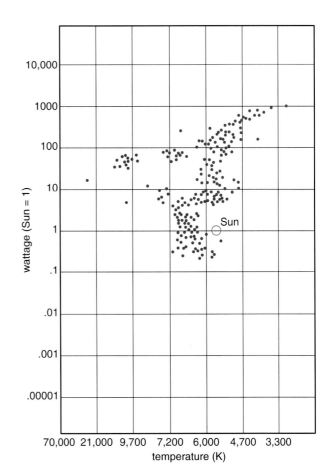

Figure 12.14
Graph of wattage vs. temperature representative of some of the stars in M 3. (The Sun is included for reference.)

Astronomers construct mathematical models of the life histories of stars. They then compare these models with plots of the wattages and temperatures of groups of stars to determine the ages of the stars making up these groups. Stars in the same group are assumed to have about the same age. Stars in groups that have been observed by astronomers have estimated ages from a few million years up to the order of 10 billion years.

HOMEWORK

1. Use the information in Table 12.1 to complete the following chart. The temperatures and energies given represent various types of stars. For the blank columns to the right, estimate the color of the photons that are emitted in the greatest number by the star (first column) and then decide what color the star would appear. Keep in mind that the star is emitting many photons of various energies.

Table 12.1	
Energy in e.v.	**Color**
1.8	Red
2.0	Orange
2.1	Yellow
2.4	Green
2.6	Blue
3.2	Violet

Classification of Stars by Temperature

energy of greatest number of photons(e.v.)	temp (K)	color associated with energy of photons	apparent color of star
9.1	21,000		
4.1	9,700		
3.1	7,200		
2.6	6,000		
2.0	4,700		
1.4	3,300		

2. If, from the spectrum of Sirius, you made a graph of the number of photons emitted vs. the energy of each photon, you would find that the star emits the greatest number of photons at an energy of 4.0 e.v. What is the approximate surface temperature and color of Sirius?

3. If, from the spectrum of Capella, you made a graph of the number of photons emitted vs. the energy of each photon, you would find that the star emits the greatest number of photons at an energy of 2.1 e.v. What is Capella's approximate surface temperature and color?

4. The chart below lists the energy of the photons that are emitted in the greatest number by each of these stars. Using this information, estimate the temperature and color of each star. (Do not worry about the strange names of some of the stars.)

Star	energy (e.v.)	Temp (K)	color
Betelgeuse	1.3		
61 Cygni	1.8		
Tau Ceti	2.1		
Alpha Centauri	2.5		
Procyon	2.8		
Deneb	3.9		
Vega	4.1		
Sirius B	4.1		
Rigel	4.2		

The following is a list of energies of photons emitted by each of the corresponding elements. Use this information to answer questions 5–7.

Element	Photon Energies (e.v.)							
oxygen	1.63	1.64						
hydrogen		1.89		2.56	2.86		3.03	
sodium			2.11					
iron		2.36	2.40		2.88			3.25 3.33
magnesium			2.39 2.40					
calcium					2.88 2.94	3.13 3.16		

5. You observe a distant star. Its spectrum shows lines at 1.89, 2.39, 2.40, 2.56, 2.86, and 3.03 e.v. What are the corresponding elements present on this star?

6. You observe another star. The spectrum of this star has the same lines as the star in question 5. It also has a line at 2.11 e.v. What are the corresponding elements present on this star?

7. A planet is observed orbiting the star in question 6. The spectrum of the planet shows lines at 1.89, 2.11, 2.36, 2.39, 2.40, 2.56, 2.86, 2.88, 3.03, 3.25, and 3.33 e.v. What is a reasonable explanation for the presence of the extra lines?

8. Examine the spectra in Color Plate 14. What type(s) of lights are in this scene? How did you determine your answer?

SELF-TEST

1. How can the temperature of a substance be determined if it is too hot to touch (for example, if the substance were hot enough to melt a thermometer)?

2. You observe a red star and a blue star in the sky. Which one has the higher surface temperature? Explain.

3. What physical properties of a star can be determined by studying the spectrum of the star?

4. Does a star emit photons at all energies? Explain.

5. Describe the general relation between the temperature and wattage of stars.

6. How does a temperature-wattage graph for a cluster like the Pleiades compare with the same type of graph for a globular cluster?

Annie Jump Cannon

When Annie Jump Cannon (1863–1941) went to college in 1884, she was one of the first women from her home state of Delaware to do so. As a student at Wellesley College in Massachusetts, she became interested in physics and astronomy. She began graduate work at Wellesley in 1894, transferred to Radcliffe in 1895, and began working at the Harvard College Observatory in 1896.

Cannon's most important work was her spectral classification of stars; she improved a method of organizing stars according to the stars' spectra, a method still used today, with some modifications. In the introduction to the Henry Draper Catalogue, she describes the method she used for gathering the spectra of stars.

Annie Jump Cannon

If you pointed your spectrometer at a star, you would only be able to see a very thin, faint spectrum. But by looking at a section of the sky through a prism and telescope, and taking a photograph of the image through both the prism and the telescope, you could get a permanent record of a much brighter and broader spectrum of the star. (A prism, usually a triangular wedge of glass, acts like the grating used in the spectrum projector and the spectrometer—it separates light into colors.) In addition, the photograph would include spectra of all the stars visible in that section of the sky, all seen through the telescope and prism simultaneously. This is the method described below.

> It was shown in May, 1885, that by placing a prism in front of the objective of a photographic telescope, excellent spectra could be obtained of all the stars of sufficient brightness in the field of the instrument. The immediate effect was that the photographic image of each star, instead of appearing as a point, was spread into a line, the rays of different wave lengths being diverted by the prism to different points upon the plate. . . . The principal lines in the spectra appear in these bands. The advantages of this method are, first, that the spectra of several hundred stars can be obtained in a single photograph, while with a slit spectroscope only one star can be photographed at a time. Secondly, the loss of light is so small that, even if stars are faint, satisfactory spectra can be obtained. Thirdly, the spectra can be identified with certainty, since they occupy the same relative positions on the photographs as stars on a chart plate, or map.
> —*Annals of the Harvard College Observatory*, Vol. 99, p. I.

Over the course of her professional career—from 1896 to her death in 1941—Cannon classified more than 350,000 stars, often working fast enough to classify up to three stars a minute. Two-thirds of these stars are listed in the Henry Draper Catalogue; Cannon did the major work on this catalog between 1911 and 1915. Annie Jump Cannon also made valuable contributions to research on variable stars, and she became the first woman to receive the honorary degree of Doctor of Science from Oxford University, England, in 1925.

ACTIVITY 12.1

GRAPHING COLOR AND TEMPERATURE

PURPOSE

To be able to relate temperature to color.

WHAT DO YOU THINK?

P1. *Do all stars appear to be the same color when you see them in the night sky? What color(s) do you see?*

P2. *Do most stars have the same temperature?*

MATERIALS

   1 colorometer
   1 laboratory thermometer (Celsius scale)
   1 chalkboard eraser
   1 paraffin photometer, from Activity 10.1
   1 spectrum projector setup, with white cardboard screens
   1 dimmer/Variac connected to the spectrum projector
   1 spectrum tube holder/power supply with hydrogen and
      helium tubes (optional)

PROCEDURE

   A. Place the spectrum projector in the center of a large table and set it up as shown in Figure 12.15. Connect the projector to a dimmer device. Turn on the projector.

   1. *What color does the projected slit appear to be? Record your answer.*

   B. Place your paraffin photometer in front of the colorometer (Figure 12.15) and move it as shown in Figure 12.16 to find the point in the spectrum that makes both halves of the paraffin appear equally bright. It helps to move the photometer back and forth several times and watch the changes in color. Set the photometer on an eraser in front of the colorometer as shown in Figure 12.16.

   2. *What colors do the two parts of the photometer appear to be?*

   C. Place the laboratory thermometer in the spectrum projector and wait 5 minutes.

   3. *What is the temperature inside the projector? Record your result.*

   D. Look at the colorometer from the position of the spectrum projector and number the colorometer blocks from left to right. List their colors in Table 12.2.

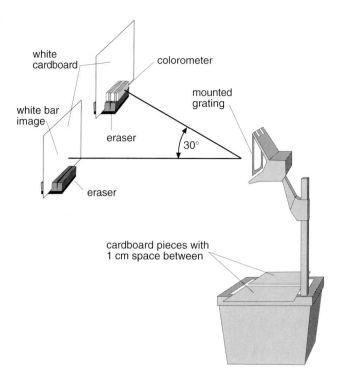

Figure 12.15

top view of colorometer and photometer

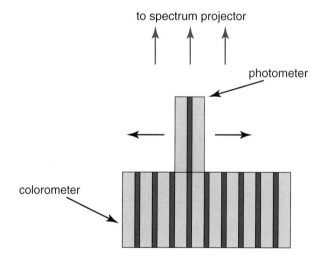

Figure 12.16

E. Judge the apparent brightness of each block. Use the scale below and record your data in the table.

0 = no color; 1 = very faint color; 2 = moderate color;
3 = very bright color; 4 = brightest color

F. Plot your points on a graph called Graph 12.1 of apparent brightness vs. block number. Connect your points with a smooth, curved line.

G. Use the dimmer switch to turn the projector bulb "down" until it is as dim as possible without the bulb turning off or flickering.

4. *What is the color of the projected slit now? How does this color compare with the color you saw in step A?*

H. Repeat step B with the dimmer setting.

5. *What color does each of the blocks now appear to be?*

6. *In what ways, if any, are the colors different from those described in question 2?*

I. Repeat step C with the dimmer setting.

7. *What is the temperature in the projector for the dimmed bulb? Record your result.*

J. Repeat step E for the dimmed bulb and fill in another Table 12.3. When you complete your observations, turn off the projector and disconnect it from the dimmer control. Do *not* try to brighten the bulb as this process causes excessive wear of the bulb.

K. Using a red pen or pencil, plot the new points on the same graph as for step F. Connect your points with a smooth curve.

8. *Based on your observations in steps B, C, H, and I and your graph, describe how you think the temperatures of objects and their colors are related.*

9. *Would a star appear redder or bluer than another star if it were much hotter than the other star?*

10. *The star Procyon has a surface temperature of 6,600°C and appears as a yellow-white star in the nighttime sky. Betelgeuse, one of the stars in the nearby constellation of Orion, has a surface temperature of 3,500°C. Does Betelgeuse appear to be redder or bluer than Procyon?*

11. *Sirius, the brightest star in the nighttime sky, appears to be a bluish/white color. Predict its temperature.*

NOW WHAT DO YOU THINK?

12. *Are all the colors in the "rainbow" spectrum equally bright?*

13. *Describe how a graph of apparent brightness vs. color for bluish/white Sirius would differ from that for the red star Betelgeuse.*

14. *Generally speaking, should hot stars appear redder or bluer than cool stars?*

15. *Our own Sun is classified as a yellow star. Predict the surface temperature of the Sun.*

ACTIVITY 12.2   MEASURING COLORS WITH THE SPECTROMETER

PURPOSE

To become familiar with the use of the spectrometer. In particular, to check the spectrometer's calibration; to become familiar with reading the spectrometer's scales and units; to observe spectra (plural of spectrum) of different light sources; and to measure the positions of dark bands in the spectra of light that has passed through different materials.

WHAT DO YOU THINK?

P1. *You have observed spectra created by ordinary lightbulbs; predict what you think the spectrum of a mercury fluorescent light will look like.*

MATERIALS

1 spectrometer
1 mercury fluorescent light
1 lightbulb and socket
1 high-voltage power supply
selection of emission tubes (or Color Plates 8–12)
bottles of transparent colored liquids
colored pencils or pens
white surface, such as a movie screen or wall

PROCEDURE

A. Turn on the lightbulb, keep the room lights on, and look at the bulb through the spectrometer. Be careful to aim the slit (on the right side of the spectrometer) at the lightbulb and look straight ahead at the spectrum on the scale. You should see a continuous spectrum of colors from red through violet. Your teacher will give you a copy of the scale below (Figure 12.17). Mark on it the colors you see where you see them. If available, use colored pencils to shade in the observed colors.

B. Read the number on the scale corresponding to the light farthest to the right that you can see and the number corresponding to the light farthest to the left that you can see. For this step and the remainder of

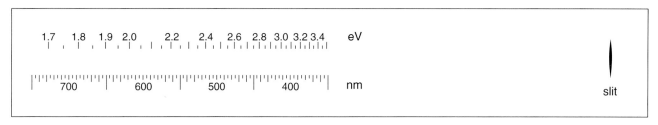

Figure 12.17

this activity, note the units (e.v. or nm) that your teacher asks you to use for these measurements. The electron volt (e.v.) units are used to describe the energies of photons (see Chapter 10), whereas the nanometer (nm) units describe the colors of the light corresponding to the different photon energies. For each value of one unit there is a unique value of the other unit corresponding to it, as you can see in Figure 12.17.

1. *The observed spectrum extends from what (e.v. or nm) to what (e.v. or nm)? What are the colors at these places on the scale?*

C. Now look at a fluorescent light through the spectrometer.

2. *Describe the spectrum you see. Is it different from the spectrum of the lightbulb that you looked at in step A?*

D. Again record the ends of the spectrum, as in step B.

3. *The colored spectrum extends from what (e.v. or nm) to what (e.v. or nm)? The spectrum from the fluorescent light should include several bright "lines." Indicate the positions of these lines on the scale.*

E. Read the positions of the bright lines on the scale. Create a table, label it Table 12.4, and record the bright-line positions in it.

F. The most common type of fluorescent light will have the mercury emission lines superimposed on a continuous spectrum (see Color Plates 7 and 8). The green line of mercury corresponds to 2.27 e.v., or 546 nm. If your value in Table 12.4 does not agree with this standard value, talk to your teacher. You may need to adjust the position of the scale in your spectrometer.

G. Point the slit of your spectrometer at a white surface that has fluorescent light shining on it, such as a wall or a movie screen, and measure the ends of the spectrum and the positions of any bright lines that you see. To record these data, create another table and label it Table 12.5.

4. *Compare the results of steps E and G. Was the spectrum that you saw from the fluorescent light similar to or different from the spectrum you saw when you looked at the white surface? Why do you think the spectra were similar or different?*

H. Look at the emission tubes that your teacher has set up. For each tube, record in another table (Table 12.6) the name of the element, the colors of the lines, and the positions of the lines on the spectrometer scale. Color Plate 12 gives you a good idea of what an emission spectrum looks like through your spectrometer. (If emission tubes are not available, examine Color Plates 8–12.)

5. *Would you expect any two of the 92 naturally occurring elements in the universe to have the same spectral line pattern? Why or why not?*

I. Look at a light source with your spectrometer. Now hold a bottle of transparent colored liquid in front of the spectrometer slit and notice how the spectrum changes. Create another table (Table 12.7) to record, for each bottle, the following data: the label on the bottle, the missing color(s), and the position(s) of the dark bands on the spectrometer scale. The dark bands, called absorption bands, are due to photons of certain energies being absorbed by the liquid. When the photons are absorbed, the colors corresponding to the photon energies are removed from the spectrum. Gaps or bands then appear in the spectrum where the missing colors would have appeared had there been no absorption.

NOW WHAT DO YOU THINK?

6. *Do you think that you could predict what the spectrum of a light source would look like by seeing the color of the light? Explain.*

7. *Where do you expect that elements would have to be located in order to cause dark lines in the spectrum of the Sun? Would the elements have to be located inside the Sun, on the Sun's surface, above the Sun's surface, in space between the Sun and the Earth, or in the Earth's atmosphere? Why?*

ACTIVITY 12.3   WHAT IS THE SUN MADE OF?

PURPOSE

To use the spectrometer to measure absorption lines in the Sun and compare them to emission lines measured in the classroom to determine some of the elements that are present in the Sun.

WHAT DO YOU THINK?

P1. *What elements do you expect would cause absorption lines in the spectrum of the Sun?*

MATERIALS

    1 spectrometer
    high-voltage power supply
    selection of emission tubes
    1 sunny day (preferably with some fluffy white clouds)
    Table 12.11, a partial listing of lines that may be observed in the
        solar spectrum

PROCEDURE

A. Refer to step H, Activity 12.2. If your teacher has set up emission tubes for any *different* elements, repeat that step here for the new elements. Create a table (Table 12.8) to record the names of the elements, the colors of the lines, and the positions of the lines on the spectrometer scale. Note the units (e.v. or nm) that your teacher asks you to use for this activity.

B. Take your spectrometer outside, or look through a window from a darkened room, and point the slit toward the bright sky near the Sun.

CAUTION

DO NOT LOOK DIRECTLY AT THE SUN! IT CAN DAMAGE YOUR EYES!!

You should see a spectrum of all the colors with narrow, dark lines superimposed (recall Activity 12.2). Measure the ends of the spectrum.

1. *The spectrum extends from what (e.v. or nm) to what (e.v. or nm)?*

C. Now measure the positions of the dark lines that you see. Record the results in another new table (Table 12.9).

D. In yet another table (Table 12.10), list any lines that you measured in step B that match measurements that you made in step A, or that match any of the measurements listed in Table 12.11.

E. The dark lines recorded in step B will be located at the same positions as the bright lines you observed in step A *if* the element you observed in step A is present in the Sun.

2. *What elements do you conclude are present in the Sun?*

3. *Do you think that you have found all the elements that are in the Sun? Why or why not?*

F. Point the spectrometer slit at a bright, white cloud.

4. *Describe the spectrum that you see. How does the "cloud" spectrum compare to the spectrum of the Sun? Does the cloud spectrum have dark lines as the solar spectrum does?*

5. *Why do you think the cloud spectrum appears the way it does?*

Table 12.11 Absorption lines in the Sun

Due to	Wavelength (nm)	Energy (e.v.)	Due to	Wavelength (nm)	Energy (e.v.)
Fe	372.8	3.33	Fe	516.8	2.40
Fe	382.0	3.25	Mg	516.7	2.40
Ca	393.4	3.167			
Ca	396.8	3.13	Mg	517.3	2.40
H	410.2	3.03	Mg	518.4	2.39
Ca	422.7	2.94	Fe	527.0	2.36
			Na	589.0	2.11
Fe	430.8	2.88	Na	590.0	2.11
Ca			H	656.3	1.89
H	434.0	2.86	O	759.4	1.64
H	486.1	2.56	O	762.1	1.63

Ca = Calcium; Fe = Iron; H = Hydrogen; Mg = Magnesium; Na = Sodium; O = Oxygen

(from the CRC *Handbook of Chemistry and Physics*)

EXTENSIONS

1. Repeat step F for the Moon. (This activity is best done at night when the Moon is bright compared to the background sky, such as when there is a full Moon visible 2 or 3 hours after sunset.) Point the spectrometer slit directly at the Moon.

   Describe the spectrum you see. How does the Moon's spectrum compare to the spectrum of the Sun? Does the lunar spectrum have dark lines as the solar spectrum does? Are they the same lines? Why or why not?

2. Use your spectrometer to observe as many different light sources as you can find. Suggested lights include the LEDs on a VCR or stereo system; bright mercury (bluish), low-pressure sodium (very yellow), or high-pressure sodium (yellowish) street lights; and ordinary lightbulbs observed through transparent, colored objects. (Color Plates 13 and 14 are photographs of different lights taken through a piece of diffraction grating of the type in your spectrometer.)

   Describe what object you observed and the spectrum you saw. Are there any bright or dark lines in the spectrum? If there are any bright or dark lines, give the positions and the colors of the lines.

Figure 12.18
The temperature of hot materials, such as molten steel, can be determined by measuring the energies of the photons they emit with instruments such as this optical pyrometer.

CHAPTER 13

The Milky Way

Starry, Starry Night

1. Some people think that the universe goes on forever in all directions and the stars are spread evenly throughout space. Is that what *you* think the universe is like? If so, why do you think so? If not, what do you believe and why?

Preview: In this chapter you will use the apparent brightness-distance relation to explore the size of the Milky Way galaxy, our "Island Universe."

The Milky Way

Turning the newly invented telescope skyward, Galileo soon learned that stars are crowded together in that faint band of light passing overhead on a dark night—the Milky Way (Figure 13.1).

Are there ways to determine where the Sun is in relation to the stars in the Milky Way? One way would be to determine the distances and directions to a large number of stars, and thereby learn how the stars are distributed around us in space. If there were more stars concentrated in one general direction and at one distance than in all others, astronomers might infer that the center of the Milky Way is located where there are the most stars.

To carry out this plan, astronomers would have to be able to determine the distances to a large number of stars. Since all stars do not have the same wattage, astronomers cannot infer the distance to a star merely by measuring its apparent brightness (see Chapter 5). But if there were some way to determine a star's wattage, astronomers could compare the star's apparent brightness with its wattage and thus determine the star's distance. Wattages of stars are, in most cases, not so easy to determine. In some special cases, however, the determination is almost easy; we now discuss these cases.

Beacons in the Sky

In Chapter 10 you learned about pairs of stars whose apparent brightnesses change because each star in the pair is regularly hidden by its companion star. These pairs of stars are identified by measuring their apparent brightnesses and noting whether they change with time in a fashion similar to the changes shown in Figure 13.2.

The changes in the apparent brightnesses of some stars display a different pattern (see Figure 13.3). Astronomers believe the patterns differ because each is produced by a different mechanism. From observations of the changes in the Doppler shift (see Chapter 10) of the photons emitted by variable stars of this second type, astronomers infer that only one star is involved, but that this star expands and contracts as it changes apparent brightness. (A star whose apparent brightness changes for any reason is called a variable star.)

One of the brightest of these stars is not too hard to find in the northern sky—it is the North Star. The changes in apparent brightness of the North Star are very small, however, and for many years were difficult to measure. The first star discovered of this type is also easy to find in the sky

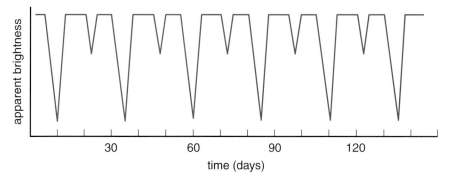

Figure 13.2

The changing apparent brightness of a pair of stars.

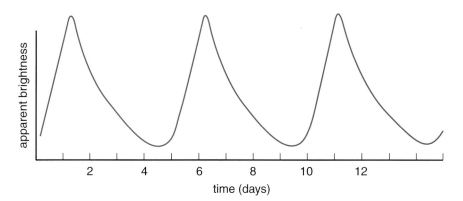

Figure 13.3

Changing apparent brightness of a Cepheid (CEF-ee-id) variable star.

(see Figure 13.4). Remarkably, stars like Delta Cephei turn out to be beacons that astronomers can treat as if they were marked with their "wattage." How could that be? The story is somewhat long, but well worth telling. For the history, see the following section; here we give the basic facts. For a variable star, the length of time between one maximum apparent brightness and the next is observed to be nearly constant, and is called the "period" of the apparent-brightness variation. For Cepheid variable stars, this period is observed to be uniquely related to the star's (average) wattage: each different period corresponds to a distinct wattage. (In fact there are two "families" of Cepheids, each with its own period-wattage relation. You will only be concerned with one of these families here.) Thus, astronomers can measure the period of a Cepheid and infer its wattage. Astronomers can then compare that wattage with the star's apparent brightness and thereby infer its

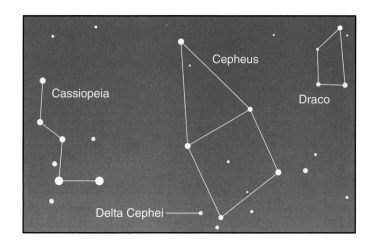

Figure 13.4

Delta Cephei (DEL-ta CEF-ee-eye), for which all Cepheid variable stars are named.

distance. This long chain of reasoning is typical in science, and, in fact, in everyday life, although you may not have realized it. *Can you think of other examples of such chains?*

The Discovery of "Standard Candles" in the Sky

In 1912 Henrietta Leavitt (Figure 13.5) was studying the changes in apparent brightness of Cepheid variable stars in two groups of stars in the southern skies—the Large and Small Magellanic (Ma-gel-AN-ic) Clouds—named after the Portuguese explorer Ferdinand Magellan (FUR-din-an Ma-GEL-an) who was one of the first Europeans to observe them. Each Magellanic Cloud appears cloud-like (see Figure 13.6), but is actually a collection of stars, gas, and dust similar to, but smaller than, the Milky Way. These "clouds" are distinct galaxies, separated from the Milky Way galaxy, as discussed further in Chapter 14. Back now to Leavitt's discovery.

For each Cepheid variable she observed, Leavitt graphed the period of the apparent-brightness variation vs. the average of the apparent brightnesses. Making such a graph is a common method scientists use to look for connections among different quantities. When she examined all the points on her graph, she found something startling. The points seemed to lie approximately on a straight line (see Figure 13.7). What did that result tell her? What could she infer from the relation between the period and apparent brightness of the Cepheids? To answer that question, it is necessary to infer something about the distances to the stars in the Large Magellanic Cloud.

All the stars in the Large Magellanic Cloud (LMC) appear to be part of one collection—a single galaxy. This galaxy also appears to have a relatively small size in the sky (small angular size). You could therefore reasonably assume that the distances between the stars in the Magellanic cloud were small compared to the distance from us to any one of these stars. That is, for any two stars in the LMC, the fractional, or percent difference in their distances from us would be small—a few percent or less. Therefore, stars in the LMC that appear equally bright to astronomers would likely have nearly

Figure 13.5
Henrietta Leavitt (1868–1921).

Figure 13.6
The Magellanic Star Clouds.

equal wattages. (Remember how you were able to use the apparent brightnesses of the stars in the Pleiades to compare their wattages?) Leavitt did not know from observations that stars in the LMC were, in fact, all at approximately the same distance from us. There was then no independent means of determining the distances from us to these stars. But since it was reasonable to assume that all the stars in the LMC are approximately the same distance from the Earth, she made this assumption. Based on it, Leavitt could then infer that a unique relation exists between the periods of Cepheid stars and their wattages (see Figure 13.7): the period-wattage relation. This relation allows astronomers to use the periods of these variable stars, which are relatively easy to measure, to infer their wattages, which otherwise would be very difficult to determine. These variable stars are now used as standards for measuring distance. Knowing the wattage of such a star and its apparent brightness, you can use the apparent brightness-distance nomogram from Chapter 10 to calculate its distance.

Using the Period-Wattage Relation

How could you use this period-wattage relation for Cepheid variable stars to find out where we are located with respect to the rest of the stars in the Milky Way? Before answering, let's consider an analogy. Imagine that you lived in the suburb of a city. If you were to count the number of streetlights you could see, you might find approximately the same number of streetlights in all directions (see Figure 13.8). You might infer that you were in the center of the city. But if you could find a hill far away from which you could see the distant lights of the city, you would know that you were far from the center of the city (Figure 13.9). On the other hand, if you were on a tall building in the center of a city, you could tell you were in the center of a city.

Determining the locations of stars in the "neighborhood" of the Sun is like determining the locations of streetlights in your neighborhood. Looking

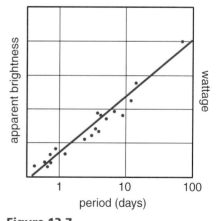

(Dots represent average apparent brightness and wattage of variable stars; the solid line is a straight line that lies close to the data.)

Figure 13.7
Graph of period vs. apparent brightness and wattage of representative Cepheid variables in the LMC. (Since these stars are all at about the same distance from the Earth, their apparent brightnesses are simply related to their wattages.)

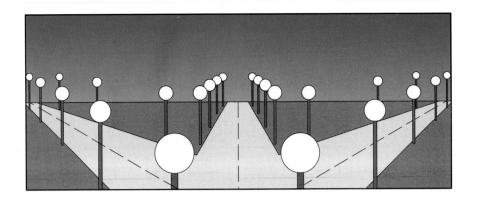

Figure 13.8
Suburban street intersection at night: equal numbers of streetlights are visible in several directions.

only in your neighborhood may not enable you to locate the center of your city or town. Because you counted an equal number of streetlights in all directions, you might conclude that you were at the center of the city. In fact, however, the center of the city might be located far away from your own neighborhood. The same problem arises from looking only at stars in the neighborhood of the Sun.

In Activity 13.1 you made a map locating open star clusters and found that they are distributed more or less regularly around the Milky Way as seen from the Earth. (Would the view be the same from the Sun? Why or why not?) This map seems to suggest that the Earth is in the middle of the Milky Way, and is analogous to a map of the streetlights in a suburb. On the other hand, in the same activity, you found that globular clusters are concentrated in the direction of the constellations of Sagittarius and Scorpius (see Figure 13.10).

In 1918 the astronomer Harlow Shapley noticed the same thing. He decided that the globular clusters might mark the center of the Milky Way, the way bright lights might mark the center of a city when viewed from well outside that center—see Figure 13.9. Shapley used the discovery by Leavitt of the period-wattage relation for Cepheid variable stars to infer the distances to globular clusters containing Cepheids. By assuming that these clusters, like the brightest city lights, are concentrated at the center of the

Figure 13.9
The heart of a city seen from the outskirts.

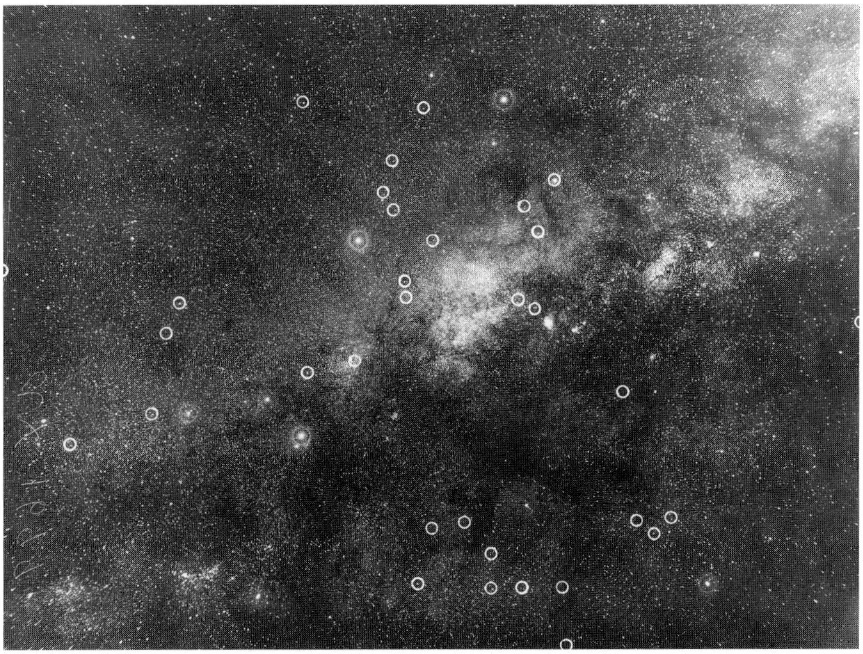

Figure 13.10
Globular clusters in Sagittarius.

"city," Shapley was able to infer that we are located far from the center of the Milky Way. He was also able to estimate how far we are from the center, thus making a major advance in our knowledge of our place in the universe.

Let us review the use of the period-wattage relation for a Cepheid star to find the distance to the star. You need to answer two questions: (1) what is the Cepheid's period, which allows you to infer its wattage; and (2) how bright does the Cepheid appear to be? You can then use the star's apparent brightness and its wattage to infer the star's distance from you by using the apparent brightness-distance relation.

PROBLEM: A Cepheid variable in a globular cluster (see Figure 13.11) is observed to take 30 days to go from one occurrence of maximum light to the next such occurrence. The average apparent magnitude of the Cepheid is +12. How far away is the globular cluster?

To use the apparent brightness and period of a Cepheid variable to determine its distance, you need to (1) use the star's period to determine its wattage, and (2) use this wattage and the star's apparent brightness to determine its distance.

STEP 1: Given the Cepheid's 30-day period, find its wattage.

In Figure 13.11, you find that a Cepheid in a globular cluster with a period of 30 days has a wattage equal to that of approximately 2.5×10^3 Suns.

STEP 2: Convert the wattage and apparent brightness into a distance.

From the apparent brightness-distance nomogram in Chapter 10, you find the Cepheid is 3×10^4 (30,000) light-years away. This is approximately the distance from the Sun to the center of the Milky Way.

PROBLEM: Suppose the size/distance ratio for the globular cluster containing the Cepheid in the previous problem is 1.4×10^{-3}. What is the diameter of this globular cluster?

Figure 13.11
A graph of wattage vs. period for
some Cepheid variables in a globular
cluster.

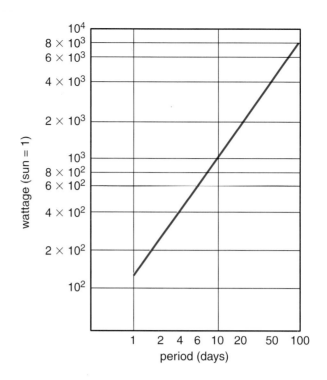

You can use the relation:

$$\frac{\text{size}}{\text{distance}} = \text{angular size}$$

$$\frac{\text{size of cluster}}{\text{distance to cluster}} = 1.4 \times 10^{-3}$$

$$\frac{\text{size of cluster}}{3 \times 10^4 \text{ l.y.}} = 1.4 \times 10^{-3}$$

Multiplying both sides of the equation by 3×10^4 l.y. yields

$$\text{size of cluster} = 1.4 \times 10^{-3} \times 3 \times 10^4 \text{ l.y.}$$
$$= 4.2 \times 10^1 \text{ l.y.}$$

QUESTION: If you were to build a scale model in which the Earth was 1 m from the Sun, how far away would you have to put the globular cluster in the above problem? How big would it be? (Hint: You need to use both the size/distance ratio for the globular cluster and the scale of your model.)

Cepheids have a high wattage, 2×10^2 to more than 10^4 times as high as the Sun's. Thus, Cepheids can be seen from great distances, and are useful for measuring the distances to remote collections of stars—some much more remote than the globular clusters and even farther away from us than the Magellanic Clouds.

A Model of the Milky Way

Photographs like Figure 13.12 clearly show the stars in the Milky Way. Astronomers infer that the dark streaks in pictures like Figure 13.12 are produced by dust—yes, dust: very small particles, of the order of 10^{-4} cm in size—that obscure the light of more distant stars. Maps made from satellite

observations also show the shape of the Milky Way (see Figure 13.13, which was made from infrared photons). Infrared photons are not scattered as readily as optical photons (see Chapter 11); therefore, satellite pictures made with infrared photons show the shape of the Milky Way, unobscured by dust. Many infrared photons—particularly those from cool objects—are absorbed by the Earth's atmosphere. A satellite located above the Earth's atmosphere is thus needed to photograph the sources that emit these photons.

Shapley's results and more recent ones based on the use of different techniques all agree that we are located approximately 3×10^4 (30,000) light-years from the center of the Milky Way, which is located in the direction of the constellation of Sagittarius (Figure 13.12). From many measurements of different types, astronomers infer that it takes the Sun about 2.5×10^8 years to make one trip around the center of the galaxy; 2.5×10^8 years is sometimes called a galactic year. *Why?*

Knowing the distance to the center of the Milky Way and the amount of time it takes the Sun to make one circuit, you can use Kepler's relation to estimate the total of all the mass closer to the center of the Milky Way than is the Sun. It is not obvious that all this mass can be treated in the same way

Figure 13.13
Map of the Milky Way made from
infrared photons.

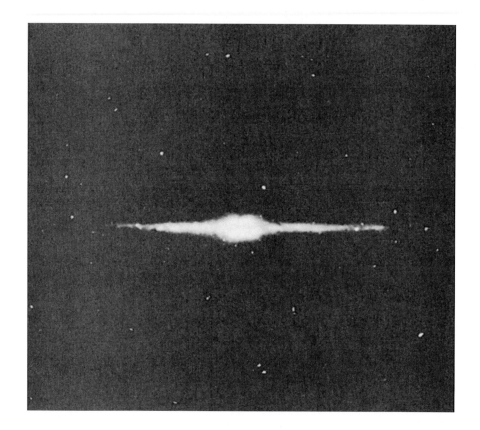

the Sun is treated when applying Kepler's relation to the planets. In fact, this treatment is only a "rough" approximation (for example, we ignore the effects of the mass farther from the center of the Milky Way than is the Sun), but a useful approximation nevertheless.

The form of Kepler's relation you used in Chapter 10 requires that distances be measured in a.u. and that time be measured in years. The period of the Sun around the galactic center is already given in years, so all you have to do is convert the distance from light-years to a.u. One light-year is approximately equal to 6.3×10^4 a.u., so 30,000 light-years is therefore equal to

$$3 \times 10^4 \text{ l.y.} \times 6.3 \times 10^4 \text{ a.u./l.y.} = 1.9 \times 10^9 \text{ a.u.}$$

You can now use Kepler's relation in the form you used in Chapter 10:

$$(\text{period in yr})^2 = \frac{(\text{distance in a.u.})^3}{(\text{mass in units of solar mass})}$$

$$(2.5 \times 10^8)^2 = \frac{(1.9 \times 10^9)^3}{(\text{mass in units of solar mass})}$$

Multiplying both sides of the equation by (mass in units of solar mass) yields

$$(\text{mass in units of solar mass}) \times (2.5 \times 10^8)^2 = (1.9 \times 10^9)^3$$

Dividing both sides of the equation by $(2.5 \times 10^8)^2$ yields

$$(\text{mass in units of solar mass}) = \frac{(1.9 \times 10^9)^3}{(2.5 \times 10^8)^2}$$

$$= \frac{6.9 \times 10^{27}}{6.3 \times 10^{16}}$$

$$= 1.1 \times 10^{11}$$

The total mass of all the stars, gas, and dust that is closer to the center of the Milky Way than is the Sun is therefore approximately 10^{11} solar masses, the mass of 100 billion Suns. Since stars make up a major portion of the mass of the Milky Way, and since an average star has about the mass of the Sun, astronomers assume that there are about 100 billion stars in the Milky Way. No one has counted them all, however. As big as the Milky Way galaxy is, it is only one "island universe" amid a vast number of similar island universes, as you will learn in the next chapter.

SUMMARY

The Milky Way has a pancake shape and contains vast numbers of stars, the whole collection being a galaxy. We are located in this galaxy. Many types of observations support this conclusion; for example, from the Earth you can observe the Milky Way as a band of light going completely around the sky. If we were outside the Milky Way, it could not surround us.

Other observations and analyses lead to the conclusion that the center of the Milky Way is in the direction of the constellation of Sagittarius and is about 30,000 l.y. away from us. This distance was first determined by using an amazing property discovered about a type of star called a Cepheid that undergoes periodic changes in apparent brightness. The interval between successive times of maximum apparent brightness is related uniquely to the star's wattage. Therefore, by observing the period of the variations in apparent brightness of a Cepheid star, the star's wattage can be inferred. Comparing this wattage to the star's apparent brightness allows you to determine the distance to the star, through use of the apparent brightness-distance relation.

The distance from us to the center of the Milky Way and the time it takes for the Sun to make one complete revolution around this center allows us to use Kepler's relation to estimate the mass of our galaxy: approximately 10^{11} solar masses; that is, the mass of the Milky Way equals the mass of about 100 billion Suns.

Homework

1. If the solar system were moved to the center of the Milky Way galaxy, which group, or groups, of objects beyond the solar system would retain the same basic distribution across the sky as is seen from the Earth in its present location?

2. If the solar system were located on the very edge of the Milky Way galaxy, and if the plane of the Earth's orbit around the Sun were parallel to the plane of the galaxy, how would the appearance of the evening sky change during 1 year? (Hint: You may want to refer to Chapter 2.)

3. A Cepheid variable is observed to take 50 days to go from maximum apparent brightness to maximum apparent brightness. Other measurements show that the Sun appears to be 4×10^{14} times brighter than the average apparent brightness of the Cepheid. How far away from the Earth is the Cepheid?

SELF-TEST

1. a) Are all objects beyond the solar system evenly distributed across the sky?

   b) What are some of the means astronomers (and you!) use to determine our location in the Milky Way galaxy?

2. Cepheid variable star P changes in apparent brightness with a period of 10 days. Another Cepheid variable star Q changes in apparent brightness with a period of 20 days. Which star has the greater average wattage?

3. Cepheid variable star S has a period of 5.5 days. Another Cepheid variable star T has a period of 1.3 days. Star T appears brighter in the sky than star S. Which star is closer to us? Explain your reasoning.

4. Toward which constellation would you look to face the center of our galaxy? List observations that support your answer.

The Milky Way Observed

The Milky Way is the name of the galaxy we live in; the Sun is one of its approximately 100 billion stars. Under the best viewing conditions, the Milky Way appears from the Earth as a broad, uneven band of faint light stretching all the way across the sky.

Until the last century, most people could view the night sky unaffected by artificial light sources. Nowadays, streetlights, store and business lights, house lights, billboard lights, and motor vehicle headlights (see Appendix 1) help you to see your neighborhood but interfere with your view of the sky above. Thus, the Milky Way is rather faint, if visible at all, in urban and sub-urban neighborhoods. But the Milky Way is a striking celestial feature on a very dark night, when there are no lights from Earth interfering with the view of the sky. It doesn't look like other objects in the sky; it doesn't trace the path of the Sun, Moon, or any planets across the sky, and it stretches from horizon to horizon. If you have been lucky enough to see the Milky Way, you might better imagine the descriptions of it given by people in earlier times. Many ancient stories mention the Milky Way: some Native Americans called it a road through the stars; the !Kung tribe in Africa saw it as the backbone of the sky; the Greeks said it was milk from the goddess Hera (hence the name "Milky Way").

By 1610, people had been wondering and guessing and theorizing about the Milky Way for thousands of years. That year, Galileo Galilei published *Sidereus Nuncius,* often translated as *The Starry Messenger* (another translation would be *Astronomical Message*). This book described the observations he made of the night sky with his telescope. Galileo was not the first person to use a telescope, but he may have been the first person to use one to study the night sky. Before Galileo, some people did think the Milky Way was made up of many stars too small to see individually, but there were other opinions as well, and no conclusive evidence was available to support anyone's idea. Because of Galileo's work, scientists and philosophers finally had information they could use to resolve these arguments about the nature of the Milky Way: it was composed of many individual stars.

> What was observed by us . . . is the nature or matter of the Milky Way itself, which, with the aid of the spyglass [telescope], may be observed so well that all the disputes that for so many generations have vexed philosophers are destroyed by visible certainty, and we are liberated from wordy arguments. For the Galaxy* is nothing else than a congeries [assembly] of innumerable stars distributed in clusters. To whatever region of it you direct your spyglass, an immense number of stars immediately offer themselves to view, of which very many appear . . . very conspicuous but the multitude . . . is truly unfathomable.
>
> Galileo Galilei, *Sidereus Nuncius*

From *Sidereus Nuncius*, translated by Albert Van Helden and published by The University of Chicago Press in 1989 (p. 62).

*Galileo used the word "Galaxy" to describe the stars and sky and space in a much less definite way than we do now. The idea that galaxies are separate, individual groupings of billions of stars developed gradually over the several centuries following Galileo's observations and wasn't well understood until the 1900s.

ACTIVITY 13.1

LOCATING THE SOLAR SYSTEM IN THE MILKY WAY GALAXY

PURPOSE

To determine the distribution on the sky of various celestial objects within and outside the Milky Way and to determine our location within the Milky Way galaxy.

WHAT DO YOU THINK?

Copies of all of the plates referred to below will be provided for you.

Plate K was taken at an observatory located in the Andes Mountains in South America. The camera used a special lens called a "fish-eye" that photographs the entire visible sky. The center of the picture is directly above the camera and the outside edge of the picture is the horizon.

P1. *When you look at this picture or at the night sky from your hometown, do you see the stars spread evenly around the sky? Describe the distribution you see.*

P2. *Given that we are inside a galaxy, do you think we are in the center of the galaxy or off to one side? How might you tell?*

MATERIALS

selection of colored pens or pencils
Chart 1
Tables 13.1–13.7
Plates A, B, C, E, F, G, K, L, M, N, P
Chart 2

PROCEDURE

By using large telescopes, astronomers have discovered objects other than stars and planets in the sky. Some of these objects are galaxies, which can be seen on plates F, G, L, M, N, and P. Galaxies come in a variety of types, each with its own name, such as elliptical or spiral, descriptive of its shape. One can think of a spiral galaxy as a "pancake"-shaped object containing about 100 billion stars, with a bump in the middle. The brighter stars form the spiral arms of such a galaxy and are visible in some of the pictures.

In addition to the billions of individual stars that make up this pancake, there are many other types of objects as well. For example, there are tenuous clouds of gas and dust, called "nebulae" (singular "nebula"). Examples of these are the Great Nebula in Orion on plates A and B and the Lagoon and Trifid nebulae in Sagittarius on plate E.

Astronomers have also discovered that some stars are grouped together in loose clusters that usually contain a few hundred stars. The Pleiades (plate C) is an example of one of these clusters. Such groups are called "open

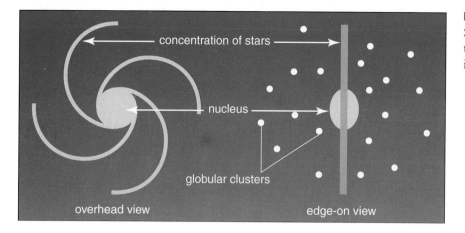

clusters" or "galactic clusters." An average spiral galaxy may have a few hundred open clusters in it.

In addition to these objects, an average galaxy contains a few hundred "globular clusters"—spherical clusters of stars that each contain a few hundred thousand stars. One such cluster, M 22, is near the upper left corner of plate E. Globular clusters are scattered in a roughly spherical distribution just outside and around the center, or nucleus, of the galaxy. They are the only visible components of most spiral galaxies that extend far away from the plane of the galaxy. Some astronomers have described globular clusters as being like bees around a flower. Figure 13.14 shows a sample distribution of stars and globular clusters in an average spiral galaxy.

Thinking of individual stars, constellations of stars, and all other celestial objects as being on the inside of a very large sphere leads to a useful mapping system. Just as the surface of the Earth, which is nearly a sphere, can be represented by different kinds of maps, such as rectangular maps, equatorial maps, and Mercator projections, so too the sky can be made into a flat map, such as the one shown on Chart 1. Only the 500 brightest stars are plotted on this chart; under good conditions the unaided eye can see a few thousand stars.

As on a map of the Earth, the line running horizontally through the center of the map is called the equator. Since it is "on" the sky, it is called the celestial equator. (See Chapter 3 and Figure 13.15.) If a celestial object, such as a star, the Sun, a planet, or the Moon, is located on the celestial equator, the object will, once each day, pass directly above a person standing on the Earth's equator.

Figure 13.15

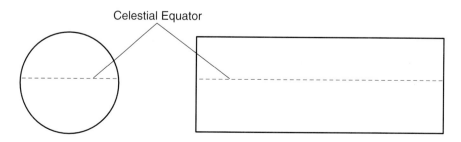

A. Locate the Big Dipper on Chart 1. It is near the top center of the chart. The Big Dipper is part of the constellation Ursa Major. Also see if you can find Scorpius. It is shaped like a fishhook and is located at −30° on the vertical axis (celestial latitude) and between 240° and 270° on the horizontal axis (celestial longitude).

B. Chart 2 is a diagram of the sky showing the areas covered by each constellation. If you cover Chart 1 with Chart 2 and hold them up to a light, you should be able to see how they match up. Look for Ursa Major and Scorpius again.

C. Looking at Chart 1, do you notice any part of the sky where there appear to be stars packed more closely together than in other parts of the sky? This part of the sky is known as the Milky Way. Part of it matches the bright-appearing region visible on the photograph in plate K.

D. Table 13.1 lists the constellations in which the brightest appearing parts of the Milky Way are located. On Chart 2, lightly shade in these constellations with a pencil or outline the constellations with a black pen.

1. *From the appearance of the Milky Way in the sky, as seen in Chart 1 and plate K, describe*

   a) *the distribution of stars seen throughout the sky.*

   b) *the brightest appearing region of stars seen in the sky.*

2. *Based on the information from question 1, where do you think our solar system is located in the Milky Way galaxy?*

E. Tables 13.2 through 13.5 are lists of Messier (MESS-ee-ay) objects. Messier objects are "fuzzy" celestial objects listed by the 18th century French astronomer Charles Messier. Messier was trying to find new comets. He realized that the sky contains many nonstarlike objects that do not move among the stars as comets do. But these objects are easy to mistake for comets because, like comets, they appear to be fuzzy rather than sharp points of light. To help with his comet searching, Messier made a catalog of all the fuzzy objects he could find. We now know that many of these fuzzy noncomets are such things as galaxies, globular and open clusters, and nebulae. Often they are identified by their Messier number, such as M 31 or M 51. A more recent catalog of "fuzzy" objects is the NGC, or New General Catalog. The NGC objects listed in the tables are too far south to have been observed by Messier.

Table 13.2 contains Messier objects that we know today to be nebulae. A nebula is a large cloud of gas and dust that marks a region in space where stars are forming or dying. The table also indicates the constellations in which these nebulae are located. Write the letter "N," or make a blue dot, in each of the constellations in which a nebula is located on Chart 2. *Make this dot or letter as **small** as you can.*

3. *Where do most of the nebulae appear to be located in the sky?*

4. *Noting these positions of nebulae in the sky, where do you think our solar system is located in the Milky Way galaxy?*

F. Using the list of open clusters in Table 13.3, write the letter "O," or make a green dot, in each constellation on Chart 2 in which a cluster is located.

5. *Where are most of these open clusters located in the sky?*

6. *Noting the positions of these open clusters in the sky, where do you think our solar system is located in the Milky Way galaxy?*

G. Using the list of globular clusters in Table 13.4, write the letter "C," or make an orange dot, in each constellation on Chart 2 in which a globular cluster is located.

7. *Where are most of these globular clusters located in the sky?*

8. *Noting the positions of these globular clusters in the sky, where do you think our solar system is located in the Milky Way galaxy?*

9. *From what you now know about our galaxy, make a new diagram of how it might look from above and a diagram of how it might look from edge-on. Compare these drawings with the answers to questions 2, 4, 6, and 8: Are they consistent? If not, in what ways are they inconsistent? Also, compare these drawings with plates K and G, and describe any important differences. Discuss your drawings with others in your class to determine how your interpretation might differ from the interpretations made by your classmates.*

10. *Given the distribution of globular clusters on the sky, as described above, would you say we are in the center, or off to one side, of our galaxy? Describe your reasoning.*

11. *How do your refined sketches of the Milky Way compare with your predictions recorded at the beginning of this activity? Look back at them and modify, as necessary, your answers to the following:*

    a) *Are the stars spread evenly around the sky and throughout the Milky Way?*

    b) *Are we, as inhabitants of the Earth, inside or outside the Milky Way galaxy?*

    c) *If we are inside the Milky Way galaxy, are we in the center of the galaxy or off to one side?*

H. Using the list of galaxies in Table 13.5, write the letter "G," or make a red dot, in each constellation on Chart 2 in which a galaxy is located.

12. *How is the distribution of galaxies in the sky different from that of the other objects you have plotted? Discuss your answer.*

13. *From this distribution of galaxies, would you conclude that these galaxies are inside or outside of our galaxy?*

14. *There is an area of the sky that seems to contain no galaxies. Should we expect galaxies to appear in all directions around the sky? Can you think of some reasons why they may not be visible in certain directions?*

Table 13.1   Milky Way Constellations

The brightest parts of the Milky Way are located in the following constellations:

Auriga	Cygnus	Hercules	Norma	Gemini
Cepheus	Aquila	Carina	Taurus	Cassiopeia
Ophiuchus	Crux	Perseus	Pyxis	Serpens Cauda
Musca	Orion	Vela	Scutum	Canis Minor
Lupus	Sagittarius	Circinus	Monoceros	Lyra
Scorpius	Centaurus	Canis Major	Vulpecula	Corona Australis
Puppis	Sagitta	Ara	Serpens Caput	Triangulum Australe

Table 13.2   Nebulae

Messier No.*	Name	Constellation	Catalog No.*	Name	Constellation
1	Crab	Taurus	IC 2948		Centaurus
8	Lagoon	Sagittarius		Eta Carinae	Carina
16	Eagle	Serpens Cauda	NGC 2237	Rosette Nebula	Monoceros
17	Omega	Sagittarius	NGC 2392	Eskimo Nebula	Gemini
20	Trifid	Sagittarius	NGC 3132		Vela
27	Dumbbell	Vulpecula	NGC 3242	Ghost of Jupiter	Hydra
42	Great Nebula	Orion			
43		Orion			
57	Ring	Lyra			
76	Little Dumbbell	Perseus			
78		Orion			
97	Owl	Ursa Major			

*Messier No. refers to the catalog of nebulous objects produced by Charles Messier in the 1700s.

*NGC refers to the New General Catalog of nebulous objects produced by J. L. E. Dreyer in the late 1800s; IC refers to Index Catalog, which Dreyer used to supplement the NGC.

Table 13.3   Open Clusters

Messier No.	Name	Constellation	Messier No.	Name	Constellation
6	Butterfly	Scorpius	45	Pleiades	Taurus
7		Scorpius	46		Puppis
11		Scutum	47		Puppis
16		Serpens Cauda	48		Hydra
18		Sagittarius	50		Monoceros
21		Sagittarius	52		Cassiopeia
23		Sagittarius	67		Cancer
25		Sagittarius	93		Puppis
26		Scutum	103		Cassiopeia
29		Cygnus			
34		Perseus	**NGC No.**	**Name**	**Constellation**
35		Gemini			
36		Auriga	3114		Carina
37		Auriga	3532		Carina
38		Auriga	3766		Centaurus
39		Cygnus	4755	Jewel Box	Crux
41		Canis Major	6067		Norma
44	Beehive	Cancer	6231		Scorpius

Note: If you wish to know the proper pronounciation of the names of any
of the constellations, look in Appendix 1 or an unabridged dictionary.

Table 13.4	Globular Clusters				
Messier No.	Name	Constellation	Messier No.	Name	Constellation
2		Aquarius	68		Hydra
3		Canes Venatici	69		Sagittarius
4		Scorpius	70		Sagittarius
5		Serpens Cauda	71		Sagitta
9		Ophiuchus	72		Aquarius
10		Ophiuchus	75		Sagittarius
12		Ophiuchus	79		Lepus
13	Great Cluster	Hercules	80		Scorpius
14		Ophiuchus	92		Hercules
15		Pegasus	107		Ophiuchus
19		Ophiuchus			
22		Sagittarius			
28		Sagittarius	**NGC No.**	**Name**	**Constellation**
30		Capricornus	10447	Tucanae	Tucana
53		Coma Berenices	2808		Carina
54		Sagittarius	5139	Omega Centauri	Centaurus
55		Sagittarius	6397		Ara
56		Lyra	6752		Pavo
62		Ophiuchus			

Table 13.5	Galaxies				
Messier No.	Name	Constellation	Messier No.	Name	Constellation
31	Andromeda	Andromeda	84		Virgo
32		Andromeda	85		Coma Berenices
33		Triangulum	86		Virgo
49		Virgo	87		Virgo
51	Whirlpool	Canes Venatici	88		Coma Berenices
58		Virgo	89		Virgo
59		Virgo	90		Virgo
60		Virgo	94		Canes Venatici
61		Virgo	95		Leo
63		Canes Venatici	96		Leo
64	Blackeye	Coma Berenices	98		Coma Berenices
65		Leo	99		Coma Berenices
66		Leo	100		Coma Berenices
74		Pisces	101		Ursa Major
77		Cetus	102		Draco
81		Ursa Major	104	Sombrero	Virgo
82		Ursa Major	105		Leo
83		Hydra	106		Canes Venatici
			108		Ursa Major

1. Table 13.6 is a list of objects called pulsars. A pulsar is thought to be the rapidly spinning remnant of a collapsed star. Radio telescopes and sometimes other kinds of telescopes detect "bursts" of light every time the "beam" of light from the pulsar sweeps by the Earth. A pulsar may be a dense sphere of matter much, much smaller than the Earth, yet it may contain more mass than the Sun! A teaspoon filled with material from a pulsar would be about as massive as a mountain.

   Write the letter "P" or make a purple mark in each constellation on Chart 2 in which a pulsar is located.

   Do the positions of these pulsars indicate that they are located in our galaxy or outside of our galaxy? Explain the reasoning that led to your answer.

2. Table 13.7 is a list of objects called quasars. Quasars are objects that seem to emit photons at an *enormous* rate. Evidence suggests that this light originates in a very small region and yet equals the output of the largest galaxies. The true nature of quasars is not yet understood.

   Write the letter "Q" or make a brown mark in each constellation on Chart 2 in which a quasar is located.

   Do the positions of these quasars indicate that they are located inside or outside of our galaxy? Explain the reasoning that led to your answer.

Table 13.6 Pulsars

Catalog number (Name)*	Constellation
CP 0328	Perseus
PSR 0138+59	Cassiopeia
3C 144 (Crab Nebula)	Taurus
PSR 1929+10	Aquila
NP 0527	Taurus
CP 1919	Sagitta
PSR 0833-45	Vela
PSR 1530-53	Norma

Table 13.7 Quasars

Catalog number	Constellation
3C 48	Triangulum
3C 273	Virgo
3C 196	Lynx
NRAO 6635	Aquarius
3C 454.3	Pegasus
3C 380	Draco
3C 279	Virgo
3C 147	Auriga

*CP, PSR, and NP refer to various catalogs of pulsars; 3C refers to the third catalog of radio sources produced in the 1960s in Cambridge, England; NRAO refers to a catalog of radio sources compiled by the National Radio Astronomy Observatory in the United States.

CHAPTER 14

Galaxies and the Universe

Ask Around

Before the next class meeting, interview one or two adults. Ask them the following questions, making sure that you write down their responses as completely as possible. Provide them with paper so that they can make sketches if they want to. Bring the answers and drawings to the next class meeting and be prepared to talk about them.

1. What is "The Milky Way"?

2. You have probably heard astronomers talk about objects called "galaxies." What do you believe a galaxy is? Draw a picture of a galaxy. What do you think a galaxy is made of?

3. How many galaxies do you think are in the universe?

4. If you were in a rocket that could travel to the Sun in 1 hour, about how long would it take you to travel across a typical galaxy at the same average speed? About how long would it take you to travel from one galaxy to another?

Preview: In this chapter you will use the apparent brightness-distance relation and the size/distance ratio to (1) explore the universe beyond the Milky Way and to (2) measure the age of the universe.

Galaxies

On a very dark night in autumn, if you know exactly where to look you can see a faint patch of light in the constellation of Andromeda (see Figure 14.1). Even in a fairly large telescope this patch of light remains a blur to the eye (Figure 14.2).

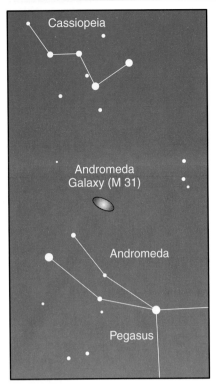

Figure 14.1
Location of faint patch of light in the constellation of Andromeda.

Figure 14.2 The Andromeda galaxy.

The nature of this and similar blurs of light was a puzzle to astronomers for many years. In 1775 the German philosopher Immanuel Kant (Ih-MAN-you-well Cahnt) guessed that some of these "nebulous stars" were isolated collections of stars, like our own Milky Way. Shapley's discovery of the size of the Milky Way (see Chapter 13) convinced him that these patches of light must be objects relatively close by, orbiting like satellites around the Milky Way. Other astronomers were just as certain that the galaxies were as large as the Milky Way. Some of them thought, therefore, that the Milky Way could not be as large as Shapley inferred.

In photographs that show considerably more detail than the eye can see, the blur of light in Andromeda, now known as the Andromeda galaxy, appears to be made up of stars, dust, and gas, just as is our own Milky Way (see Figure 14.3). But how far away is the Andromeda galaxy? And how big is it? The astronomer Edwin Hubble used Shapley's own tool, Cepheid variables, to answer those questions. In the process he demonstrated something that often happens in science: Even the best scientists can be right about some things and wrong about others. The only way to be sure of what is right is to make measurements and observations.

Hubble showed Shapley was wrong about the distance to the Andromeda galaxy. Hubble also showed that Shapley's critics were right about the size of the Andromeda galaxy—it is about the size of the Milky Way—but wrong about how big the Milky Way is—Shapley was right on that count. Astronomers now believe that the Andromeda galaxy is approximately 2×10^6 l.y. from the Earth. Like our own Milky Way galaxy, the Andromeda galaxy is about 10^5 l.y. in its largest dimension. These two galaxies are thus separated by a distance about 20 times the largest dimension of either galaxy. The Milky Way and the Andromeda galaxy are each vast collections of stars; the stars in each galaxy orbit around the center of their galaxy under their mutual gravitational attraction. Such a collection of stars is called a galaxy.

Figure 14.3
Another view of the Andromeda galaxy showing more detail.

Figure 14.4
A galaxy similar to the Andromeda galaxy.

Astronomers see a wide variety of galaxies in the sky. Some look similar to the Andromeda galaxy (see Figure 14.4). Others look like the Andromeda galaxy might look from different positions in space (Figure 14.5). Some galaxies have different shapes (Figures 14.6 and 14.7). Astronomers are uncertain as to why galaxies come in this wide variety of shapes and compositions. Astronomers have learned, however, that there is more mass in these galaxies than they see.

Dark Matter

There are two ways astronomers use to measure the mass of, that is, the amount of matter in, distant objects. One is based on the assumption that the mass of an object is proportional to the light it emits. Almost all stars emit light, for example—so starlight indicates the presence of mass. In the second way, the amount of mass is inferred from its gravitational effects.

Figure 14.5
Galaxies seen at various orientations: "edge on" and "face on."

Figure 14.6
Another type of galaxy.

Figure 14.7
Yet another type of galaxy.

Figures 14.8 and 14.9
The graph (14.9) below the photograph of the galaxy (14.8) shows the speeds determined from the Doppler shift associated with each part of the galaxy.

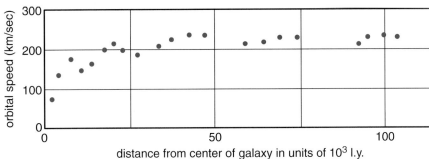

distance from center of galaxy in units of 10^3 l.y.

Both ways for measuring mass are illustrated by Figures 14.8 and 14.9. From Figure 14.8, you can be sure there is mass in the central portion of the galaxy because you see light coming from that region. Astronomers can use the Doppler shift (see Chapter 10) to measure the speed, toward or away from the Earth, of the stars orbiting at different distances from the center of a galaxy. If a galaxy is oriented almost "edge-on" to the Earth, the speed obtained from the Doppler shift of some of the stars that appear to be located on the long axis, as seen from the Earth, is approximately equal to the speeds of these stars around the center of their galaxy. Astronomers can then use Kepler's relation, as you did in Chapter 13, to estimate how much mass there is at different distances from the center of the galaxy. Such a graph of speed obtained from Doppler shifts vs. distance from the center of a galaxy is shown in Figure 14.9.

In this way, the astronomer Vera Rubin and her colleagues first discovered in the 1970s that a large fraction of the mass of most galaxies extends well beyond the visible portion of the galaxy. Otherwise, the speeds shown in Figure 14.9 would decrease for the points corresponding to distances farther from the center than the visible edge of the galaxy: Astronomers know of no other way that the measurements of speed could be as shown in Figure 14.9 except if they were caused by gravity, and gravity requires mass. The mass producing this effect is not visible in the photograph, however. This invisible mass is called dark matter. In a typical galaxy, there seems to be several times as much dark matter as visible matter. One model proposed for a galaxy consists of a core of visible, light-emitting mass surrounded by a giant halo of invisible matter. But no strong evidence has yet been found to support this model.

QUESTION: If a galaxy is surrounded by dark matter, how can we see the galaxy?

Astronomers were startled to realize that so much of the whole universe seems to be dark matter. What is this dark matter? No one knows.

Theories have ranged from black holes to tiny stars to exotic new kinds of subatomic particles.

The Big-Bang Model

In 1929, the American astronomer Milton Humason measured the Doppler shift of many galaxies. At the same time, Edwin Hubble also observed Cepheid variables in these galaxies. By comparing the Cepheids' apparent brightnesses with the wattages inferred from their periods, Hubble was able to infer their distances from the Earth. Hubble discovered that almost every galaxy he measured is moving away from the Milky Way with a speed proportional to the distance between the galaxy and the Milky Way. Thus, for example, a galaxy, twice as far from the Milky Way as another galaxy, is moving away from the Milky Way twice as fast as is the closer galaxy.

Hubble believed that the Milky Way was not a special galaxy, except for our living in it, and so he assumed that the universe must look about the same from any place within it. An observer in any other galaxy would thus see what Hubble saw—other galaxies would appear to be flying away from the observer's galaxy with speeds proportional to their distances from it. This model is called the expanding universe or Big-Bang model, described below.

If the galaxies are moving away from each other, then they would have been closer together in the past. At some definite time in the past, all the matter in the universe must have been crammed together. From the rate of expansion today, astronomers can estimate this time: about 10 to 20 billion years ago. It is called the beginning of the universe, or the Big Bang. In the 1920s, theoretical physicists, particularly the Russian Alexander Friedmann (Alec-SAND-er FREED-mahn) and the Belgian Georges Lemaitre (Jorj Le-MATE-ruh), worked out a mathematical theory of the expansion of the universe. This mathematical theory was proposed before Hubble's discovery

Whispers and Gas from the Big Bang

In 1948, the physicist George Gamow (Jorj GA-moff) and his colleagues predicted the existence of a "bath" of radio waves filling all space. According to their calculations, these radio waves would have been produced when the universe was approximately 100,000 years old. In 1965, this radiation was discovered accidentally by Arno Penzias (Arno PEN-zee-ess) and Robert Wilson, who won the Nobel Prize in physics for their finding. These radio waves have precisely the predicted spectrum, and provide very important evidence consistent with the Big-Bang model.

The universe is composed of various chemical elements, such as hydrogen, carbon, and oxygen. Scientists have long puzzled over how these elements were formed and what determined their relative proportions. Astronomers now think that the heavier chemical elements were formed in nuclear reactions at the centers of stars. However, the two lightest elements, hydrogen and helium, are thought to have been formed during the first few minutes after the Big Bang.

In the 1960s physicists calculated how much hydrogen and helium should have been produced according to the Big-Bang model. They concluded that about 75% of the mass of the universe is hydrogen and about 25% helium. (*All* the remaining chemical elements contribute much less than 1%!) These predicted numbers agree with observations combined with inferences of the abundance of the chemical elements in various objects in the universe, and provide further observational evidence consistent with the Big-Bang model.

and influenced his interpretation of his observations. It is still the most plausible model conceived to explain what astronomers see.

According to the Big-Bang model, the universe began in a sort of mighty explosion. However, this was not an ordinary explosion, in which a localized region of flying debris spreads out into a surrounding region of space. The Big-Bang model assumes there was no surrounding space for the universe to move into, since any such space would be part of the universe. The concept boggles the imagination, but it is easier (*not easy,* mind you) to visualize if one pictures individual objects in the universe. Starting with the Big Bang, all objects in the universe move away from each other, carried along by the expansion of space, just as the ink marks on a rubber band move apart as the band is stretched (Activity 14.2). In this analogy the rubber band represents space itself. This concept is *very* hard to understand, because it is not related at all to your everyday experience of the world.

Was there a Big Bang? No one knows, but you now know some of the evidence. This evidence is enough to convince most scientists that the universe began approximately 10–20 billion years ago and has been expanding ever since.

SUMMARY

Objects once thought to be inside our Milky Way galaxy turned out to be collections of stars comparable in size to the Milky Way. These objects have shapes that range from spirals to spheres and ellipsoids. They each contain billions of stars and are called galaxies. The distances to nearby galaxies can be determined by observing Cepheid variables in those galaxies. The periods of these variable stars indicate their wattages. From knowledge of the wattage of a star and its apparent brightness, the distance to the star, and to the galaxy, can be estimated using the apparent brightness-distance relation from Chapter 10.

The orbital speeds of stars in some galaxies can be determined by observing the Doppler shifts of the light coming from them if they are oriented almost "edge-on" to us. Kepler's relation then allows us to estimate the

mass of the galaxy. The result implies that there is more mass around the galaxy than can be seen. This unseen material is called "dark matter."

Edwin Hubble showed that the farther away a galaxy is the faster it is moving away from us. This observation has been interpreted to mean that the universe is expanding, and that it was born in a "Big Bang." Not enough is yet known to allow astronomers to infer the fate of the universe—whether it will keep expanding forever or some day collapse in a "Big Crunch."

Homework

1. A supernova results from the explosion of a star. (Which stars explode and why are fascinating questions, but we do not discuss them in this book.) The supernova of 1987 was a star that exploded in the Large Magellanic Cloud (LMC). The supernova's greatest apparent magnitude was +3.0. The LMC is about 170,000 l.y. from the Earth.

   a) Determine the supernova's greatest wattage.

   b) How many times larger is this maximum wattage than the Sun's wattage?

2. The diameter of the image of galaxy B on a photographic plate is 1/10 the diameter of an image of the Andromeda galaxy taken with the same telescope. The period and apparent brightness of a Cepheid variable in galaxy B indicate that the star is 15 times farther away from the Earth than is a Cepheid of the same period observed in the Andromeda galaxy. What do you conclude is the distance from the Earth to galaxy B and why?

3. Imagine that you are an astronomer and that you have discovered a galaxy with a Doppler shift that indicates it is moving toward us; other measurements indicate that the galaxy is 300 million light-years away from the Earth. What potentially important discovery have you made? What would be a responsible action for you to take?

SELF-TEST

1. Which galaxies, aside from the Milky Way, can be seen from some location on the Earth with the naked eye?

2. How are the distances to nearby galaxies determined?

3. a) A Cepheid variable is observed in galaxy G to have a period of 11 days. A different Cepheid variable is observed in galaxy H to have a period of 6.5 days and appears brighter than the variable star in galaxy G. Which galaxy is closer to us?

   b) Through the same telescope, the image of galaxy G appears the same size as the image of galaxy H. Which galaxy has the larger diameter? Explain your reasoning.

4. In photographs made with the same telescope, an image of the Andromeda galaxy appears about 10 mm long and the image of another galaxy appears 2 mm long. If the Andromeda galaxy is 2 million light-years away from the Earth, how far away from us would you estimate the second galaxy to be? What assumption did you use to make your estimate?

ACTIVITY 14.1 DETERMINING GALAXY SIZES AND DISTANCES

PURPOSE

To estimate the size of our Milky Way galaxy and the distance to other galaxies using the apparent brightness-distance relation and size/distance ratios.

WHAT DO YOU THINK?

Look at plates F (M 51) and G (M 31). Both of these photographs were made with the same telescope; therefore the scale is the same for both pictures.

P1. *Based on these pictures only, decide which galaxy is farther away from the Earth. Describe your reasoning.*

P2. *Approximately how many times farther from the Earth is the more distant galaxy than the nearer galaxy?*

PART A ESTIMATING GALAXY SIZES AND DISTANCES USING APPARENT BRIGHTNESSES

PURPOSE

To estimate the size of our galaxy and the distances to other galaxies by using the apparent brightness-distance nomogram.

MATERIALS

Plate E
ruler
apparent brightness-distance nomogram

PROCEDURE

Some stars vary noticeably in apparent brightness, appearing more and less bright over time, while remaining the same distance from us. These are called "variable stars," of which there are several types. One type is a "Cepheid" variable star (see Chapter 13), which varies in apparent brightness over periods of days or weeks. Another type of variable star is called a "nova." Still another type of variable is called a "supernova." All of these types of variable stars have been used to determine celestial distances; here we will make use of yet another type called an "RR Lyrae" (arr-arr-LIE-ray) variable star.

RR Lyrae stars are much larger than average (that is, they are "giant") stars whose apparent brightnesses go through a full cycle in less than a day. They are named after the constellation Lyra, because the first such variable star was discovered in that constellation. They are also called "cluster variables" because they are generally found in globular clusters. By studying the light from RR Lyrae stars, astronomers have estimated that each of these stars has an average wattage of about 50 Suns.

Use this information and the nomogram your teacher gives you (see also Activity 10.3) to answer the following questions.

1. *Refer to plate E. In the constellation of Sagittarius is M 22, one of the brightest and largest appearing of the Messier globular clusters. Is M 22 one of the nearest or one of the farthest clusters from us? (Hint: If all globular clusters were about the same size, what would you think their apparent sizes on photographs would tell us about their distances?)*

2. *One of the RR Lyrae stars in M 22 has an apparent magnitude of +13. How far is it from us?*

3. *Also in Sagittarius is M 75, one of the dimmest and smallest appearing of the Messier globular clusters. Is it one of the nearest or one of the farthest clusters from us?*

4. *One of the RR Lyrae stars in M 75 has an apparent magnitude of +18. How many light-years is it from us?*

5. *You have determined the distance to one of the nearest and one of the farthest globular clusters. If you assumed that the nearest cluster were on one edge of our galaxy and the farthest cluster at the opposite edge of our galaxy, what would you estimate the diameter of our galaxy to be?*

In the Southern Hemisphere, two irregularly shaped galaxies are visible in the sky. They are called the Large Magellanic Cloud (LMC) and the Small Magellanic Cloud (SMC). These collections of stars were observed in 1520 by Magellan on his voyage of exploration and are named in his honor (see Chapter 13). At that time they were not recognized as galaxies. We now know that these collections of stars are galaxies near our Milky Way galaxy. Through a telescope, they have been observed to have their own globular clusters and these clusters contain some RR Lyrae-type stars.

6. *An RR Lyrae star in one of the clusters that belongs to the LMC has an apparent magnitude of about +23. How far is this galaxy from the Earth?*

7. *A Cepheid variable star, which has an average wattage of 4×10^{30} watts, is visible in the Andromeda galaxy. (The Andromeda galaxy is a collection of stars similar to the Milky Way.) This star has an average apparent magnitude of +20. What is the distance from us to this star (and, therefore, to the Andromeda galaxy)?*

PART B ESTIMATING DISTANCES TO GALAXIES USING SIZE/DISTANCE RATIOS

PURPOSE

To determine the distances to some nearby galaxies by using size/distance ratios.

MATERIALS

Plates F, G, and L through P
metric ruler

PROCEDURE

A. Figure 14.10 shows the size/distance ratio of a galaxy whose diameter is labeled XY. The size of the image of this galaxy as seen in the telescope is labeled AB. The length of the telescope is labeled L; the distance from the telescope to the galaxy, D, can then be found using the relation that you discovered in Activity 6.3, Part A, question 7, between the size/distance ratio for an object and the object's image. This relation can be used here only because all galaxies have small size/distance ratios as seen from the Earth.

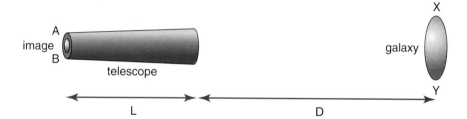

Figure 14.10

In the following problems, assume that a galaxy has a diameter ("size" in the size/distance ratio) of 100,000 l.y. (about the same diameter as the Milky Way galaxy has). This assumption, although not strictly valid, allows you to obtain reasonable estimates for the distances to other galaxies. Also assume that the size of the galaxies in the photographs is the size the image appears in the telescope (line AB in Figure 14.10).

Plates F and G were taken with a telescope with a *length of 310 cm* (122 in.).

1. *Plate G is a photo of the Andromeda galaxy (M 31). Measure the longest diameter of the image (in centimeters).*

2. *From the image size and telescope length, calculate the size/distance ratio for M 31.*

3. *The Andromeda galaxy is how many of its diameters away from us?*

4. *What is your estimate of the distance to the Andromeda galaxy?*

5. *Plate F is a photo of the Whirlpool galaxy (M 51). Measure the longest diameter of the image (in centimeters).*

6. *Calculate the size/distance ratio for M 51.*

7. *M 51 is how many of its diameters away from us?*

8. *What is your estimate of the distance from us to M 51?*

B. Tape plate G to a wall. Hold plate F at arm's length (about 75 cm). Move away from or toward plate G until the image of M 51 appears as big as the image of M 31.

9. *How many times farther from you must M 31 be than M 51 for them to appear to be the same size? Discuss your results.*

10. *Determine the distance to the galaxies on the following plates. These plates were also made with a telescope with a focal length of 310 cm.*

   Plate L —M 101   Plate M—M 104   Plate N—NGC 5371
   Plate O—Hercules galaxy cluster (measure only one galaxy)
   Plate P—NGC 4565 (edge-on spiral)

ACTIVITY 14.2

THE UNIVERSE ON A RUBBER BAND

PURPOSE

To model the expansion of the universe with a rubber band.

WHAT DO YOU THINK?

P1. *A rubber band is marked at 1-cm intervals. The band is stretched from both ends so that the mark originally 1 cm from the center of the band moves a distance of 1 cm farther from the center of the band. How far from the center will the mark originally 2 cm from the center move?*

MATERIALS

   1 large rubber band
   1 pair of scissors
   1 meterstick
   1 pen

PROCEDURE

A. Cut the rubber band so that you have a single length of band at least 20 cm (8 in) long.

B. Lay the rubber strip next to the ruler. Do *not* stretch the strip. Use the pen to make a mark on the strip every 1 cm. Each mark represents a galaxy.

C. Select a mark to represent our galaxy, the Milky Way. Grasp both ends of the rubber strip and hold it next to the ruler so that the mark representing the Milky Way is next to the 1-cm line. See Figure 14.11. Stretch the strip until the mark that was at the 2-cm line is at the 3-cm line. Be sure to keep the Milky Way mark next to the 1-cm line.

Figure 14.11

D. The mark that moved from the 2-cm line to the 3-cm line increased its distance from the Milky Way mark by 1 cm; it also doubled its distance from the Milky Way mark (from 1 cm away to 2 cm away).

1. *How did the positions of the marks at the 3-, 4-, and 5-cm lines change in relation to the Milky Way mark? Did the other marks move 1 cm farther away from the Milky Way mark or double their distances from the Milky Way or move some other distance?*

E. Select another mark to represent the Milky Way. Repeat steps C and D.

2. *How did the positions of the marks at the 3-, 4-, and 5-cm lines change in relation to the Milky Way mark? Did the other marks move 1 cm farther away from the Milky Way mark or double their distances from the Milky Way or move some other distance?*

3. *How do the results described in questions 1 and 2 compare to each other? Were the distances moved the same or different? If different, by what percents did they differ? How do these results compare to your prediction in P1?*

4. *Does it take the same time or different times for the marks at the 2-, 3-, 4-, and 5-cm lines to move to their final positions? If different, by what percents do the times differ? In general, then, how are the speeds of the marks related to the changes in position of the marks?*

5. *Based on your answers to questions 1–4, do you think it is necessary for our galaxy, the Milky Way, to be located in a "special" position, such as the center of the universe, for us to observe the motions of the galaxies as modeled in this activity?*

PURPOSE

To study the relation between the distances to galaxies and the motions of galaxies, and to discuss the general structure of the universe.

WHAT DO YOU THINK?

As you can tell from looking at photographs of galaxies, some of them appear to be smaller than others. Most often those that appear smaller are farther away. As the distances to galaxies increase, it is difficult to determine their apparent sizes. Astronomers have therefore developed a different method for calculating the distances to very distant galaxies—a method that does not involve the sizes of galaxies.

Most astronomical knowledge is based on the study of light. One piece of information that can be learned from studying the light from an astronomical object is the speed at which the object is moving toward or away from us. We can determine this speed by means of the "Doppler effect" or the Doppler shift (see Chapter 10). By studying the Doppler shift in the light from galaxies, astronomers can determine their speeds toward or away from us. By using this effect, an American astronomer, Edwin Hubble, discovered a remarkable relation between galactic speeds and their distances. This relation is easy to find when the data are presented in a graph.

Scientists often use graphs to illustrate and present their data to help themselves and others to better understand their experiment. This activity will give you a glimpse into motions of objects in the universe and it will help you with graphing skills. Being able to graph information is an important skill for many kinds of work. Let's consider an example first.

Imagine that you often have friends over to watch videos. You usually serve 8-oz. cups of soda to your friends. In the past you have entertained groups of two to six people, but this coming week you are entertaining seven people and you are not certain how much soda you should buy for this group. Fortunately, you remember your friends' past soda consumption. To estimate how much soda to provide for the upcoming party, you can graph past consumption and use this graph to predict how much to buy.

Using your data from past parties, you plot the number of people at each party on the horizontal axis (often called the "X" axis) and the amount of soda consumed at each party on the vertical axis (or "Y" axis). At the party attended by two friends, for example, your friends drank a total of 40 oz. of soda. So you put a point on the graph that corresponds to 2 on the X axis and 40 on the Y axis. After plotting all the points, you draw a straight line that passes near all of the points on the graph. If the line is straight and passes close to all of the points, you may have uncovered what scientists call a "linear" relationship. If this relation holds for future events, the graph will enable you to make useful predictions about the future.

P1. *Examine the graph. How much soda should you buy for the party with seven guests?*

No. of Persons Attending	Amount of Soda Consumed (oz)
6	152
2	40
5	128
4	88
3	64

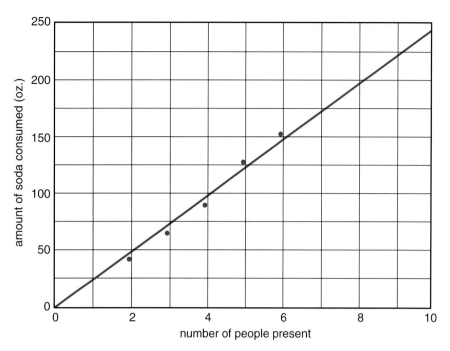

You can use a similar graph to begin to understand information that was gathered by astronomers.

You will use the best available values for the distances to some galaxies and their speeds to construct a graph similar to the one described above. From this graph you will be able to predict the distance to even more distant galaxies in much the same manner that you predicted how much soda to buy for your party.

MATERIALS

Plates F, J, and L through P
2 sheets of millimeter graph paper

PROCEDURE

A. Refer to plates F, L, M , and N. You will need the distance information from your answers to question 10 from Activity 14.1, Part B. Distance will be expressed in units of millions of light-years (ml.y.).

1. *M 51 (F) is moving away from our location in the Milky Way galaxy at a speed of 900 km/sec. How far away from us is it?*

2. *M 101 (L) is moving away from us at 390 km/sec. How far away from us is it?*

3. *NGC 4565 (P) is moving away from us at 1,200 km/sec. How far away from us is it?*

4. *NGC 5371 (N) is moving away from us at 2,700 km/sec. How far away from us is it?*

5. *Plot a graph of the information in questions 1–4 (as well as in your answers to them) on the graph paper. Put speed on the vertical scale and distance on the horizontal scale. Your teacher will give you additional instructions on plotting the graph.*

6. *From this graph, what conclusions can you draw about the relation between the distance of a galaxy from us and the speed with which it is moving away from us?*

7. *Using your graph and the value for the distance to one galaxy in the Hercules cluster (Plate O) from question 10 in Activity 14.1, Part B, find the speed with which that galaxy is moving away from us. What is this speed?*

B. Use your graph to answer the following questions:

8. *M 66 (J) is moving away from us at 600 km/sec. How far away from us is it?*

9. *M 87, in the Virgo cluster of galaxies, is moving away from us at 1,300 km/sec. How far away from us is it?*

HOMEWORK

Use the data from Table 14.1 on the next page to plot a second graph with distance on the horizontal axis and speed on the vertical axis. Use this graph to answer the following questions:

1. As time goes on, are the galaxies getting farther apart, closer together, or maintaining the same distance from each other? Explain your reasoning.

2. How, if at all, does the speed of a galaxy relative to us depend on its distance from us?

3. Do the data points on your second graph fit perfectly on a straight line? If your data points do not all fall on a straight line, what are some of the possible reasons?

4. Use your graph to determine the distances (in ml.y.) to the following galaxies:

   a) M 65, which is moving away from us at 700 km/sec.

   b) M 81, which is moving away from us at 140 km/sec.

   c) Quasar 3C 273, which is moving away from us at 50,000 km/sec.

   d) NGC 1275, in the Perseus cluster, which is moving away from us at 5,300 km/sec.

   e) Quasar 3C 9, which is moving away from us at 160,000 km/sec.

5. Are the numbers you calculated in question 4 exact distances to these galaxies? Give some of the reasons why or why not.

6. From these data and/or your graph, determine what you think may be the "age of the universe." Explain your reasoning.

7. Is the universe expanding, contracting, or remaining the same size? Discuss the reason(s) for your answer.

Table 14.1 Some Galaxies That Appear Relatively Bright

NGC no.*/ Messier no.	Distance (ml.y.)	Speed (km/sec)	NGC no./ Messier no.	Distance (ml.y.)	Speed (km/sec)
55	10	120	4486 /87	72	1,190
247	10	620	4594 /104	55	910
253	14	520	4631	39	630
300	8	650	4649 /60	72	1,180
628 /74	55	520	4736 /94	22	360
1068 /77	81	540	4826 /64	23	370
1291	49	530	4945	23	280
1313	17	270	5055 /63	35	570
2403	12	310	5128	23	260
2903	31	490	5194 /51	36	570
3034 /82	12	430	5236 /83	22	280
3521	42	650	5457 /101	25	390
3627 /66	39	620	6744	42	680
4258	33	540	6946	22	350
4449	16	260	7793	14	250
4472 /49	72	850			

Odds & Ends

What Do You Think?

A couple has had four male children in a row and is now expecting a fifth child. Which of the following statements about this next baby is likely to be true?

1. The couple probably will have another boy.

2. The couple probably will have a girl.

3. It is equally likely for the couple's next baby to be a boy or a girl.

    Explain why you selected the statement that you did.

What Do Your Classmates Believe?

Before the next class meeting, take a survey of five students in your school who are not using this textbook and who have not already responded to the statements below. Ask the students if either or both of these statements apply to them; keep track of the total number of people who answered "yes" or "no." Bring your tally sheet to the next class meeting.

"I read my horoscope in the newspaper almost every day."

"I believe that the position of the Sun, Moon, stars, and planets partly affects my personality and the events in my life."

Preview: In this chapter you will be introduced to the basic concepts of probability by examining the outcomes of tossing coins and tossing dice. You will then use probability theory to determine if an astrological prediction of the personality of an individual, based on the person's birthdate and birthplace, is more accurate than a prediction made by simple guessing.

Table 15.1	
First toss	**Second toss**
H	H
T	T

Table 15.2	
First toss	**Second toss**
H	H
T	T

Table 15.3
All possible outcomes of tossing one coin twice

HH	HT	TH	TT

Probability

Suppose you toss a coin twice. How many different outcomes are possible? First, look at the possibilities for each toss, listed in Table 15.1. On the first toss, the coin can come up either heads (H) or tails (T); the same is true for the second toss. Because for "fair" coins, coins not rigged or otherwise changed to produce a desired outcome, the result of one toss does not affect any future tosses, either of the results of the first toss can be followed by either of the results of the second toss. These possibilities are indicated by the arrows pointing from the "First toss" column to the "Second toss" column in Table 15.2. For example, H on the first toss can be followed by either H or T on the second toss.

All of the possible outcomes of tossing a coin twice are shown in Table 15.3. In this table, the letter sequence represents the order in which the coin landed. For example, HT means that heads came up on the first toss and tails came up on the second toss. Table 15.3 shows that there are four possible outcomes for tossing one coin twice. How many ways are there to get one head and one tail? Although there is only one way to get two heads (HH) and only one way to get two tails (TT), there are two ways to get one head and one tail, a head on the first toss followed by a tail on the second toss (HT), or a tail on the first toss followed by a head on the second toss (TH). Activity 15.1 provides direct experience with the behavior of coins.

How can you describe these outcomes in terms of their likelihood? Mathematicians have developed the theory of probability for this purpose. They have defined the probability of any outcome as a number that must lie between 0 and 1. A probability of zero means that the outcome cannot occur—it is impossible; a probability of 1 means that the outcome will definitely occur—in fact, it will *always* occur. (Imagine a coin rigged so that it always lands showing "heads"; for any toss, such a coin has a probability of 0 of showing "tails" and a probability of 1 of showing "heads.") If all outcomes of an "experiment" are *equally* likely—the coins are not rigged or "loaded"—and no outcome affects any other outcome, then the probability that a desired outcome will occur can be determined by dividing the number of outcomes that are "desired" by the total number of ways the experiment can turn out. Suppose you consider tossing one coin twice. There are four possible patterns—a total number of four possible outcomes for the experiment. (See Table 15.3.) In only one of these four possible outcomes do both tosses result in a head. Therefore, the probability of getting two heads is one divided by four, or 1/4. Note that the probability of this outcome is within the limits set for the probability of any outcome: 1/4 lies between 0 and 1.

Question: If you toss one coin twice, what is the probability of getting two tails? of getting a head followed by a tail? of getting a head and a tail in any order?

Question: Suppose you toss a "fair" coin three times. How many different outcomes, or patterns, are possible? How many patterns are made up of one head and two tails? one tail and two heads? three tails? three heads? What is the probability of getting three heads?

✳ The Universe in Your Hands

Question: If the probability of parents having a child of a particular sex is 1/2, and if the sex of a child has no effect on the sex of any child born after it, what is the probability of their having three girls in a row? of having three boys in a row?

To help you understand better how probabilities are determined for "independent events," that is, outcomes that are not affected by previous results, such as tossing a coin, let us determine the probability of getting three heads if you toss a coin three times. The possible outcomes for a three-toss "experiment" using one coin are shown in Table 15.4. There are eight possible outcomes for this experiment. The outcome of three heads occurs only once. Therefore, the probability of getting three heads in three tosses of one coin is one divided by eight, or 1/8.

Consider now the following question: What is the probability of getting two heads in three tosses of one coin? You can look back at Table 15.4 and determine the probability rather quickly: there are three ways to get two heads, out of eight possible outcomes. The probability is therefore 3/8 for getting two heads in three tosses. However, Table 15.4 was prepared for you—you did not have to fill it in yourself. If you did not have Table 15.4, how might you determine the probability?

The desired outcome of two heads from three tosses of a coin occurs in *all* of the following outcomes:

HHT   HTH   THH

The desired outcome is not a unique event: there are three different outcomes that are acceptable as the desired outcome, that is, an outcome that contains two heads. However, only one outcome can occur in a single three-toss experiment. For example, if the result of three tosses of one coin is HHT, it cannot be HTH or THH. But each outcome that is acceptable as the desired outcome is a unique event, a single result out of eight possible outcomes for three tosses of one coin. Therefore, each acceptable outcome for the series of three events—HHT, HTH, and THH—has a probability of 1/8. Because there are three possible ways to get the desired outcome, each with a probability of 1/8, you can calculate the overall probability for the desired outcome by *adding* the separate probabilities: 1/8 + 1/8 + 1/8 = 3/8. Remember, though, that this procedure works only for *independent* events; if the outcome of any toss of a coin affected the outcome of any subsequent toss, the coin tosses would not be independent and the procedure used above could not be used.

Without looking at Table 15.4, can you determine the probability of getting at least one tail in a three-toss series? Consider that getting at least one tail means that only one outcome is not acceptable, three heads (HHH); every other outcome of a three-toss series includes at least one tail, the desired outcome. Since each of the remaining seven possible outcomes includes at least one tail, the probability of getting at least one tail in three tosses is 7/8, which is the sum of the probabilities of all acceptable outcomes: 1/8 + 1/8 + 1/8 + 1/8 + 1/8 + 1/8 + 1/8 = 7/8.

Keep in mind that you are assuming that the coin tossed is equally likely to come up heads or tails. If a coin came up heads every time you flipped it, then you might suspect it was "rigged"; if it were rigged, you

Table 15.4			
All possible outcomes of tossing one coin three times			
HHH	HHT	HTH	THH
HTT	THT	TTH	TTT

The Multiplication Principle and Probabilities

The outcomes for a three-toss experiment are provided for you in Table 15.4, so it is relatively easy to find the probability of any desired outcome. When the numbers involved in an experiment get large, it is time-consuming (and boring) to list all possible outcomes. Is there an easier way? In some cases, the answer is "yes." When the coin tosses are *independent* of one another, that is, the outcome of a toss has no effect on the next toss, the mathematics is easy. Each time you toss the coin, the probability that you will get heads is the same: 1/2. How can you use this probability and the fact that the coin tosses are independent events to determine more easily the probability of getting a head on each of three tosses? Notice that the probability of getting three heads in three tosses, 1/8, can also be obtained by multiplying the probabilities of getting heads for each individual toss, 1/2 × 1/2 × 1/2 = 1/8. This is no coincidence or trick; it is derived from a basic mathematical rule sometimes called the "multiplication principle."

The multiplication principle could also be called the "special addition principle." Why? First, the multiplication principle is only used for determining the probabilities of independent events. That fact makes the principle "special," since many events are not independent. Second, multiplication is a shorthand form of addition. Consider this simple problem: How many sneakers do you have if you have four pairs of sneakers? Since one pair of sneakers contains two sneakers, the total number of sneakers in four pairs can be found by addition: 2 + 2 + 2 + 2 = 8. But you can calculate the total number of sneakers more quickly by multiplication: 4 × 2 = 8.

The multiplication principle can be stated as follows: If some outcome can occur in A different ways and some subsequent, independent outcome can occur in B different ways, then the total number of different ways these outcomes can occur equals A × B. This reasoning can be extended indefinitely for as many successive outcomes as you need to consider. For three successive tosses of one coin, there are two possible outcomes for the first toss, two possible outcomes for the second toss, and two possible outcomes for the third toss. Applying the multiplication principle, the total number of possible outcomes for three tosses is 2 × 2 × 2 = 8.

The desired outcome of the three-toss experiment, three heads, can occur only if a head comes up on each toss. For three successive tosses of one coin, there is only one desired outcome possible on the first toss (heads), one desired outcome possible on the second toss (heads), and one desired outcome possible on the third toss (heads). Applying the multiplication principle again, the total number of desired outcomes that can occur is 1 × 1 × 1 = 1. Thus, an examination of the number of desired outcomes and the total number of possible outcomes reveals that there is only one outcome out of a total of eight that fits the description of the desired outcome—all three tosses come out heads. Therefore, the probability of getting three heads by tossing a coin three times is 1 out of 8, or 1 divided by 8, or 1/8.

An alternate way to calculate the probability of any outcome for a series of independent events, such as the coin tosses previously mentioned, is to multiply the probabilities of the desired outcomes of the individual events together. You can test the validity of this method by checking to see if it yields the same answer as does the method discussed above. Since the probability of getting a head on one toss of a coin is 1/2, you can use the multiplication method to find that the probability of getting three heads from three tosses of a coin is 1/2 × 1/2 × 1/2 = 1/8. This answer, 1/8, does agree with the result obtained in the preceding paragraph.

You can always check the reliability of an answer found by multiplication by using addition. But it can be tedious.

would have to refigure all the odds (or get another coin). Remember also that coin tosses are *independent* events: a coin has no "memory" of how it landed on previous tosses. The outcome of one toss or of 100 tosses of a coin has no effect on the next toss. If, by chance, you do get heads on each of 100 tosses, and the coin is not rigged, the probability of getting heads on the next toss is just 1/2. Any time you toss a coin, there are two possible outcomes, of which only one will occur. The coin doesn't "know" that it's been tossed 100 times or that it's shown heads 100 times in a row. The fact that *you* know what the coin has done influences only your personal feelings about the likelihood of the next toss; your knowledge and feelings have no effect on the coin's behavior. A coin never remembers and it doesn't care how you feel!

Suppose you had been tossing two dice instead of tossing a coin. Each die (singular of dice) has six faces. Each face has a number of dots on it, from one to six, with no two faces having the same number of dots. There are 36 possible outcomes for one toss of two dice; these are listed in Table 15.5.

The memories of dice are just as bad as those of coins: they have no memories. A die, like a coin, behaves independently: a die is unaffected by the results of previous trials. Dice are also independent of one another: If you toss two dice at the same time, the outcome for one die is not affected by the outcome for the other die. The probability of any one outcome of a toss of a die is the same as for any other outcome; for example, for either die a three is just as likely to come up as any other number. However, if a die is rigged ("loaded"), some outcome will be more likely to occur than another. Activity 15.2 investigates the behavior of unrigged dice.

Question: (See Table 15.5.) Assume that two dice are not rigged and behave independently when they are tossed. How many patterns can the two dice display? How many patterns have a total of 10 dots each? What is the probability of tossing a 10? a 12? Which total is "easier" (more probable) to toss, a four or a five? Why? Suppose you had tossed four sevens in a row, what is the probability you would get a seven on the next toss?

So far, we have used the theory of probability only to investigate the outcomes of tossing coins and dice. However, probability theory has much wider applications. A concern of critical importance to scientists is the accuracy of a theory. For a theory to be a useful scientific tool, it must make accurate predictions about the phenomena for which it was developed. To learn how the theory of probability can be used to determine whether a theory is useful, we will consider astrology and astronomy.

What Do the Stars Tell Us?

Astronomy is often confused with astrology. The two are quite different. Although both subjects deal with the positions of planets and stars, they have different goals and use different methods. By considering these differences, you will gain a better understanding of the methods of science. Strangely, these differences can be studied easily by considering a common property of these subjects: Astronomy and astrology both make predictions. You will examine the results of the predictions of both: Are the predictions accurate virtually without exception, based on an understanding of the basic phenomena, or do the predictions turn out no better than could be expected purely on the basis of chance? To answer that question, you will employ the theory of probability, drawing upon your experience with tossing coins and dice.

What Is Astrology?

The most fundamental claim made by astrology is that the relative positions of the Sun, Moon, planets, and stars at the time of a person's birth have an influence on the personality of the individual and the future pattern of that person's life. Furthermore, astrologers claim that the positions of celestial objects continue to exert influence on a person's life day by day, the pattern

Table 15.5: Possible results of rolling two dice

First Die	Second Die	Sum of dots on both dice
1	1	2
	2	3
	3	4
	4	5
	5	6
	6	7
2	1	3
	2	4
	3	5
	4	6
	5	7
	6	8
3	1	4
	2	5
	3	6
	4	7
	5	8
	6	9
4	1	5
	2	6
	3	7
	4	8
	5	9
	6	10
5	1	6
	2	7
	3	8
	4	9
	5	10
	6	11
6	1	7
	2	8
	3	9
	4	10
	5	11
	6	12

Astrological Signs

You may have seen the astrology columns that appear in most newspapers. You may even know your own astrological sign. But what is an astrological sign?

Astrological signs are also called Sun signs or the signs of the zodiac. Originally they referred to the constellation that the Sun appeared within on the date a person was born. As a result of the Earth's movement around the Sun, the Sun is "seen" against different constellations at different times of the year. (You plotted the apparent path of the Sun, the ecliptic, against the background of the stars on your celestial sphere in Activity 3.1.) By 2,500 years ago, Babylonian observers had determined the apparent path of the Sun on the celestial sphere and found that it passed through 12 constellations. (The constellations had already been named; some of the constellation names, such as the bull and the scorpion, are thought to be very ancient, perhaps more than 4,000 years old.) Astrologers then divided the ecliptic into 12 sections, one for each of the ecliptic constellations. The set of 12 ecliptic sections, or signs, was named the zodiac. Astrologers didn't begin to refer to the zodiac by name until about 2,500 years ago. Table 15.6 lists the zodiac signs and the birthdates associated with them, as used in many astrological columns in U.S. newspapers.

Some astrology charts differ by a day from a few of the dates shown in Table 15.6, based on when the astrologer considers the Sun to have entered or left a sign. One of the reasons for these differences is that the Sun has a definite angular size, about 0.5°, which means the Sun cannot pass instantly from one sign to the next. Just as a car takes a certain amount of time to cross a state line while traveling on a highway, with part of the car in Wisconsin and the rest in Minnesota, the Sun takes time, about 12 hours, to cross the dividing line between two signs. Twelve hours is 1/2 day, which by "rounding off" from 1/2 to 1 can account for a one-day difference. Another reason for variations in the dates is that the boundaries between signs can be slightly different on charts used by different astrologers. Many astrologers resolve the problem of assigning signs to persons born on the first or last date of a sign by placing the person under two signs. For example, a person born on June 20 would be placed under both Gemini and Cancer. A person born on June 21 would also be placed under both of these signs.

Table 15.6		
ARIES Mar 21–Apr 19	TAURUS Apr 20–May 20	GEMINI May 21–June 20
CANCER June 21–July 22	LEO July 23–Aug 22	VIRGO Aug 23–Sept 22
LIBRA Sept 23–Oct 22	SCORPIO Oct 23–Nov 21	SAGITTARIUS Nov 22–Dec 21
CAPRICORN Dec 22–Jan 19	AQUARIUS Jan 20–Feb 18	PISCES Feb 19–Mar 20

of the influence changing as the positions of the celestial objects change. In addition, the influence exerted by the specific arrangement on the sky of celestial objects on a particular day differs according to the astrological sign of the person.

Astrologers make predictions for the future of people's lives by using horoscopes, which are charts of the positions of the Sun, Moon, and planets relative to the astrological signs. Astrologers claim to be able to predict an individual's personality and the general trends of a person's life by using the date, time, and place of birth of the individual. The date of birth is used to determine the positions of the celestial objects relative to each other and to the astrological signs. The place of birth locates the person on the Earth's surface, which, in combination with the time of birth, determines where the celestial objects and astrological signs were in the sky relative to the horizon, for example, whether a sign was rising or setting. Astrologers claim that the rising of a particular sign at the time of birth influences an individual's personality and life.

Astrologers make daily predictions for people born under each of the 12 astrological signs by using the pattern of celestial objects and signs for each day and by using the way these patterns supposedly affect people born under each sign. Apparently where a person lives is not a factor, since the same astrologer will have the same predictions printed in newspapers nationwide. Nor does it seem to matter who the persons are or what they do. The predictions made by an astrologer apply to all persons born under the same sign. Thus, a 37-year-old bank executive living in Los Angeles supposedly has the same basic future on a particular day as a 53-year-old homeless person living on the streets of New York City, as long as they were born under the same sign. Indeed, since there are nearly equal numbers of people born under every sign, about 1/12 of the population is covered by the prediction for a particular sign. The United States has a population of about 275,000,000. The number of people born under a particular sign is therefore 275,000,000 × 1/12, or about 23,000,000 per sign. Thus, when an astrologer makes a prediction for people born under any sign, he or she is actually predicting the same type of day for 23,000,000 Americans. Applied to the total world population of more than 6,000,000,000, the daily prediction for each sign is being made for 6,000,000,000 × 1/12 = about 500,000,000 people! No astrologer whose predictions are published nationally in U.S. newspapers includes "caution" messages with the predictions,

The President and the Scientist

On February 12, 1809, two babies were born only hours apart on opposite sides of the Atlantic Ocean. One was born into a poor farming family in Kentucky, the other into a wealthy physician's family in England. The Kentucky baby was named Abraham Lincoln; the British baby was christened Charles Robert Darwin. Lincoln—with only about 1 year of formal education—became a lawyer, then a U.S. congressman, and finally president of the United States. Darwin attended university where he studied to be a minister (he first tried medicine but could not endure seeing children in pain), but his interest in science led him to be accepted as the naturalist for the 5-year round-the-world voyage of the British survey ship Beagle. Partly as a result of his experiences on the voyage, Darwin developed the theory of evolution.

Darwin published his theory of evolution in 1859; Lincoln was elected president in 1860. While Lincoln plunged into the heated politics preceding the U.S. Civil War and emerged as a powerful leader, Darwin withdrew from the controversy surrounding the publication of his theory, leaving it for his colleagues to debate in favor of his theory. Lincoln died from an assassin's bullet on April 15, 1865; Darwin died quietly of old age and illness on April 19, 1882.

Both men's lives involved bitter controversy. Both were considered to be fundamentally kind and intelligent. Both died in April. Is this sufficient evidence to believe that their lives were alike because they were born on the same day? Were the differences between them due to different astrological influences caused by their births occurring at different times in different places? Or were the similarities and differences due to characteristics inherited from their parents and the effects of the environments and people each man was exposed to during his life? Which influences were most important in the lives of these two people? Was it the influence of the planets and stars or the experiences each person encountered in his life? How much of their lives was locked in place at the moment of birth (or conception?) due to the positions of celestial objects and how much occurred as a result of a series of events, many happening by chance?

such as "valid only for Chicago residents" or "not valid outside the United States." It is therefore reasonable to assume that the astrologer intends the predictions to apply to all persons born under the same sign.

Scientists know of no mechanism, involving, say, gravity or light, that could explain how the position of celestial objects at the moment of your birth could have any effect on your future. Therefore, scientists are skeptical about astrological predictions. (A skeptical person is one who, based on examination of the available evidence, holds doubts about something, such as a method of prediction.) Should you be skeptical? Many babies are born at almost the same time—do they have the same future even if one is born to poor parents and one to wealthy parents? The birth of some children occurs early or late due to the use of medical procedures. Will the baby have a different future because it was born 2 weeks earlier or 2 days later? Why is the moment of birth and not the moment of conception important? Here there is disagreement between modern Western astrology and the astrology that developed in China. Chinese astrology does emphasize the time of conception; the traditional Chinese method of calculating a person's age is from that time, not from the date of birth. Which method is "correct"? Saturn is much farther from the Earth than is Venus; why do astrologers say that Saturn has an equal or stronger effect on some people's future than has Venus?

Astrologers claim to be able to predict the future. Weather forecasters and stock market analysts also claim to be able to predict the future. How can you tell whether such predictions are reliable?

Many people have had the experience of an astrological prediction turning out to be accurate. Does such an experience prove that astrologers can be relied upon for accurate predictions? Not necessarily, for the same reason that you can sometimes predict that you will get heads on each of three tosses of a coin and then have that outcome occur. You did not have any information in advance concerning the outcome of tossing the coin. But you were predicting an event that was reasonably likely to occur by chance. You could visit different people, ask to use a coin provided by them to show that there was no trick intended, and set about predicting outcomes for various coin toss series. Suppose you decided to do five series of three tosses for each person. How often do you think your predictions for all five series would turn out to be accurate? In all likelihood, not very often. However, because it is possible for your predictions and the outcomes to match by chance, you might make five correct predictions in a row. The person who observed those five correct predictions might think that you could predict future events and be impressed. Indeed, imagine someone telling you that she could predict the outcome of five series, each involving tossing a coin three times, and then proceeding to do exactly that! If you pressed her for a sixth prediction and she failed, would you think she couldn't make accurate predictions or was perhaps simply "tired" from making five correct predictions in a row?

One problem with testing astrological predictions, in contrast to those for tossing coins, is that the former are often vague. Suppose you were told that something bad will happen to you next week. It's hard to imagine a week that is so good that nothing bad happens. But "bad" includes missing a bus as well as being hit by a bus. If a description is sufficiently vague, it is easy to think that it applies to you. There are so many things that can be considered "bad," ranging from a minor inconvenience to total catastrophe, that if you're looking for something to label "bad," you'll probably have no difficulty finding it. Consider the difference between being told that something bad will happen to you next week and being told that next Wednesday at 10:30 a.m. you will get a paper cut on the thumb of your left hand. While you will probably find something to label "bad" out of next week's events, the very specific prediction about the paper cut will almost certainly turn out to be wrong.

Making and Testing Predictions

Anyone can make a prediction about anything. However, there is no evidence that anyone can predict *accurately* the future of the stock market. Astronomers are very good at predicting the future locations of the Sun, Moon, and planets. But with complicated systems, such as the weather and human behavior, nobody has much success with predictions. In fact, scientists believe that for many systems, accurate predictions are fundamentally impossible to make because of the very nature of these systems. For example, the weather depends so sensitively on some factors that there may never be accurate long-range (for example, a month ahead) forecasts.

One way to determine if a particular method is capable of making accurate predictions is to compare the success of the method's predictions with the success that might be expected from chance alone. If the success rates are about the same, there is no need to invoke the method; you can forget about causes and effects—all you have to do is guess! How do the predictions made by astrologers, who use the method of prediction called astrology, compare to those made by simply guessing? If astrological signs do tell us something about our mental and physical abilities, perhaps outstanding athletes, statesmen, entertainers, and scientists tend to be born under different astrological signs. In Activity 15.3, you will test how accurately an astrological profile matches the person for whom it was written, based on the location and date of the person's birth.

Each January first, a number of astrologers and psychics (people who predict the future based on "feelings" or "visions," rather than the positions of celestial objects or some other method) predict what will happen during the year just starting. You might find it interesting to put those forecasts away and look at them on the next January first to see how accurate they were. But if the predictions are vague, such as "a famous rock star will experience health problems," ignore them—should you count one performer's back trouble as the successful outcome of the prediction, or the heart attack suffered by another as the intended outcome? Of course you can't tell which was the intended outcome, so you can't use such predictions. (Don't be surprised if you have no predictions left to check after using this guideline.) By December first, both the Old Farmer's Almanac and the U.S. National Weather Service have made their predictions concerning the severity of the coming winter. Try comparing these predictions with the weather. You can also go to the library and check the forecasts from previous years with what happened; this check would give you a larger sample to test for accuracy. Remember that you can predict three heads in a row and get this result by chance, but it's very unlikely that you can predict the toss outcome correctly 10 times in a row—you're only guessing. One prediction of a winter that turns out to match the outcome accurately is no better an indicator of prediction accuracy.

Because astrological forecasts are usually vague, it is easy to find evidence that "supports" astrology. It is a lot harder to know what kind of evidence would convince a believer in astrology that astrology does not work. By contrast, there are many examples of evidence that has convinced astronomers that something they previously believed was not true. For example, until 1977 astronomers believed that Saturn was the only planet in the solar system with rings; now they know that Jupiter, Uranus, and Neptune also have rings.

Conclusion

To test a theory, apply it to new circumstances that the theory is supposed to "handle" and check the results. Did the theory accurately predict the outcome of the new tests? If you continue to test the theory under different conditions and get accurate results, that is, the theory's predictions turn out to be true, then you can be more confident in the theory. If a prediction is not accurate, it indicates that the theory is flawed in some way. The theory must be revised so that it does predict that result accurately; moreover, testing of other predictions should be made. If you continue to get inaccurate results, you may find that the theory cannot be modified to include all of your results. The theory may then have to be abandoned in favor of a new theory based on a new approach.

By using probability theory to test if a model's predictions are more accurate than simple guessing, you can tell whether a model is a useful scientific tool to make consistently reliable predictions or is just a useless idea. For example, there are eight possible outcomes for tossing one coin three times. Since each of the eight outcomes is equally likely to occur if the coin is not rigged, each outcome has a probability of 1/8. If you guessed the outcomes of many three-toss series, only about one guess out of eight would match the results—the probability of a guess being correct would be 1/8. Now imagine a theory that, on average, predicted correctly the outcome of a

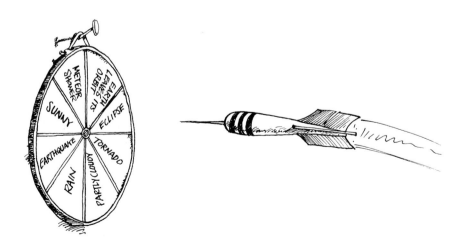

three-toss series once in eight tries. The probability of a prediction being correct would be 1/8. Since a prediction made by the theory would have the same probability of being correct as would a guess, the theory would likely be useless. Suppose, however, that another theory were developed that made use of detailed information about the way you tossed a coin, how the air affected it, and how the coin interacted with the floor. Suppose further that this theory allowed you to predict correctly the outcome of a three-toss series five times for every eight tries. The probability of a prediction made by this theory being correct would be 5/8, much better than the 1/8 probability of a guess being correct. Since the theory's predictions would be correct much more often than the results obtained by simple guessing, the theory would be useful. But is such a theory a reliable tool? A theory that makes five correct predictions out of eight tries also makes three *incorrect* predictions out of eight tries—the probability of a prediction being *wrong* is 3/8. Obviously, the theory cannot be relied upon to provide a correct prediction each time. A reliable theory would always make an accurate prediction, that is, the probability of the theory's prediction being correct would be 1. Scientists strive to construct such reliable theories. However, in some cases, such as constructing a theory that accurately predicts the weather for a specific day 1 year ahead, the amount of information needed and the extreme sensitivity of the predictions to exceedingly tiny errors in this information make a reliable theory impossible to construct. In such cases, it is useful to have a theory that, while not always yielding accurate predictions, does for some circumstances yield results that are more accurate than those obtained by guessing.

Some phenomena, such as those occurring at the small scales of molecules and atoms, cannot be predicted accurately because of the basic properties of nature. An extremely useful theory, called quantum mechanics, has, however, been developed for these phenomena. But this theory does not predict outcomes; rather, it predicts the *probabilities* of outcomes. The behavior of the small components of the universe can only be described by probabilities. If you think that seems strange, don't worry—Albert Einstein thought so, too.

Summary

The likelihood of a particular event occurring can be defined as a probability and assigned a number between 0 and 1. If all outcomes of an event are equally likely and independent, that is, no outcome affects any other outcome, the probability of a desired outcome occurring can be determined by dividing the number of desired outcomes by the total number of possible outcomes. Successive tossing of fair coins and unrigged dice are examples of independent events.

The usefulness of a theory is often judged by determining the probability that the theory will make an accurate prediction for a particular phenomenon. Ideally, a theory should be reliable, that is, it should always make an accurate prediction. However, a theory is judged to be useful if the probability of the theory making an accurate prediction is greater than the probability of getting an accurate prediction by simple guessing. The probability that a prediction based on astrology will be accurate is no better than the probability obtained by guessing. Astrology is therefore neither reliable nor useful for making predictions.

HOMEWORK

1. What is the probability of tossing a coin six times and getting at least four heads in sequence?

2. A woman has given birth to three children—a boy, then a girl, then a boy. Assuming she is equally likely at each birth to have a girl or a boy

   a. What is the probability of this sequence?

   b. What is the probability of a fourth child being a girl?

3. It was reported that in 1950 a man tossed dice 28 consecutive times, getting either a 7 or 11 on each toss. (The man used two dice on each toss.)

   a. What is the probability that a person can toss a 7 or an 11?

   b. What is the probability that a person can do so 28 consecutive times?

4. A deck of cards has four suits (hearts, diamonds, spades, and clubs) with 13 cards in each suit (2-10, Jack, Queen, King, and Ace).

   a. What is the probability that the top card is an Ace (any Ace) if the deck is well shuffled?

   b. What is the probability that the top card is an Ace of spades if the deck is well shuffled?

Self-Test

1. What is the probability of getting four heads in four tosses of one fair coin?

2. What is the probability of getting at least three tails in a row from five tosses of one fair coin?

3. What is the probability of tossing two unrigged dice once and getting a total of 3?

4. The rules for the board game Monopoly state that if you toss the two dice and get a "double," that is, both dice show the same number of dots, you get an extra turn. If you toss a "double" (any "double") on the extra turn, you get another extra turn. But if you throw a "double" on that turn, you must go directly to jail (Do not pass GO!). What is the probability of tossing three "doubles" in a row, using two fair dice?

ACTIVITY 15.1   TOSSING COINS

PURPOSE

To investigate probability by tossing pennies.

WHAT DO YOU THINK?

P1. *If you tossed a penny 10 times and it came up heads each time, do you think it would come up heads or tails on the 11th toss? How certain are you of your prediction: absolutely certain, very certain, fairly certain, cannot tell, or just a guess?*

P2. *If you tossed 10 pennies together, what do you think the most likely outcome would be? Specify how many coins would come up heads and how many would come up tails in this most likely outcome.*

MATERIALS

10 pennies (9 tarnished and 1 shiny)
1 box or other container with a secure cover or lid and an inside height much greater than the diameter of a penny

PROCEDURE

A. When a coin is tossed, there are only two possible outcomes, heads or tails. (A coin could land on its edge, but that is so unlikely, it is not considered as a possible outcome.) If a coin is tossed more than once, however, do the outcomes of the past tosses have any effect on the outcome of the next toss? Toss a penny nine times and record your results, writing "H" to represent heads and "T" to represent tails.

1. *Which side came up more often, H or T? Predict the outcome of the next toss. How certain are you of your prediction? Why?*

2. *What was the outcome of the 10th toss? Was your prediction in question 1 correct?*

3. *Predict the outcome for 10 more tosses by writing down the number of H and T you expect to come up. (The sequence does not matter for this example.)*

B. Toss a penny 10 more times and record the results of these 10 tosses as in step A.

4. *What were your results for these 10 tosses? How do the results compare to your prediction in question 3?*

5. *How many times do you think you would have to toss 10 pennies before your prediction matched the results? Try it and record your results.*

6. *Did you do better with your prediction in question 5 than in questions 1 or 3? If so, why; if not, why not? How many times do you think you would have to toss a penny to be certain that your prediction of the results would be correct?*

C. Place all 10 pennies in the container, secure the lid, and shake the container. Open the lid and count the number of pennies that came up H and the number that came up T. Record your results.

7. *How did the results from tossing 10 pennies together compare to the results from tossing one penny 10 times (see questions 1 and 4)? Are the results of shaking up 10 pennies simultaneously more predictable, less predictable, or about as predictable as the outcomes of tossing one penny 10 times?*

D. Repeat step C five times. Record the tally of H and T for each trial in a table. Also note whether the shiny penny came up H or T in each trial.

8. *Is there any pattern to the results of tossing 10 pennies together?*

9. *How did the results for the shiny penny compare to the overall result for the 10 pennies? Were the outcomes of tossing the single penny more predictable, less predictable, or about as predictable as the results for 10 pennies together?*

10. *Compare your results for step D with those of your classmates. Does any pattern appear in the results from tossing the 10 pennies together? Does any pattern appear in the results for the shiny penny?*

11. *How do the predictions that you made in questions P1 and P2 compare to the results obtained in this activity?*

12. *If you tossed 1,000 pennies together, what do you think the outcome would be? How certain are you of your prediction? Why? Would the expected outcome be different from tossing one penny 1,000 times? Why?*

13. *Could you ever toss a penny and know with certainty what the outcome would be? Describe such circumstances.*

EXTENSIONS

1. Combine your results for step D with those of your classmates. Does a greater amount of data change the results? If so, how?

ACTIVITY 15.2   TOSSING DICE

PURPOSE

To investigate probability by tossing dice.

WHAT DO YOU THINK?

P1. *Which is more likely, to toss one die and get 5 to show face up, or to toss two dice and get a total of 5?*

P2. *Which total number is most likely to result when two dice are tossed? Why?*

MATERIALS

2 dice

PROCEDURE

A. Since a die has six sides, there are six possible outcomes when you toss a die. Table 15.5 in the text shows all possible outcomes for tossing two dice. Note that there are 36 possible outcomes, but only 11 different sums (you cannot get 1 with two dice). Some totals are more likely to result than others because there are more ways for those totals to be formed (see text for a more complete explanation). For any one outcome, the probability is 1 in 36 of that outcome occurring; this expression can be written as a fraction, 1/36. The probabilities (also known as "odds") for all possible totals resulting from tossing two dice are summarized in Table 15.7.

B. Toss two dice 36 times, recording the total for each toss. Add up the number of times each total occurred and, in a table, record the results as fractions of the total number of tosses. For example, if the total 5 came up 7 times during the 36 tosses, write 7/36 next to the 5 in your table. If a particular total did not occur, write 0 next to that total.

1. *The most likely total to result from tossing two dice is 7. Was 7 your most common result? If not, which total was the most common? What is the predicted probability in Table 15.7 for your most common result?*

2. *Did any totals not show on any of the tosses (zeros in your Results column)? For each such total, what is the probability of occurrence given in Table 15.7?*

3. *Although you tossed the dice 36 times, your overall results are most likely not identical to the probabilities given in Table 15.7. Could you ever toss the dice 36 times and get results that match the probabilities? Why or why not?*

Table 15.7	
Odds	**Totals**
1/36	2
	12
2/36	3
	11
3/36	4
	10
4/36	5
	9
5/36	6
	8
6/36	7

4. *Could you toss two ordinary (not "loaded") dice 36 times and get a total of 2 every time? If you don't think this could happen, explain why. If you think it could happen, calculate the probability of such an event (read the text first!).*

DISCUSSION QUESTION

1. There is a difference between stating that a particular event is impossible (it can never happen) and that an event is improbable (unlikely, but possible). There is a popular phrase that says "nothing is impossible." This is not a true statement. Make a list of five impossible events (they do not have to involve coins or dice) and explain why you think each event is impossible. Then list five improbable events and state why you think each event, though unlikely, could occur. (If you can, calculate or estimate the probability of occurrence of each event.)

ACTIVITY 15.3

USING ASTROLOGY TO IDENTIFY A "FAMOUS" PERSON

PURPOSE

To attempt to identify a well-known person by using an astrological prediction.

WHAT DO YOU THINK?

P1. *Given a list of 12 well-known people and one horoscope, do you think you could match the horoscope to the right person? Explain why you think you could or could not do so.*

MATERIALS

list of 12 famous people, Table 15.8
1 computer-generated horoscope

PROCEDURE

A. The persons in Table 15.8 are listed in alphabetical order by last name. No two persons have the same Sun sign. A computer astrology program, written by an astrologer, generated a horoscope for one of the 12 persons based on the date and place of birth of that person. The horoscope provides personality traits based on the location of the Sun, Moon, and the planets vs. the signs of the zodiac. The Sun sign is not

Table 15.8	
Person and Brief Description	
Corazon Aquino:	President of the Philippines after the downfall of Ferdinand Marcos
Marie Curie:	Chemist who won two Nobel Prizes for work on radioactive materials
Diana:	Former Princess of Wales, anti-landmine activist
Clint Eastwood:	Actor of "tough guy" roles, usually in Western and police dramas
Albert Einstein:	Physicist who developed the theories of relativity, peace activist
Geraldine Ferraro:	1984 Democratic party vice-presidential candidate, lawyer
Mick Jagger:	Rock and roll performer, lead member of the group "Rolling Stones"
Martin Luther King:	Civil rights leader, advocate of nonviolent protest
Vladimir Lenin:	Communist revolutionary
Olivia Newton John:	Singer and actress in musicals, environmentalist
Sandra Day O'Connor:	U.S. Supreme Court justice, appointed by President Reagan
Steven Spielberg:	Producer, director, and writer of popular adventure films

given, but the personality traits of the sign are given at the top of the horoscope.

B. Carefully read the horoscope summary. Then, based on what you know about the persons in the list (you can look up additional background information in encyclopedias or, if the person is living, in *Who's Who*), match the horoscope to the person who you think is best described by the horoscope. Your teacher will tell you the correct match.

1. *Was your match correct?*

2. *How many of your classmates made a correct match? What percent of your class members made a correct match?*

3. *What is the probability of making one correct match by simple guessing? Show your calculations.*

4. *Compare the probability of getting a correct match to the probabilities for getting certain results when tossing dice. Which results of tossing two dice have the same probability as making a correct match by guessing?*

Trekking among the Stars

This appendix is a guide to help you view the nighttime sky. It is designed to be used with a northern star chart, such as the star finder from Activity 2.2.

OBSERVING THE NIGHTTIME SKY

This appendix will assist you in learning to identify some of the stars and constellations of the evening sky as seen from the continental United States. Occasionally we discuss conclusions drawn from models. But these are presented differently in this appendix than in the chapters. Here we present conclusions as "facts" and do not discuss their basis, because this appendix is intended primarily as a guide to observing the nighttime sky. If you want to learn about the origins and supporting evidence for the "facts" mentioned in this appendix, you can find such information or useful references in most comprehensive college-level astronomy textbooks.

Before you begin observing the nighttime sky, you should be aware of some general observing tips. First, find as dark a location to observe from as possible. If you can, turn off the outside lights and draw the curtains and shades on the side of the building you'll be standing near. Try standing so that the building helps to block the light from streetlights and passing cars. Wait outside away from any lights for at least 10 minutes to let your eyes adjust to the lower light level—you'll then be able to see the stars more easily.

Observing is best done from a dark location. However, you *must* consider your personal safety first. The darkest location may not be a safe one. Bring others with you when you go observing; it is safer and you will also be able to share your observations. You may be surprised how much easier it is to learn the locations of stars if you explain what you are doing to someone else.

CAUTION

Once your eyes are "dark adapted," that is, adjusted to seeing dim lights, you need to preserve your dark adaption. If you have a good, dark site, it will be too dark to read this page or to see the details on your star finder. An ordinary flashlight should not be used to help you see as its light will ruin your "night vision." A simple solution is to wrap a piece of red cellophane around the head of a flashlight, securing the cellophane with an elastic band. Red light does not greatly disturb dark-adapted eyes. Do not be concerned if things look strange, or even seem to disappear, when using the red light; as you will learn in Chapter 11, how you see things depends partly on the color of the light shining on the objects that you are looking at.

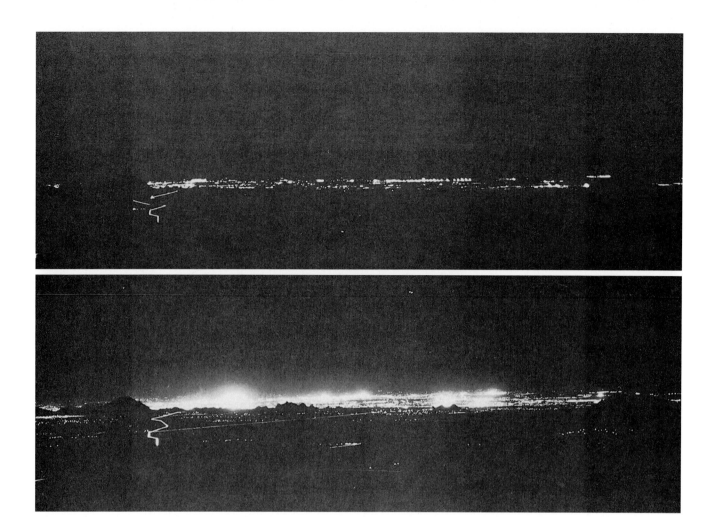

Figure A.2
Two views of light pollution in Tucson, Arizona, from the Kitt Peak National Observatory. The top photograph is from 1959; the bottom from 1980.

There are approximately 6,000 stars that can be seen from the Earth with the unaided eye. From any location on the Earth's surface, only half of the sky is visible at a given time, so only about 3,000 stars can be seen at any one time. For most stargazers, though, the full beauty of the nighttime sky is hard to see.

Artificial lighting from streetlights and buildings (known as "light pollution") brightens the sky in urban and suburban areas, limiting the number of stars that can be seen to a few hundred, or even fewer. (See Figures A.1, A.2, and A.3.) Haze and smog caused by air pollutants create additional problems for the stargazer. Even if the weather satellite image on the evening news shows no clouds over a city, an observer on the ground may see nothing but a pale sky, the stars being obscured by light and air pollution. However, about 15 stars, as well as the Moon and the planets Venus, Jupiter, Mars, and Saturn appear bright enough to be visible through most light pollution and some can even be seen from the centers of cities on clear nights. One amateur astronomy group routinely sets up its telescopes near a busy intersection in downtown San Francisco and invites passersby to have a look at the Moon or any planets that are visible. It is often the first time a "city person" has noticed the nighttime sky, let alone looked through a telescope.

Because most people in the United States live in areas with at least moderate amounts of light pollution, we will use only the brightest stars of

each season as markers to explore the nighttime sky. If you are lucky enough to live in a location with dark skies, you can use any one of several constellation guidebooks to help you locate fainter stars along with your star finder from Activity 2.2.

Getting Oriented

The most widely recognized star pattern visible from the Northern Hemisphere is the Big Dipper. The Big Dipper can be seen from any location north of the equator and is visible all night on every clear night of the year for observers anywhere in the United States. To locate the Big Dipper, use a magnetic compass or a map of your area to help you face north. During fall

Figure A.4
The diagram shows the positions of the Big Dipper and the "pointer" stars with respect to the North Star in the evening sky for each of the seasons.

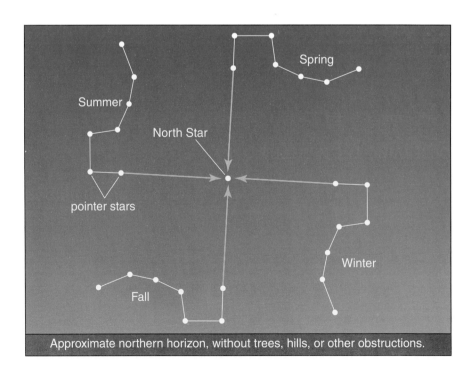

evenings, the Big Dipper appears "right-side up" just above the northern horizon. In winter, it appears to be standing on its handle. On spring evenings, it appears upside down and nearly overhead. On summer evenings, the Big Dipper appears to hang by its handle from an invisible hook in the sky. Refer to Figure A.4.

The two stars that form the "front" of the Big Dipper's bowl define a line that, when extended away from the "mouth" of the bowl, points toward the North Star. (Refer again to Figure A.4.) For that reason, these stars are often called the "pointer" stars. The North Star has no close neighbors of similar apparent brightness, so you should be able to pick it out fairly easily. To check if the star you have located using the pointer stars is the North Star, use your hand (see Activity 1.1) to measure the angle from the point on the horizon directly below the star to the star. This angle will be about 30° for locations in the southern half of the continental United States and about 40° from locations in the northern half of the country (excluding Alaska).

The North Star, also called Polaris, is perhaps the best-known star, even though there are about 50 stars that appear brighter. (Yes, you read correctly, the North Star is not the brightest star.) Its fame is due to its location above the north point on the horizon and the fact that its angle above the horizon is related to the observer's location on the Earth. Because the North Star appears to be almost stationary in the sky, it is used by navigators as a reference point.

When you are facing the North Star, you are looking north. Make a one-quarter turn to your left and you'll face west; a one-quarter turn to your right points you east. Turn around and face away from the North Star and you are looking south. Since the North Star always appears above the north point on the horizon, you can use the star to reference compass directions from any location north of the equator (the imaginary circle around the Earth halfway between the North and South Poles), and to locate other stars on any night.

We will now explore the brighter stars and constellations of the evening sky for each of the seasons, beginning with the fall sky since you are probably reading this appendix in September or October. If this is a second-

---

Celestial Names

The Big Dipper is not an "official" constellation; however, it is an easily recognized group of stars. Most constellations are *not* named because of their appearance. Just as we name schools, airports, mountains, and other objects after famous people, the ancients named portions of the sky as memorials or tributes to legendary figures, human and animal. In fact, we carry on the tradition of naming celestial features after people and animals, real and mythical. Comets are named for their discoverer(s). Asteroids have a variety of names, including those of Hindu gods, artists, the crew of the shuttle *Challenger*, the Beatles, and even the editor of this book. Comets and asteriods are the only celestial objects that can bear the names of living people, according to international

agreement among astronomers. Craters on the Moon have been named for ancient philosophers and science fiction authors. Features on the planets and their moons are usually given names in keeping with the object's name. For example, most of the features on Venus, the only planet bearing a female name, are named either for famous women or female characters from the myths of many different cultures.

All celestial names must be approved by the International Astronomical Union (IAU), a worldwide organization of professional astronomers. Names given to celestial objects by other organizations or individuals without IAU approval are not considered "official" and are not used by most astronomers.

semester course, it's probably January or February, so you can skip ahead to the winter sky.

The descriptions that follow are useful for any location in the continental United States for between 8 p.m. and 10 p.m. Use your star finder to help orient yourself and to guide your viewing at other times during the night.

NOTE: In the following sections, you will be introduced to the names of numerous constellations, stars, and other celestial objects. Nearly all of these names are derived from mythology; none of the names has any scientific significance. You should therefore treat the names as being of cultural interest only—no scientific concepts are involved. If you attach any importance to learning the positions and names of celestial objects, it should be based on personal interest and the potential satisfaction and pleasure of sharing your knowledge of the night sky with others.

THE FALL EVENING SKY

An impressive set of four stars visible above the eastern horizon in September is the Great Square of Pegasus (PEG-ah-sus). The stars appear to be nearly the same brightness and form a large square with no bright stars inside it. The Square is part of Pegasus, the winged horse of Greek mythology.

If you start at the "top left" star of the Great Square, you can follow a chain of three additional stars trailing away from the Square (see Figure A.5). These stars are part of the constellation Andromeda (An-DROM-eh-dah), a legendary princess of Ethiopia. The middle star of the three-star chain serves as a guide to the most distant object visible to the unaided eye. About 10° "up" from the middle star is the Great Galaxy in Andromeda, more simply known as the Andromeda galaxy. In a dark, clear sky, the galaxy will appear as a very faint, hazy spot, about as large as the width of a pencil held at arm's length. This galaxy, thought by astronomers to be similar to our

Milky Way galaxy, is so distant that the light from it that enters your eyes left the galaxy's stars more than 2 *million* years ago. And Andromeda is the nearest major galaxy to us. The Milky Way and Andromeda galaxies, along with about 20 other "neighboring" galaxies, form a cluster of galaxies known as the Local Group. Except for two small galaxies near our own, none of the other members of the Local Group is visible to the unaided eye. These two small galaxies are the Large and Small Magellanic (Ma-GEL-an-ik) Clouds and can only be seen from locations near to or south of the equator.

The Great Square is also useful for locating one of the 20 brightest stars visible from the Earth. If you look "down" along the line formed by the two "right-hand" stars of the Square for a distance equal to about 3 times the separation of those stars, you will come to an isolated bright star, Fomalhaut (FOE-mal-ot). Fomalhaut will be low in the sky, probably only about 20° above the horizon, and therefore may be blocked by trees, other objects along the horizon, or haze. (Refer to Figure A.5.)

Fomalhaut is the only bright star visible in that part of the sky, but you may see a bright object nearby. This will not be a star (unless you've discovered a supernova), but one of the planets of our solar system, most likely Jupiter, Saturn, or Mars. The other planets are either too dim to see or would not be seen near Fomalhaut in the fall. Is there any difference in appearance between a star and a planet? Although much bigger than the planets in our solar system, the stars are much, much farther away. As a result, stars appear as points, sending narrow beams of light through the Earth's atmosphere. The atmosphere is always in motion and causes the narrow beams to dance around a bit, so the star's light shimmers or "twinkles." The "nearby" planets appear larger, with wider light beams. The light beams from the planets are also disturbed by the atmosphere, but the width of a planet's light beam is large compared to the amount of shimmer, so the planet's beam appears as a steadier light. As proof, look through a pair of binoculars and you will see that a planet, like Jupiter, appears as a tiny disk, while a star still looks like a point.

Figure A.5
The directions of the Andromeda galaxy and the bright star Fomalhaut with respect to the Great Square of Pegasus.

THE WINTER EVENING SKY

Many people who have stargazed on a cold winter night have noticed how bright the stars appear and thought this appearance was due to the colder, drier air. Although the air appears to be less hazy in winter than in other seasons, that is not the main reason the stars look brighter. Their appearance is due to the types of stars they are and to their being relatively close to the Earth. Although the evening sky of each season has some bright stars, eight of the 20 brightest stars seen from the Earth are visible in the winter evening sky. One of these, Canopus (ka-NO-pus), cannot be seen from the northern half of the United States.

The centerpiece of the winter sky is the constellation Orion (o-RYE-on), the hunter, marked by seven bright stars that form a rather distinct humanlike figure, including a "belt" of three evenly spaced stars. In early December, Orion can be seen rising above the eastern horizon. By February, Orion is centered in the southern sky.

Although most stars look white, they do vary in color. Orion's two brightest stars serve as good examples of the color differences among stars. Betelgeuse (commonly pronounced "BEETLE-juice," but more properly pronounced "BET-al-juz") is the "upper left" star in Orion; on a dark night, Betelgeuse appears distinctly reddish. Diagonally opposite Betelgeuse, in Orion's "lower right" corner, is Rigel (RYE-jel), which has a bluish-white appearance.

The star that appears brightest in the night sky is Sirius (SIR-ee-us), part of the constellation Canis Major (KAY-nis MAY-jer), the big dog. Sirius appears rather low in the sky, 30° or less above the southern horizon. Sirius is located to the lower left of Orion. Although it can appear to be very bright, Sirius may appear dimmer than other stars due to light pollution or haze along the horizon. Sirius is most easily located when Orion is in the southern sky; if Orion is rising, Sirius will still be below the horizon.

Sirius is also known as the "dog star" because it is in Canis Major. It is mentioned in Chapter 1 that the ancients knew that the stars were in the sky during the daytime. The Sun is nearest to Sirius in mid-June, the beginning of summer for locations north of the equator. Centuries ago, people believed that the presence of Sirius and the Sun together in the sky was the cause of the hot summer weather and Sirius's nickname led to summer being called the "dog days."

At the start of the "dog days," Sirius can be seen rising just before the Sun. Three thousand years ago, the priests of ancient Egypt would watch for this appearance of Sirius; it occurred at the same time that the Nile River began to rise in the annual flood that kept Egypt's fields watered and fertile. Egypt's calendar was linked to Sirius, not the Sun, and the Egyptian new year therefore began in late spring rather than in early winter.

Above Orion is Capella (ka-PEL-ah), second only to Sirius in apparent brightness in the winter sky as seen from the northern United States. Capella is in the constellation Auriga (o-RYE-ga), the chariot driver.

If you follow the line of Orion's belt stars to the right, you will come to Aldebaran (al-DEB-ah-ran), considered as the "eye" of the bull, Taurus. To the upper right of Aldebaran is a small cluster of stars, five or six of which are visible to the eye. These are the Pleiades, located within the constellation Taurus. The Pleiades look a bit like a miniature Big Dipper (Figure A.6.). (The Pleiades cluster is also the only real star pattern used by an automobile company for its emblem.)

Returning to Orion, note two more bright stars and a constellation that can be located by looking along a line from Rigel through Betelgeuse to a distance from Betelgeuse equal to about twice the separation of Rigel from Betelgeuse. These bright stars are Castor (KAS-ter) and Pollux (POL-uks), representing the heads of the twins, Gemini (JEM-eh-nye). In Greek mythology, the twins are sons of Zeus, king of the gods. They are an adventurous pair who went with Jason on his expedition to find the Golden Fleece. Legend has it that the twins saved Jason's ship, the *Argo*, from a storm. Ancient sailors made offerings to the twins to ensure a safe voyage. Another custom among sailors was to invoke their name as an oath, "by Gemini." This expression spread and has survived as the phrase "by Jiminy."

The bright winter stars, taken together, are sometimes called the "Winter Oval." Starting with Sirius, you can trace the oval through Rigel, Aldebaran, Capella, Castor, and Pollux, returning to Sirius by passing through the star Procyon (PRO-see-on) in Canis Minor, the little dog.

THE SPRING EVENING SKY

You can use the Big Dipper to locate the bright stars of the spring sky. On a spring evening, the Big Dipper will appear upside down nearly overhead. The stars of the Dipper's handle form an arc pointing toward the south and east. If you follow the arc defined by the handle away from the Dipper's

bowl down into the eastern sky, you will find Arcturus (ark-TOO-rus). Arcturus is the brightest star in the spring sky and the third brightest visible from the Earth. The star is located in the constellation Bootes (bo-O-teez), the herdsman.

Following the line of the arc through Arcturus, you will come to Spica (SPY-ka), the brightest star in Virgo (VUR-go), the maiden. The use of the Big Dipper's curved handle to locate Arcturus and Spica can be remembered by the phrase: "Arc to Arcturus, speed on to Spica."

The remaining bright star of the spring sky, Regulus (REG-uh-lus), can be identified by using the pointer stars of the Big Dipper. Instead of following the pointer stars to the North Star, follow them in the opposite direction, down into the southern sky. About halfway from the Big Dipper to the southern horizon you will see the constellation Leo, the lion. Regulus appears as the bright point at the base of a star pattern that looks like a backwards question mark; these stars form the head of Leo and are a key feature of the spring sky.

THE SUMMER EVENING SKY

About an hour after sunset on a summer's evening, you can look up about 40° from the southern horizon and see a bright star, Altair (al-TARE), in Aquila (AK-wah-lah), the eagle. If you look almost overhead, you will see two more stars, Vega (commonly pronounced "VAY-gah," but correctly pronounced "VEE-gah") and Deneb (DEN-eb). Together, these three stars form a distinctive pattern known as the "Summer Triangle." These stars are bright enough that they are usually the first stars visible after sunset in the summer. Vega is in Lyra (LYE-rah), the Lyre, and Deneb is in Cygnus (SIG-nus), the swan, which is also known as the "Northern Cross" because of the pattern formed by its five brightest stars.

The Summer Triangle can be used to locate another star, Antares (an-TAY-reez). If you start at Deneb and follow a line passing halfway between Vega and Altair towards the southwest, Antares will be a reddish star near the horizon. Located in the center of Scorpius (SKOR-pee-us), the scorpion, Antares is the creature's "heart."

Antares gets its name from its reddish color and brightness, which make it appear similar to the planet Mars, the Roman god of war, known to the Greeks as Ares (AH-reez, although often pronounced A-reez). The Greeks considered the star's appearance as a rival to that of Ares, thus the name Antares, literally "anti-Ares." Due to Antares's location near the horizon, the star may be hard to see, appearing dimmer than expected due to light pollution and haze, or the star may be blocked by objects along the horizon.

To the east (left) of Antares and Scorpius is the constellation Sagittarius (SAJ-eh-TAY-ree-us), the archer, often pictured as a centaur (half man, half horse) holding a bow and arrow. Although Sagittarius does not contain any bright stars, it is marked by a rather compact pattern of stars that looks like a teapot, complete with a handle and spout. In fact, this portion of Sagittarius is commonly known as the "teapot." If you can spot the teapot, you will be looking directly toward the center of our galaxy.

Vega and Stellar Photography

In 1850, William Bond, director of the Harvard College Observatory, made a daguerreotype of Vega, the first photograph ever made of a star. Bond used the observatory's main telescope, the 38-cm (15-in.) "Great Refractor," at the time the largest telescope in the United States and the twin to the largest in the world, the 38-cm refractor at the Russian Imperial Observatory. (See Figure A.7.)

In 1983, another image of Vega, this one made by the Infrared Astronomical Satellite (IRAS) from Earth orbit, showed a belt of particles surrounding the star. Vega, believed by astronomers to be a young star, may serve as an example of how the debris remaining from the formation of a star leads to the development of planets orbiting the star.

Figure A.7
The 38-cm (15-in.) "Great Refractor."

You may have noticed that six of the constellations mentioned have the same names as six of the "zodiac signs": Taurus, Gemini, Leo, Virgo, Scorpius, and Sagittarius. This is no coincidence; the signs of the zodiac are derived from these constellations. The other six constellations from which zodiac signs were derived (Capricornus [KAP-rah-KOR-nus], Aquarius [ah-KWARE-ee-us], Pisces [PICE-eez], Aries [A-reez], Cancer, and Libra [LYE-bra, although it is often pronounced LEE-bra]) were not mentioned because these constellations do not contain any bright stars. The overall pattern of the 12 constellations is marked by four of the bright stars previously mentioned. Each season has one bright star in or near a "zodiacal" constellation. These four stars were named the "royal" stars by the priests of ancient Mesopotamia. The stars are Fomalhaut (fall), Aldebaran (winter), Regulus (spring), and Antares (summer).

The Moon and Other Earth Satellites

Although only a part-time occupant of the night sky, the Moon, when present, appears brighter than any other celestial object. The Moon is also the only natural satellite of the Earth. There are several thousand artificial satellites, some working, some not, others just pieces of debris from rocket launches. Many are only a few hundred kilometers above the Earth's surface and are visible to us. Figure A.8 shows a satellite orbiting the Earth, passing over three locations on

the night side. For 2 or 3 hours after sunset (position 1), you can spot satellites as tiny points of light moving steadily across the sky, usually from west to east. If you're up early (or late) satellites are also visible for 2 or 3 hours before sunrise (position 3). They are not visible in the middle of the nighttime because their orbits take them through the Earth's shadow (position 2). More information about the Moon is presented in Appendix 2.

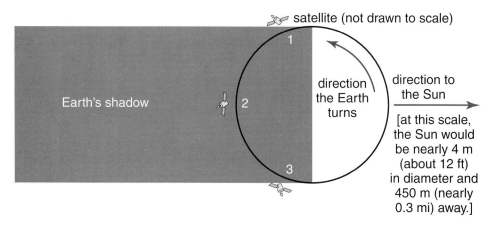

satellite (not drawn to scale)

1

Earth's shadow

2

direction the Earth turns

direction to the Sun

[at this scale, the Sun would be nearly 4 m (about 12 ft) in diameter and 450 m (nearly 0.3 mi) away.]

3

Figure A.8
This illustration shows the Earth and the inner (dark) region of its shadow as viewed from above the North Pole. A satellite is shown passing over three observers on the Earth at three different positions in the satellite's orbit. Only the observers at positions 1 and 3 would be able to

see the satellite when it passes over them; the satellite would not be visible to the observer at position 2, when it passes there, because the satellite would not be reflecting any sunlight. See the section on lunar eclipses in Chapter 7 for more about the visibility of objects in the Earth's shadow.

Portraits of the Planets

This appendix provides descriptive information about the Moon, the planets in our solar system, except the Earth, and some of their moons. The appendix is designed to be read in conjunction with Chapter 8. You may be better able to appreciate the sizes and distances discussed in this appendix if you have done Activity 8.2.

THE MOON

When Galileo first looked at the Moon through his new telescope he discovered that the dark and light areas that make up the "man in the Moon" represent different kinds of lunar terrain. Typically, the light areas are mountainous regions covered with many craters. The dark regions are smoother. They are called maria, the Latin word for "seas" because people once thought they were lunar oceans—we now know that there is no liquid water on the Moon. (See Figure A.9.) A square kilometer on a dark area of the Moon has many fewer craters than a typical square kilometer on a light area.

The cause of the lunar craters puzzled people for quite some time. The craters do not resemble volcanoes on the Earth. But the lunar craters do resemble some craters on the Earth. Astronomers finally decided that the craters on the Moon must be produced by the same kinds of objects that occasionally hit the Earth. Some astronomers argued that the craters left by the impact of these objects could be used to tell something about the ages of these craters. How?

Imagine that there is a town that cleans its statues once a year. How could you tell if cleaning time were near? If you looked at an outdoor statue and found that there were relatively few bird droppings on it, you would suspect that statue had been cleaned recently. If, on the other hand, there were lots of droppings, that statue would probably be due for a cleaning soon. How could you tell if one bird dropping were more recent than another? If the first bird dropping partially covered the second, you would

Figure A.9
The Moon.

know that the one doing the covering was younger than the one being covered. The same approach can be used on the Moon. Moreover, people reasoned that since the lunar highlands are covered with craters, they must be older than the maria, which are not so covered.

When astronauts first landed on the Moon in 1969, they brought back rocks. Scientists were able to measure the radioactivity in these rocks and to discover that many were formed between 4.1×10^9 and 4.5×10^9 years ago. Those rocks are older than the oldest ones found on Earth (see box). Further, since so many of the rock samples were formed during that interval of time, scientists inferred that there was a period of very intense meteor bombardment of the Moon in these early years of the solar system. The

As Old As the Hills

Scientists can tell the age of a rock by measuring its "radioactivity." Some elements can transform naturally to other elements. For example, a form of rubidium can change into a form of strontium. By measuring the relative amounts of such rubidium and strontium in a rock, scientists can infer how long ago the rock was formed.

Astronomers believe that the solar system formed about 4.7×10^9 (4.7 billion) years ago. No solar system object whose age has been estimated is older. What is meant by the age of an object? One usually reckons age from the time the object first took on approximately its present form. The White House's age is based on when it was first built, in 1792, not on when the trees started to grow whose wood is used in the White House, nor on when the White House was last repainted. The age of a rock is usually based on when it soldified from some molten form. The oldest rocks known on the Earth were formed about 4.0×10^9 years ago. The youngest rocks on the Earth are brand new, being formed from hot lava from the most recent eruption of a volcano. This volcanic and related "internal" activity of the Earth is responsible for the Earth's rocks being, on average, much younger than the Moon's.

---

maria are believed to have filled with molten rock after that bombardment period, leaving them covered with fewer craters. Although younger than the heavily cratered lunar highlands, the maria are still more than 3.0×10^9 years old. Since the lunar surface has remained unchanged for so long, the Moon must be much less active internally than is the Earth.

A compass would be useless for finding your way on the Moon since the Moon has no magnetic field of its own. Finding your way around the Moon would be a minor problem compared to just staying alive. The Moon essentially has no atmosphere and the only water present is bonded with other substances in the rocks. Since the same side of the Moon always faces the Earth, the Moon must turn once on its axis in the same time that it takes the Moon to make one orbit around the Earth. The daylight period for most locations on the Moon, including the side that faces away from the Earth, lasts about 2 weeks, followed by 2 weeks of nighttime. The Moon's surface temperature ranges from about 130°C (260°F) in the daytime to around −110°C (about −170°F) during the nighttime.

Instruments left on the Moon by the Apollo astronauts have recorded very little activity. The instruments have recorded the impact of space debris on the lunar surface, but only very weak earthquakes (or "moonquakes"). The Moon is a very quiet place compared to the Earth.

MERCURY

Being so close to the Sun, Mercury is hard to observe, even with a telescope; thus, astronomers knew very little about this planet until the last part of the 20th century. For example, only in 1965 was it discovered, from radar observations, that Mercury turns on its axis three times for each two trips it makes around the Sun. Mercury is the only planet whose "day" is linked to

its "year." Only because Mercury is so close to the Sun, can the Sun control Mercury's day.

Astronomers got their first good look at Mercury in 1974 and 1975 when the U.S. spacecraft *Mariner 10* flew past the planet three times. The pictures *Mariner 10* sent back by radio to the Earth showed a world that looks very much like the Moon (see Figure A.10). Like the Moon, Mercury is a virtually airless world, and like much of the Moon, Mercury's surface seems to have been little altered since the great meteor bombardment that ended about 4.0×10^9 years ago. However, Mercury does possess a magnetic field of its own and a very, very thin atmosphere. But Mercury's daytime and nighttime conditions are more extreme than on the Moon: the temperature of Mercury's surface can reach 230°C (about 440°F) during the daytime and drop to –170°C (nearly –280°F) during the nighttime. It may be surprising that the planet nearest the Sun can get so cold, but Mercury lacks a thick, cloud-filled atmosphere to "hold" heat during the nighttime.

VENUS

Venus is Earth's twin in many ways. It is almost the same size as the Earth and has nearly the same mass. Cloud-wrapped Venus fascinated people for many years (Figure A.11). Clouds suggested rain and constant rain made people think of jungles. Some even speculated that Venus might be a younger version of the Earth in which dinosaurs still roamed. In fact, Venus is not nearly so hospitable to people as would be a dinosaur-filled jungle.

Radar observations in the early 1960s gave the first reliable determination of Venus's rotation on its axis: Venus rotates "backwards" from the Earth—the Sun rises in the west and sets in the east. Further, Venus spins slowly: daytime on Venus lasts about 117 Earth days.

Mariner 2, the first spacecraft to fly past Venus (or any other planet), confirmed observations made with radio telescopes on the Earth: the temperature on the surface of Venus is nearly 480°C (about 900°F), hot enough to melt lead. The Soviet spacecraft *Venera 9* landed on the planet in 1975, and before it expired from the heat, sent back the first picture of the surface of Venus. The clouds that make Venus so brilliant in the morning and evening skies are not made primarily of water droplets as are clouds on the Earth; clouds on Venus contain sulphuric acid. Venus is not exactly a tourist's delight.

Radar techniques have been used to penetrate Venus's clouds to produce images of most of Venus's surface. Some of these images have been made by radars on the Earth, but the best pictures have come from radars on board spacecraft, such as the U.S. probe *Magellan,* placed in orbit about Venus in 1990. These radar pictures show the surface of Venus to be very different from the surface of the Moon and Mercury. Although the thick atmosphere of Venus has played a role in protecting the planet, radar images sent back by *Magellan* do show impact craters. The images also revealed a belt of volcanoes along a portion of the planet's equator; whether there are any active volcanoes on Venus has yet to be determined. The surface of Venus does appear similar to the Earth's surface in one respect: There are regions of the surface that are much higher and much lower than the "average" surface.

This pattern is similar to the continents and ocean basins found on the Earth. But Venus has no oceans and its "continents" are fewer and much smaller than the Earth's. The North Pole of the Earth is covered by an ice-filled ocean; Venus's "north pole" is covered by high mountains wrapped in heat. Venus also lacks a magnetic field.

MARS AND ITS MOONS

Even primitive telescopes showed that Mars has polar caps that grow and melt with the changing seasons on Mars. In 1907, the American astronomer Percival Lowell drew a map of Mars showing a network of fine lines on the surface of the planet. Lowell drew his map based on what he thought he had seen while observing Mars through a telescope. He thought these lines represented vegetation growing near canals built by Martians to preserve their dwindling water supply. Where the lines came together he thought he could see oases where Martian cities might have been built.

But the first spacecraft to image Mars from close by showed a surface that looked more like the Moon than any place on Earth. Later spacecraft showed a world with craters like the Moon (see Figure A.12), but with many different features, including Olympus Mons, what many believe is the largest volcano in the solar system (Figure A.13). However, Olympus Mons, and the other volcanoes on Mars, are not active and may not have erupted for hundreds of millions of years. Some pictures even show what appears to be evidence for ancient water flows.

Figure A.12
A *Viking* image of Mars.

The atmosphere on Mars is very thin and the temperature very low compared to the Earth's atmosphere. Liquid water would quickly evaporate on Mars. The differences in the daytime and nighttime temperatures on Mars are much greater than on the Earth: a difference of 35–50°C (60–90°F) between daytime and nighttime temperatures in one day. A summer daytime high temperature on Mars might be about 30°C (80°F); a winter night might have a temperature of –120°C (about –190°F). As noted, like the Earth, Mars has polar caps, but the martian caps contain frozen carbon dioxide ("dry ice"), as well as frozen water.

The two U.S. *Viking* spacecraft landed on Mars in 1976 and took images that showed the landing sites to look something like a desert on the Earth. The planet's surface is a reddish color, making Mars look as if it is rusting. In fact, the red coloring of the rocks is due to the same chemical process, oxygen combining with iron, that causes rusting on the Earth: most of the oxygen on Mars appears to be "locked up" with the iron in its rocks. The *Viking* spacecraft did not detect any magnetic field around Mars. Of the four planets nearest to the Sun, only the largest (Earth) and the smallest (Mercury) have detectable magnetic fields.

Mars has two small moons, Phobos (FOE-bos) and Deimos (DEE-mos), discovered by Asaph Hall in 1877. Phobos, the larger moon, is only about 25 km (15 mi) wide. The orbiters for the *Viking* spacecraft took images of both moons (see Figure A.14). The moons are irregular in shape, looking a bit like potatoes.

The information from the *Viking* missions has been supported and supplemented by other missions, notably the U.S. *Pathfinder* mission, which in 1998 placed a robotic minirover on the martian surface that was used to determine the chemical composition of surface rocks.

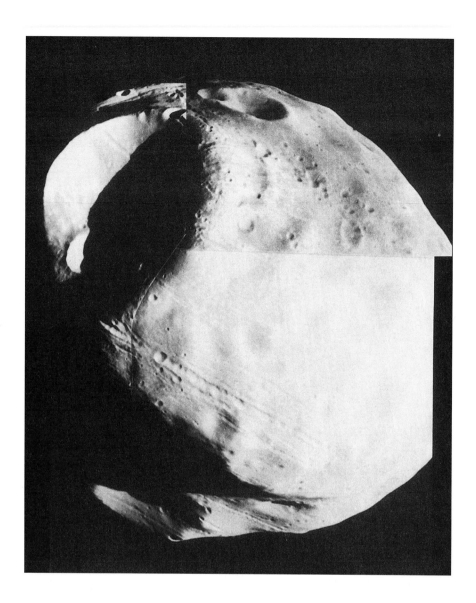

JUPITER AND ITS MOONS

When Galileo first turned his telescope on Jupiter, he saw four bright "stars" very near the planet. When he looked the second night, one of these "stars" had disappeared. Galileo soon realized that they were not stars but moons, or satellites, traveling around Jupiter just as the Moon travels around the Earth.

Even small telescopes allow you to see two bands in the clouds surrounding Jupiter and for more than 100 years astronomers have followed the changes in the shape, size, and position of a "Great Red Spot" in Jupiter's atmosphere. The first spacecraft (*Pioneer 10*) passed Jupiter in 1973; images taken from the spacecraft and radioed to the Earth showed many more details than astronomers had ever seen before, including giant storms in Jupiter's ever-changing atmosphere.

Most of the information about Jupiter and its moons was collected by three spacecraft, the two *Voyager* spacecraft, which passed the planet in 1979, and the *Galileo* spacecraft, which began orbiting the planet in 1995. (See Figure A.15.) A surprising discovery made by *Voyager 1* was that Jupiter has a very thin ring system around it. We now know that all four of the large planets in the solar system have some sort of ring system, but the most spectacular rings still belong to Saturn.

Before the first spacecraft reached Jupiter, scientists knew it possessed a magnetic field and was surrounded by radiation belts because Jupiter had been discovered to emit radio bursts. However, the information gathered by the *Pioneer* and *Voyager* probes indicated that the magnetic field and radiation belts were much stronger than some scientists had expected.

The images of the satellites of Jupiter were even more surprising. Each satellite was different. The outermost satellite seen by Galileo, Callisto (kah-LIS-toe), has a surface as cratered as the Moon's, suggesting that its surface too has not been changed much since the formation of the solar system. But in contrast to the Moon, the centers of Callisto's craters are white, suggesting that this satellite has a layer of ice just below its dark surface. Images and other data transmitted by the *Galileo* spacecraft suggest that an ocean of liquid water might lie beneath the icy layer.

Ganymede (GAN-ah-MEED), the largest of Jupiter's moons, is bigger than the planet Mercury. Much of Ganymede's surface looks just like Callisto's. But patches of bright material cover some of the ancient terrain. These bright patches have relatively few craters compared to the rest of the satellite's surface and therefore are probably younger than the heavily cratered darker areas. This observation suggests that there has been some

Figure A.15
Jupiter.

activity inside Ganymede since it was formed; the discovery by the *Galileo* spacecraft of a magnetic field around Ganymede provides further evidence for some type of internal activity. Astronomers think that the bright material may be ice formed from material forced out onto the surface from Ganymede's interior.

Europa (u-ROW-pah) is about the size of our Moon. Europa's surface appears to be covered with ice. There are almost no craters on Europa's surface, suggesting its surface has undergone changes fairly recently, compared to the age of the solar system. Europa may also possess an ocean beneath its icy crust.

The innermost large moon, Io, is almost the size of our Moon. (The satellite's name is commonly pronounced as "EYE-oh," but some people, using the ancient Greek pronunciation, call it "EE-oh.") Io held the greatest surprise of all. Looking, someone said, like a large pizza with extra cheese, the surface of Io was undergoing changes even as *Voyager 1* flew past the satellite and imaged volcanoes erupting on its surface (see Figure A.16). This was the first time volcanic activity had been observed on an object other than the Earth. In fact, Io is probably the most volcanically active

Figure A.16
A volcanic eruption can be seen on the horizon of Io, one of Jupiter's moons.

object in the solar system; the *Galileo* spacecraft observed widespread volcanic activity during its many flybys of the satellite over a 5-year period. Io's surface is covered mostly with sulfur-rich materials, which give the satellite its orange-yellow color. Io is so active that its surface is constantly reshaped by material erupted from the volcanoes, making Io's surface probably the youngest in the solar system. Io's intense activity is due to tremendous internal heating of the moon caused by a gravitational tug of war on Io between Jupiter and other moons. The stresses on Io caused by these objects keep Io's "insides" stirred up and its volcanoes busy; some of its volcanoes erupt lava much hotter than that erupted by volcanoes on the Earth.

SATURN AND ITS MOONS

The first look at Saturn through a telescope, by Galileo, provided a shock. Something was very different about this planet. Some astronomers thought the planet consisted of three parts; others said it had "ears." When telescopes improved, astronomers saw that Saturn was circled by many rings. (This is a good example of the value of a telescope's ability to "bring" an object within the resolution limit of human eyes, as is discussed in Chapter 4.) The rings are very thin and seem to nearly disappear about every 15 years, when we

Figure A.17
Saturn.

see them edge on. The rings are not solid, but are composed partly of icy particles probably ranging in diameter from several meters down to much less than a millimeter. Each particle is orbiting around Saturn; if you were to count the ring particles as "moons," Saturn would have trillions of moons.

Pioneer 11 passed Saturn in 1979; data from that flyby revealed the presence of a magnetic field. *Pioneer 11* also radioed back the first close-up images of Saturn. But the *Voyager* spacecraft, in 1980 and 1981, provided the best look astronomers have ever had at the ringed planet (see Figure A.17). The rings proved to have detailed structure never imagined before. The broad rings seen through Earth-based telescopes were found to be composed of thousands of narrower rings (Figure A.18). Some rings appear to be "controlled" by small moons, less than 200 km in diameter, orbiting on either side of the rings, the gravity of the moons acting on the particles in the rings. The moons "tending" these rings have been nicknamed "shepard" moons. But, as for Jupiter, some of Saturn's biggest surprises were reserved for its satellites.

The small satellite Mimas (MIME-as) appears to be composed largely of ice, and is completely covered with craters, resembling the surface of Mercury and Callisto. Enceladus (en-SELL-a-dus) appears to be a mixture of the Jovian satellites Europa and Ganymede. Titan (TITE-en), Saturn's largest satellite, has its own atmosphere, made up mostly of nitrogen, like

Figure A.19
A comparison of the "tilts" of the axes
of rotation of Uranus and the Earth.

North Pole

Earth

"North Pole"

Uranus

NOTE: Planets shown to correct scale sizes.

the Earth's. The surface of Titan is, however, very cold, nearly –180°C (about –300°F) and possibly covered in places by liquid methane—not very hospitable. (You might occasionally see a T-shirt or bumper sticker inviting you to "Surf Titan"; similar items also proclaim "Ski Mars" or "Dive Europa." These activities would be the ultimate "extreme" sports!) Among Saturn's other unusual satellites are Hyperion (hi-PAIR-ee-en), which tumbles chaotically as it circles the planet, and Iapetus (YAP-et-us), which, surprisingly, scatters much less sunlight from one side than from the other.

URANUS AND ITS MOONS

All of the planets mentioned so far are visible to the unaided eye and have been known since ancient times. Uranus (YOUR-in-us) was the first planet to be discovered with a telescope, in 1781.

Uranus's most unusual feature is that it spins on its "side" (see Figure A.19). In 1977, observations of Uranus made with telescopes on the Earth resulted in the discovery of the planet's rings. Uranus's rings were not discovered earlier because they are very narrow and made up of very dark particles. Detailed information about Uranus was provided by *Voyager 2*, which flew past the planet in 1986. Figure A.20 shows two views of Uranus; Figure A.21 is a close-up image of the planet's rings.

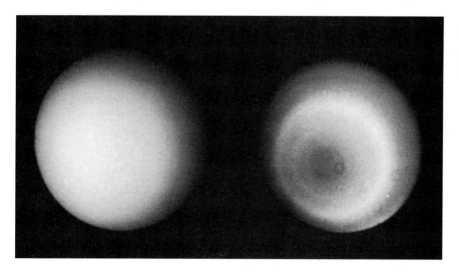

Figure A.20
Two views of Uranus; the cloud features are enhanced in the right-hand image.

Uranus was discovered to have a magnetic field. Unlike the fields of most other planets, the axis of Uranus's field is not closely aligned with the planet's axis of rotation. While the "source" for a planet's magnetic field has been thought by some scientists to be located in the planet's core, Uranus's field appears to have its "source" located nearly one-third of the way out from the core toward the surface. The magnetic field is relatively strong and it has "trapped" charged particles—like electrons—in it that emit photons, most corresponding to the "colors" of radio waves.

Figure A.22
Miranda, one of Uranus's moons. Note the different types of surface features.

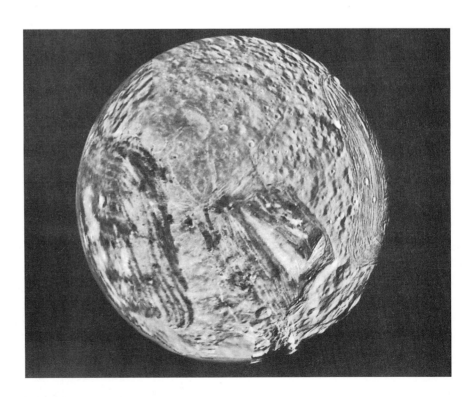

Most of Uranus's satellites are icy objects, none more than 1,600 km (1,000 mi) in diameter. The most interesting moon is Miranda (mah-RAN-dah), only about 500 km (300 mi) in diameter. Miranda looks like it has been patched together from different pieces of material (see Figure A.22).

NEPTUNE AND ITS MOONS

Neptune was the first planet discovered as the result of mathematical calculations. Uranus had been carefully observed since its discovery and by the early 1800s it was known that Uranus's motion was not what was expected. Some unknown object seemed to be pulling on Uranus. In 1846, a German astronomer used a telescope to discover Neptune. The astronomer found Neptune where a French mathematician had predicted a planet might be located that could account for Uranus's observed motion around the Sun. An English astronomer-mathematician had independently calculated the position of the unknown planet in 1843. But British astronomers failed to look seriously for the planet; one astronomer observed it, but thought it was a star. The French mathematician had been frustrated trying to get a French astronomer to do a search. He then wrote to an acquaintance at the Berlin Observatory, giving his prediction; the German astronomer located Neptune within hours of receiving the prediction, mainly because he had updated star charts that showed no star located at the position he saw Neptune.

Not much was known about Neptune until *Voyager 2* passed the planet in 1989. Although Earth-based observations in the mid-1980s showed the presence of parts of rings, it took the images radioed back to the Earth from *Voyager* to show that Neptune has a system of four faint rings (Figure A.23). *Voyager* also uncovered a large disturbance in Neptune's atmosphere similar to the "Great Red Spot" on Jupiter, which can be seen in Figure A.24. Neptune's

Figure A.23
The rings of Neptune. The rings are so faint, Neptune was blocked out so the camera could image the rings.

Figure A.24
Neptune; note the Great Dark Spot.

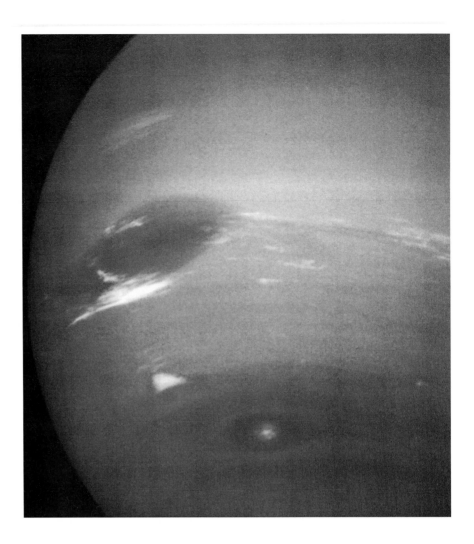

feature has been named the "Great Dark Spot." A magnetic field similar to Uranus's was found: The field axis is not closely aligned to Neptune's axis of rotation, and the field's "source" appears to be located almost halfway from the planet's core to the surface. The reason why some planets have magnetic fields is not well understood and the results from Neptune, combined with those from Uranus, have left scientists with much to think about.

Like Saturn and Uranus, Neptune's moons are mostly small and icy. Neptune's largest satellite, Triton (TRITE-en), was discovered to have volcanoes that erupt cold nitrogen vapor instead of molten rock. The upper portion of Triton's crust appears to contain liquid nitrogen. Some process acts on this liquid, forcing the nitrogen out through cracks in the surface. Triton also moves around Neptune in the opposite direction from the other moons. If you looked down on Neptune from above its "north pole," you would see Triton move clockwise around the planet while the other moons move counterclockwise. Another moon, Nereid (NEAR-ee-id), has a very elliptical orbit.

PLUTO AND ITS MOON

As was the case with Uranus, Neptune's motion around the Sun was carefully observed after its discovery. By the late 1800s, some astronomers thought they could detect a difference between Neptune's motion and its motion as predicted by Newton's theory of gravity, based on the gravitational effects of the other known planets. Thus, searches for an unknown planet affecting Neptune were underway by the early 1900s, the most intensive search having been conducted by Percival Lowell. It was not until 1930, however, that Pluto was discovered by Clyde Tombaugh. By coincidence, he found Pluto near to where the "missing" planet was predicted to be by Lowell. It was coincidence because Pluto is not nearly massive enough to disturb Neptune's orbit to the extent Lowell thought that it was. Indeed, it now appears that most of the "unpredicted" motion of Neptune was not any real motion of the planet, but errors made in the observations of the positions of the background stars with respect to which Neptune's position was obtained. Whether one or more major planets orbit the Sun beyond Pluto is unknown. However, it is believed that comets come from a huge collection of icy objects orbiting the Sun at a distance of nearly 1 light-year, more than 1,000 times the distance from the Sun to Pluto. This collection of objects, named the Oort (ORT) cloud after the Dutch astronomer who proposed the idea, could be considered the outer limits of the solar system.

Pluto is so small (smaller than the Moon) and remote from the Earth, that information about the planet is limited. No spacecraft has passed Pluto (the *Pioneer* and *Voyager* spacecraft followed paths that did not take them near Pluto), so all information about Pluto has been obtained with telescopes on or near the Earth. Pluto might be an example of a class of large icy objects thought by many astronomers to orbit the Sun in a region between Pluto's orbit and the Oort cloud. An object in this region, called the Kuiper (KOY-per) belt after the Dutch-American astronomer whose model for the formation of the solar system suggested such a belt, might have been detected by the *Pioneer 10* spacecraft. In 1992, the probe experienced an unexpected course change 56 a.u. from the Sun, perhaps caused by the gravitational pull of an object roughly the mass of Pluto. (*Pioneer 10* is more than twice as far from the Sun as is Pluto, heading out of the solar system at 12 km/sec [about 27,000 mi/hr] toward the star Aldebaran. If the probe stays on course, it will pass Aldebaran in about 2 million years, about the time the 200,000th edition of this book will be published. Pre-order now!)

One fact about Pluto that has been known for some time is that Pluto's orbit passes inside the orbit of Neptune (see Figure A.25). Although Pluto is considered the farthest planet from the Sun, when Pluto is traveling along the portion of its orbit that is inside Neptune's orbit, Neptune is actually the farthest planet from the Sun. During the 249 years it takes Pluto to orbit the Sun once, the planet spends about 20 years inside Neptune's orbit. Pluto passed inside Neptune's orbit in 1979 and passed back outside in 1999. During this period, Pluto made its nearest approach to the Sun and the Earth. Not surprisingly, most of the information gathered about Pluto has been collected since the beginning of this "near" (about 7×10^9 km, or 4.5 billion mi) approach to the Earth.

Although Figure A.25 shows the orbits of Neptune and Pluto crossing, there is no danger of the planets colliding. The planets do not come closer to each other than about 4.5×10^9 km (3 billion mi). Even if Neptune and Pluto arrived at a "crossing" point at the same time, they would not collide:

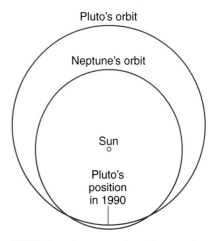

NOTE: Drawing approximately to scale. The orbit of the Earth cannot be shown easily at this scale; it is too small.

Figure A.25
The orbits of Neptune and Pluto.

The orbits are not in the same plane; the planets would pass each other like two cars traveling on separate highways at an overpass, only the planets would be separated by millions of kilometers instead of the height of an overpass bridge.

Pluto's single moon, Charon (CARE-en), was discovered accidentally in 1978 by Robert Harrington, a sharp-eyed astronomer at the U.S. Naval Observatory who was looking at an image of Pluto. Studies of Pluto and Charon have revealed that Charon is about half the diameter of Pluto. No other moon is so large compared to the planet it orbits. Because Pluto and Charon are roughly the same diameter, some astronomers refer to the two objects as a "double planet."

Pluto takes about 6.4 days to turn once on its axis, the same amount of time that it takes Charon to make one orbit around Pluto. That means that one side of Pluto always faces Charon. If you stood on the side of Pluto that faces Charon, Charon would appear to remain almost motionless in the sky—it would never set. A recent discovery is that Pluto spins nearly on its side, much like Uranus.

The temperature on Pluto's surface is about –220°C (around –370°F). Pluto's "supercold" surface is covered by frozen gases. When Pluto passed "close" to the Sun, some of the frozen gases vaporized to create a thin atmosphere. As Pluto moves farther from the Sun, some of the gases will freeze back onto the surface. Pluto will not be as close to the Earth again until about 2240, so the observations being made now are important. If a spacecraft were soon sent to image Pluto from close-up, it would reach Pluto during your life. One proposal for a U.S. probe to Pluto estimates that it would take the spacecraft 14 years to reach Pluto. This is not far-fetched; *Voyager 2* took 12 years to reach Neptune.

GLOSSARY

angular height The angle, as seen by an observer, between the direction to the horizon and the direction to the object being observed.

angular size The size (for example, the diameter) of an object measured as an angle from the observer's eyes. As the distance from the observer to an object increases, its angular size decreases. Angular size is related to the diameter/distance ratio for an object: for small diameter/distance ratios, the angular sizes in degrees are about 57 times the diameter/distance ratios.

apparent brightness The brightness of an object as seen by an observer. The apparent brightness of an object is proportional to the object's wattage, if it emits its own visible light, or to the amount of light scattered or reflected by a nonemitting object. The apparent brightness of an object is also proportional to the inverse square of the distance of the observer from the object. Apparent brightness depends, too, on observing conditions, such as the presence of haze.

apparent magnitude A measure of the apparent brightness of an astronomical object, as observed from the Earth. The scale of magnitudes is logarithmic. On this scale, a difference of one magnitude corresponds to a ratio of about 2.5 in apparent brightnesses, and, for example, a difference of 5 magnitudes corresponds to a ratio of 100 in apparent brightness.

astronomical unit (a.u.) A unit of distance equal to the Earth's average distance from the Sun. This distance is equal to about 150,000,000 km or about 93,000,000 mi.

celestial equator A great circle on the celestial sphere in the same plane as the Earth's equator. The zenith for any observer standing at the Earth's equator passes through the celestial equator.

celestial sphere An imaginary sphere with an "enormous diameter" and with the Earth at its center. All objects in the sky appear to us as if they are on the inside surface of this sphere.

Cepheid variable A type of star that varies in apparent brightness with a period between 1 and 100 days. The period and wattage of a Cepheid variable are related, which allows an estimate to be made of the star's distance based on the measurement of its period and apparent brightness. Because Cepheids can be detected in other galaxies, these variable stars serve as useful tools for determining the distances to such galaxies. The star type is named after the star Delta Cephei.

constellation A pattern of stars named for a particular object, person, or animal; also, the area of the sky assigned to such a particular pattern.

Doppler shift The change in the energy of photons measured by an observer when the source of these photons is moving toward or away from the observer. If the source is moving toward the observer, the energies of the photons will appear to be higher than if the source were at rest with respect to the observer. If the source is moving away from the observer, the photon energies will appear to be lower. The differences between the observed photon energies and the energies expected if the source were motionless with respect to the observer allow the speed and direction of the source to be determined. The Doppler shift is also known as the Doppler effect.

eclipsing binary A binary star system oriented so that, when viewed from the Earth, one star passes directly in front of the other star, creating "eclipses." An eclipsing binary appears as a single star whose brightness varies in a very regular pattern over a period of time.

ecliptic A great circle on the celestial sphere that is the path apparently followed by the Sun each year. In fact, this path is due to the Earth orbiting around the Sun. The ecliptic is tilted 23.5° to the celestial equator and crosses it at two points. The Sun appears at these points on the dates of the equinoxes.

electron volt (e.v.) A very small unit of energy. The energies of individual photons can be measured conveniently in electron volts.

equinox One of two points on the celestial sphere where the ecliptic crosses the celestial equator. The Sun appears to be at one of these points at the beginning of the spring (vernal equinox) and at the other of these points at the beginning of the autumn (autumnal equinox) seasons.

escape speed The speed that an object must attain so that it can "escape" from the gravitational pull of another object. The escaping object will not return to this other object, although it will always "feel" the gravitational pull of this object. The pull, however, is too weak to cause the escaping object to return. For example, if a rocket launched from the Earth's surface reaches escape speed, it will not return to the Earth or go into orbit around the Earth. The escape speed is proportional to the mass of the object (for example, the Earth) and inversely proportional to the distance from the center of the object to the center of the "escaping" object (for example, a rocket).

field of view The angular size, usually measured in degrees, of an object that just fills the field that can be seen when looking through a telescope or binoculars. The field of view is a characteristic of a telescope or of binoculars.

focal length The distance from a lens or a concave mirror to an image when the object being viewed is very far away. Focal length is a basic characteristic of a lens or a concave mirror.

galaxy A collection of billions to hundreds of billions of stars; our Milky Way galaxy is a typical example.

galaxy cluster A group of galaxies "near" to one another.

globular cluster A collection of hundreds of thousands of stars that, together, look like a sphere from far away. Many such clusters are seen in our Milky Way galaxy and in other galaxies.

horizon A circle on the celestial sphere 90° away from the zenith point of an observer. This circle could also be described as the circle represented by the meeting of the sky and the water as seen by an observer in a boat in the middle of a large, quiet ocean.

infrared photons Photons with energies between 0.01 e.v. and 1.8 e.v. Warm objects that are not glowing emit infrared photons. Infrared photons are more energetic than radio photons, but less energetic than photons of visible light. Infrared literally means "below red," from the fact that the energy of an infrared photon is less than that of a photon of red light.

light-year (l.y.) The distance light travels in 1 year: nearly 10 trillion kilometers (10,000,000,000,000 km) or six trillion miles (6,000,000,000,000 mi).

magnification The ratio of the apparent size of an image when viewed through an optical device to the corresponding apparent size of the object as seen without the optical device.

Milky Way The bright patch of stars that forms an arc across the sky; these billions of stars are in our Milky Way galaxy.

Milky Way galaxy   The galaxy to which the Sun belongs.

nebula   A large collection of dust and gas that usually appears as a fuzzy object in telescopes at low magnification.

noontime   The time of day when the Sun is at its greatest angular height from the horizon. At this time the Sun will be directly south, directly north, or at the zenith, depending on the latitude of the observer and the season of the year. The time of this event will not exactly match noon on a clock for most locations for most days of the year.

North Celestial Pole (N.C.P.)   The point where the rotational axis of the Earth coming through the Earth's North Pole would touch the celestial sphere. The N.C.P. would be directly overhead for an observer at the North Pole of the Earth.

objective lens   The primary lens of a telescope that collects the light from the object being observed. The diameter of the objective lens is the aperture or "size" of the telescope.

ocular   The eyepiece of a telescope; the lens on a telescope through which the observer looks.

open cluster   A comparatively loose or "open" cluster of stars, containing from a few dozen to a few thousand members; also known as a "galactic cluster."

parallax   The apparent change in the position of an object with respect to the background when it is observed from two different positions.

photometer   A device designed to measure the apparent brightness of an object. The word literally means "light measurer."

photon   A "particle" of light. The model of light used in this book describes light as being composed of such particles that travel in straight lines at a speed of 300,000 km/sec through empty space or air. Each photon has a particular value of energy and is thereby associated with a particular color.

pulsar   A rapidly rotating star from which we detect "bursts" of light or radio waves every time the "beam" of such light "sweeps by" the Earth. It is believed that pulsars are the spinning cores of collapsed stars, with masses somewhat greater than the Sun's mass packed into spheres only about 10 km in diameter!

quasar   A very distant object of very high wattage; thought by some astronomers to be a very young galaxy.

radar   A device from which radio photons can be emitted in a direction toward an object and the photons that are reflected back toward the device can be detected. By analyzing these echoes, the device can determine the distance to the object and its speed toward or away from the device. The word "radar" is an acronym: *r*adio *d*etection *a*nd *r*anging.

radio photons   Photons with energies less than 0.01 e.v. The signals for radio, non-cable TV, and radar are composed of radio photons of various energies that are emitted by a transmitting device.

resolution limit   As used in this book, the ratio of the smallest distance between two side-by-side objects, for which the objects can be seen through a device as two objects, to the distance to them. Every device used to observe objects has a resolution limit. Your eyes have a resolution limit.

RR Lyrae star   One of a class of stars whose variable wattage goes through a full cycle in less than 1 day. The apparent brightness of such an object also goes through the same cycle.

scale model   An imitation, at a different size, of an object or group of objects.

solstice   The position of the Sun on the ecliptic when the Sun is at its greatest angular distance from the celestial equator. There are two such positions: one when the Sun is north and one when the Sun is south of the celestial equator. Both of these positions are on the ecliptic. The Sun passes through one in June, which event marks the beginning of summer (winter) in the Northern (Southern) Hemisphere; the Sun passes through the other in December, thus marking the beginning of winter (summer) in the Northern (Southern) Hemisphere. At these two times, the Sun is, respectively, 23.5° north and south of the celestial equator.

South Celestial Pole (S.C.P.) The point on the diametrically opposite side of the celestial sphere from the North Celestial Pole. The S.C.P. would be directly overhead for any observer standing at the Earth's South Pole.

spectrometer A device that produces a spectrum of the light emitted or reflected by an object and contains a scale so that the energies (or wavelengths) of the photons making up the spectrum can be measured.

spectrum A separation of light into its component colors; in the photon model, a separation of photons by their energy. The most familiar spectrum is that of visible light, the so-called "rainbow" spectrum.

star cluster A large number of stars that are near one another; some clusters may contain hundreds of thousands of stars.

ultraviolet photons Photons with energies above about 3.2 e.v., but below about 100 e.v. Ultraviolet photons are more energetic than photons of visible light, but less energetic than X-ray photons. Ultraviolet literally means "beyond violet," from the fact that the energy of an ultraviolet photon is greater than that of a photon of violet light. Ultraviolet photons, sometimes simply called UV, are emitted by the Sun. Absorption of UV by the skin can result in a sunburn.

variable star A star whose wattage and apparent brightness vary with time. In some cases, these variations repeat in a (nearly) regular manner; examples are Cepheids, pulsars, and RR Lyrae stars.

visible photons Photons with energies between 1.8 e.v. and 3.2 e.v. When many photons with energies in this range enter your eyes, you can see. The color you see depends on the energies of the photons that enter your eyes. The lowest energy photons of visible light are associated with the color red, whereas the highest energy photons of visible light are associated with the color violet.

wattage As used in this book, the amount of energy per second emitted by an object; wattage is here measured in watts. Wattage is a physical characteristic of an object that does not depend on the distance between the object and the observer. If two objects are at the same distance from your eyes, the object with the higher wattage will appear brighter.

x-ray photons Photons with energies above about 100 e.v., but less than about 1 million e.v. X-ray photons are emitted by metal that is hit with electrons traveling at very high speeds. X-ray photons are more energetic than ultraviolet photons, but not as energetic as gamma-ray photons (which are not mentioned elsewhere in this book). The first experiences that scientists had with the effects of X rays could not be linked to any known rays, so the rays were labeled "X" for "unknown."

zenith The point on the celestial sphere directly overhead, or straight up, for any observer, or, equivalently, the point where a straight line from the center of the Earth through any observer touches the celestial sphere.

zodiac The region of the sky located about 8°–9° on either side of the ecliptic in which the Sun, the Moon, and those planets known to ancient cultures are found. The term itself means "circle of animals."

ANSWERS TO SELF-TEST QUESTIONS

Chapter One

1. East.

2. West.

3. South.

4. Noontime.

5. There are many reasons why people believe that the Sun is directly overhead at noontime every day. One reason is that the Sun is often said to be at its highest point in the sky for the day at noontime. While that statement is true, some people interpret it to mean that the Sun is as high as possible, that is, directly overhead. Because very few people check such ideas with observations, the idea is not challenged and remains fixed in the person's mind as being true.

6. A good scientific model should allow you to understand what has been observed and also to predict accurately what will be observed under new conditions. A good model should also be simple.

Chapter Two

1. West.

2. East.

3. The Moon's shape became fuller.

4. The Moon was farther to the east (left) of the Sun for each successive observation.

5. As the Earth moves in its annual path around the Sun, the nighttime side of the Earth faces toward different stars. You can model this effect by walking around an object that represents the Sun (your head represents the Earth). As you walk around the Sun, you must face it to model daytime—the Sun must be visible to you. To model nighttime, you must face away from the Sun—the Sun cannot be visible. Notice that when you look away from the Sun at different positions in your path around the Sun, different scenes are visible to you. The different scenes are like the different sky views visible from the nighttime side of the Earth as it moves around the Sun.

Chapter Three

1. Two (the first day of spring and the first day of fall).

2. Beginning with the first day of winter in December, the Sun's rising and setting points move northward until the first day of summer in June. After the first day of summer, the Sun's rising and setting points move southward until the next first day of winter. Only on the first day of spring and the first day of fall does the Sun rise due east and set due west. The Sun's rising and setting points change because the Earth's axis of rotation is tilted with respect to the perpendicular to the plane of the Earth's orbit and is fixed in space, while the Earth travels in a nearly circular path around the Sun. A scale model is useful to help in understanding these facts.

3. Slightly more to the west. The "day" would be shorter by about 4 minutes because the star rises about 4 minutes earlier each day.

4. The cause of the seasons is the tilt of the Earth's axis (see 2, above). As the Earth travels around the Sun, the Sun's angular height at noontime changes, reaching its lowest height on the first day of winter and its greatest height on the first day of summer. When the Sun is at a greater angular height, more of its light strikes a given area on the ground than is the case when the Sun is at a lower angular height. (The length of the daylight period also changes, but this change has less effect on the seasons than does the angular height of the Sun at noontime.)

5. The Sun's angular height changes by 47° for locations in the continental United States. This change is the result of the Sun appearing between 23.5° north (on June 21) and 23.5° south (on December 21) of the celestial equator: the overall range is 23.5° + 23.5° = 47°.

6. The Sun's position relative to the celestial equator changes because the Earth's axis is tilted 23.5° from the perpendicular to the plane of the Earth's orbit around the Sun and is fixed in space, while the Earth travels around the Sun in a nearly circular orbit.

Chapter Four

1. 400 m.

2. 6 m.

3. 13.2 m.

4. 0.3° (about one-third of a degree).

Chapter Five

1. A photon in space travels in a straight line at a speed of 300,000 km/sec. The path of the photon can change if it strikes a surface or passes through different substances.

2. a) 4 bulbs.
   b) 16 bulbs.

3. Yes; light must be present if you are able to see. The light is entering the room through cracks or openings around doors and shades. The

light could be coming from lights in another room, the Sun (if it is daytime), sunlight scattered by the Moon, or the stars (if it is night).

4. Yes; light must be reaching your eyes if you can see the wall. The wall is scattering photons from the flashlight toward your eyes.

Chapter Six

1. The image would be 0.05 cm long.

2. 1.2 m.

3. You have to make it shorter. The farther away the object is from the lens, the closer the image is formed to the lens.

Chapter Seven

1. About 25 times smaller: the Earth-Moon ratio is about 4/1 and the Sun-Earth ratio is about 100/1.

2. About 400 times smaller.

3. Last quarter.

4. First quarter.

5. Waning gibbous.

Chapter Eight

1. The angular size of the Sun as seen from Mercury would be about 1.4°; the Sun's angular size as viewed from Saturn would be nearly 0.06° (about 1/16 of a degree).

2. Humans have traveled to the Moon, which is about 400,000 km from the Earth; that trip, made by the Apollo astronauts, took about 3 days. Mars is about 56 million km from the Earth at its closest approach. A trip from the Earth to Mars would therefore require covering a distance at least 140 times greater than that from the Earth to the Moon.

Chapter Nine

1. The period of the 50-cm pendulum is shorter than the period of the 70-cm pendulum.

2. The orbital period for the planet 400 million km from the Sun is about 3.5 years; the orbital period for the planet 800 million km from the Sun is about 10 years.

3. 14 kg (30 lbs).

4. 220 kg (480 lbs).

Chapter Ten

1. No; there could be two or more stars so close together that they appear as a single star from the Earth.

2. 1/2,500,000,000; −4 (using the apparent brightness-distance nomogram); Sirius, with an apparent magnitude of −1.5.

3. Sirius. From Kepler's relation between the orbital period and the separation between two stars, we see that as the total mass of the system increases, the orbital period decreases. Hence, the pair of stars with the shorter orbital period has the greater total mass.

4. 195,000,000 km (120,000,000 mi). Alpha Centauri's wattage is 1.75 times that of the Sun's. Using the inverse-square law for apparent brightness, the distance from you to Alpha Centauri would have to be the (square root of 1.75) times the distance from the Earth to the Sun, or about 1.3 times the Earth-Sun distance.

5. About 20 a.u. (using the apparent brightness-distance nomogram).

6. About 25,000%. Deneb has the greatest wattage compared to the Sun's: Deneb's wattage is 60,000 times that of the Sun's. If Deneb were assumed to have the same wattage as does the Sun, the distance to Deneb would be underestimated by a factor of the square root of 60,000, or about 250 times too short. An error factor of 250 equals a percentage error of about 25,000%.

7. a) False. The wattage stays the same because it is a physical property of the star; the star's apparent brightness would decrease.
   b) Perhaps false. (If the stars were all the same wattage, it would be true.)
   c) False. The triangle method (parallax) for determining stellar distance is possible because the apparent shift in a star's position is due to the Earth's motion around the Sun; if the Earth did not move, the star would not appear to shift.

8. System L. From Kepler's relation between the orbital period and the separation between two stars, we see that as the total mass of the system increases, the orbital period decreases. Hence, the pair of stars with the shorter orbital period has the greater total mass.

9. System B. Using Kepler's relation again, we see that, if the orbital periods are the same, the total mass must be greater for the system with the greater separation between the two stars.

Chapter Eleven

1. White light is composed of photons with energies corresponding to all of the colors in the visible spectrum.

2. A photon is a "particle" of light with a particular energy. Photons with energies in the range of 1.8 e.v. to 3.2 e.v. are associated with visible light.

3. The electron volt (e.v.) is a very small unit of energy used to describe the energy of a photon, because such energies have values of the order of 1 e.v., rather than, say, one-trillionth in some other unit.

4. The light is separated into its component colors, the "rainbow" spectrum. More specifically, the path of each photon that passes through the grating is changed in a way that is related to the photon's energy. Therefore, the photons are "spread out" by the grating according to their energies.

5. It comes out as red light. (If the red light is not a "pure" red, that is, if the light is composed of photons of different energies, then the light will be separated into its component colors.)

6. Only the photons associated with blue light are passed by the filter; most of the other photons are blocked. A "pure" blue filter will allow only photons of a specific energy associated with blue light to pass through; all other photons will be absorbed.

7. Object A must be at the lower temperature since most of its photons are of a lower energy than those from the other object. (The red photons from object A have a lower energy than the green photons from object B.)

8. Object X: If visible at all, it would appear to be a very dim red (some photons with energies near 1.8 e.v. may be emitted).
   Object Y: Orange. (Photons with an energy of 2.0 e.v. are associated with orange light.)

9. Photons with energies between 0.01 and 1.8 e.v.—infrared photons.

10. It is less expensive to place a telescope on the Earth's surface; a telescope in space has the advantages of being free from the "smearing" of images due to atmospheric motions and from absorption by the atmosphere.

Chapter Twelve

1. Pass the light emitted by the substance through a spectrometer and see which color is brightest. The brightest color of the emitted light is associated with the substance's temperature.

2. The blue star is at the higher temperature. Since blue photons have more energy than red photons, objects at higher temperatures emit more blue photons than do cooler objects, which emit more red photons.

3. Its temperature and its chemical composition.

4. Yes; a star emits photons of almost every energy. As the surface temperature of a star increases, the star emits relatively more photons with higher energies.

5. The higher the surface temperature of a star, the greater is its wattage per unit area. One square meter of the surface of a hot star emits more energy per second than one square meter of the surface of a cool star.

6. In general, a globular cluster contains stars with relatively low surface temperatures and relatively high wattages compared to the values of these quantities for stars in the Pleiades.

Chapter Thirteen

1. a) No.
   b) All objects, except the globular clusters, are located along the Milky Way. The globular clusters are found mostly in one region of the sky, centered on the constellation Sagittarius. Therefore, we appear to be off to one side within the galaxy, not at its center. (If we were

located at or near the galactic center, we would see globular clusters in all directions.)

2. Star Q.

3. Star T. Because star T has a shorter period than does star S, T must have a lower wattage than S. However, since T has a greater apparent brightness than does S, star T must be the closer of the two to the Earth.

4. Sagittarius. Globular clusters appear to be centered on or near the direction to Sagittarius. Other objects also appear to be more concentrated in the direction of Sagittarius, as demonstrated in Activity 13.1.

Chapter Fourteen

1. Andromeda galaxy (M 31) and the Magellanic Clouds, although all of them cannot be seen from every location on the Earth.

2. By observing the periods of Cepheid variables. From the period of a Cepheid, you can estimate its wattage. Using the star's wattage and its apparent brightness, and the apparent brightness-distance rule (or apparent brightness-distance nomogram), you can determine the distance to the star and the galaxy that it is in.

3. a) Galaxy H. The Cepheid star in H has a shorter period than the Cepheid in G and therefore has a lower wattage. Thus, since the Cepheid in H appears brighter than the one in G, galaxy H must be closer to the Earth than is galaxy G.
   b) Galaxy G. Galaxy G is farther from us than is galaxy H, but since G has the same apparent size as H, galaxy G must have a greater diameter than does H.

4. About 10 million light-years. The other galaxy appears to be one-fifth the apparent size of the Andromeda galaxy. Assuming that the other galaxy has the same diameter as the Andromeda galaxy, we use the size/distance ratio to infer that the other galaxy has to be 5 times farther away from us than is the Andromeda galaxy. As the Andromeda galaxy's distance is about 2×10^6 l.y., then the other galaxy's distance is about 10×10^6 l.y. (10 million light-years).

Chapter Fifteen

1. 1/16. Each toss has only one outcome that matches the desired outcome, a head. The probability of getting a head on one toss is 1/2. For four tosses of one fair coin, the probability of getting four heads is $1/2 \times 1/2 \times 1/2 \times 1/2 = 1/16$.

2. 7/32. The desired outcome is at least three tails in a row in five tosses. For five tosses of one fair coin there are 32 possible outcomes: $2 \times 2 \times 2 \times 2 \times 2 = 32$. How many of these outcomes can have three tails in a row? There are seven ways: TTTTT, HTTTT, THTTT, TTTHT, TTTTH, HHTTT, and TTTHH. Thus, the probability is 7 out of 32, or 7/32.

3. 1/18. There are 6 × 6 = 36 possible outcomes for one toss of two fair dice. There are only two ways to get a 3: die #1 shows one dot and die #2 shows two dots, or die #1 shows two dots and die #2 shows one dot. Two desired outcomes out of 36 possibilities yields a probability of 2/36, which simplifies to 1/18.

4. 1/216. For one toss of two fair dice, there are six ways to get a "double": die #1 shows one dot, as does die #2; die #1 shows two dots, as does die #2; and so on up to die #1 shows six dots, as does die #2. There are 36 possible outcomes for one toss of two fair dice. Since six of these outcomes are "doubles," the probability of getting a "double" on one toss is 6/36, or 1/6 (not bad odds). However, to toss three "doubles" in a row is much harder (much less likely). Since each toss is independent of the others (the dice don't know when you roll a "double"), the probability for three "doubles" in a row can be found by multiplying the probability for a "double" together three times: 1/6 × 1/6 × 1/6 = 1/216.

SOME ASTRONOMY RESOURCES ON THE WORLD WIDE WEB

Listed below are some web sites that are both useful and stable (i.e., unlikely to be discontinued during the "life" of this book). A brief summary of each site's content is provided.

The sites below are hosted by reputable organizations, but this listing does not constitute an endorsement of any organization or company; many other resources can be found on-line by conducting keyword searches. However, we caution readers that not everything found on the Internet is accurate: Browser Beware!

http://cfa-www.harvard.edu

> The official web site of the Harvard-Smithsonian Center for Astrophysics (CfA), where this course was developed. This site provides links to all scientific and educational activities carried out by the world's largest astrophysical research center.

http://www.iau.org

> The International Astronomical Union (IAU) is the primary organization for worldwide coordination of astronomy efforts. Among its many activities is granting recognition to astronomical discoveries, including the formal naming of comets and asteroids. Its web site provides a wide range of information for astronomers, educators, and students.

http://www.aas.org

> The American Astronomical Society (AAS) is North America's major professional organization for astronomers, other scientists, and individuals interested in astronomy. The AAS provides a variety of education services for teachers.

http://www.aspsky.org

> The Astronomical Society of the Pacific (ASP) long ago extended its efforts beyond California and is now the world's largest general astronomy society. The ASP's primary focus is the dissemination of astronomical information, including educational materials.

http://www.nasa.gov

> The National Aeronautics and Space Administration's (NASA) official web site provides up-to-date information about human spaceflight (including live video during shuttle missions), automated interplanetary probes and space-based observatories such as the Hubble Space

Telescope. The web site provides links to all NASA centers and affiliated research sites.

http://www.skypub.com

Sky & Telescope magazine publishes articles aimed at astronomers and serious amateur observers. Its web site includes astronomy news items, sky charts, and observing tips.

http://www.kalmbach.com/astro/Welcome.html

Astronomy is the most widely read English-language magazine for astronomy enthusiasts. Its articles are, in general, written at a less technical level than those in *Sky & Telescope*. The *Astronomy* web site provides astronomy news and information for observing the sky, including charts.

ILLUSTRATION CREDITS

Computer Graphics: Mike Meyer, Kerry J. Rasmussen

Cartoons: Jon McIntosh

Photographs:

214	10.3	HCO
218	10.6	NASA
250	11.2	Courtesy of Applied Infrared Technologies, Beverly, MA
250	11.3	Courtesy of David H. Loeb, D.M.D., Concord, MA
252	11.6	NASA
252	11.7	NASA
275	12.3	Photograph by Andrew MacFadyen
279	12.11	Courtesy of Celestron International
279	12.12	NOAO (National Optical Astronomy Observatories)
283		HCO
291	12.18	Bethlehem Steel
294	13.1	HCO
296	13.5	HCO
297	13.6	HCO
298	13.9	California Institute of Technology
299	13.10	HCO
301	13.12	HCO
302	13.13	NASA
314	14.2	NOAO
315	14.3	HCO
315	14.4	NOAO
316	14.5	NOAO
316	14.6	NOAO
316	14.7	NOAO
317	14.8	NOAO
342	A.1	Courtesy of International Dark-Sky Association
343	A.2	NOAO
344	A.3	U.S. Air Force Photo
349	A.6	HCO
351	A.7	HCO
354	A.9	NASA
356	A.10	NASA
357	A.11	NASA
358	A.12	NASA
359	A.13	NASA
360	A.14	NASA
361	A.15	NASA
362	A.16	NASA
363	A.17	NASA
364	A.18	NASA
365	A.20	NASA
366	A.21	NASA
366	A.22	NASA
367	A.23	NASA
368	A.24	NASA

INDEX

Moon, *continued*
    gravitational pull of Earth on, 195, 196, 199
    journal for tracking, 35–37
    lunar eclipses, 150–53, 155
    maria on, 361, 362, 363
    orbit and rotational period, 363
    phases of, 150, 155, 163–67
    physical features of, 361
    preconceptions about, 143
    rock samples from, 362–63
    scale model of, 160–62
    solar eclipses and, 77, 153–55, 153–55
    temperature of, 363
    viewing artificial satellites and, 360
    water on, 363
    weight and gravity on, 197
    wobble of, 152
Moonnoon, 166
Moonquakes, 363
Moonrise, 77, 166
Moons
    of Jupiter, 186, 188, 369–71
    of Mars, 186, 188, 367
    of Neptune, 186, 188, 376
    of Pluto, 186, 188, 378
    of Saturn, 186, 188, 372–373
    of Uranus, 186, 188, 374, 375
Moonset, 166
Multiplication principle, probability and, 334
Mural Quadrant, 33, 34
Musca, 310

N

Nebulae, 306, 310
Neon, spectrum from, CP–6
Neptune, 375–76
    average distance from Sun, 185, 187, 192
    diameter of, 185, 187
    discovery of, 375
    escape speed from, 201
    Great Dark Spot on, 376
    magnetic field of, 376
    moons of, 186, 188, 376
    orbital period, 192
    orbits of Pluto and, 377–78
    rings of, 375
    Voyager 2 mission and, 375
Nereid, 186, 188
New General Catalog (NGC), 310
New moon, 164
Newton, Isaac, 196
    Einstein's theory of gravity vs. Newton's, 199
    formula for gravitational pull, 194–97, 201
    ideas of gravity of, 191, 194
Newton's constant, 196
NGC (New General Catalog) objects, 310, 324, 327, 329
Night, defined, 3, 28
Nighttime sky, 21–30, 349–59
    apparent motion of Moon in, 23, 26, 35–37
    apparent motion of stars in, 23–25
    artificial satellites in, 360

Big Dipper in, 352–53
    in fall, 354–55
    light pollution and, 350, 351–52
    North Star in, 21, 352, 353
    observation tips, 349–50
    in spring, 357–58
    in summer, 358–59
    in winter, 355–57
Nomograms, 204–6
    for apparent brightness-distance, 239
    for apparent magnitude, 236
    for apparent magnitude problems, 239
    for celestial distance problems with, 322
    for escape speed, 205–6
    for Kepler's relation, 226–28
Noontime, 3
Norma, 310, 312
North celestial pole (NCP), 62, 63
North Star (Polaris)
    apparent magnitude of, 236
    apparent position of, 21, 29–30
    changing apparent brightness of, 294
    determination of Earth's radius by angle of, 145–46, 147
    distance from Earth, 240
    line-up of with Earth's axis of rotation, 44, 54
    locating in nighttime sky, 352, 353
Northern Cross, 358
Northern sky, position of stars in, 26, 27–28
Novas, 321
Numbers, scientific notation of, 57–58

O

Oberon, 186, 188
Observation lines, Mayan, 10
Observations
    of lunar eclipses, 153
    of Milky Way, 305
    of Moon's apparent motion, 35–37
    of nighttime sky, 349–50
    role in model creation, 4
    of sky by ancient peoples, 10
    of solar eclipses, 154–55
Observatories, 31
Occam, William of, 3–4
Occam's razor, 3–4, 25–26, 100
Olympus Mons, 366
Omega Centauri, 311
Omega nebula, 310
Oort cloud, 225, 377
Open clusters, 306–7, 310
Ophiuchus, 310, 311
Optical fibers, 233
Optical pyrometer, 291
Orbital periods, planet, 192–93, 201, 203
    discovery of, 192, 201
    methods for determining, 192–93, 222–23
Orbits, 172–75, 179–81
Orion, 66, 294, 310
    apparent size of, 73
    locating with homemade telescope, 138–39
    observation of in winter sky, 355–57
Owl nebula, 310

Ozone, filtering of Sun's ultraviolet light by, 10–11

P

Paraffin block photometer. See also Colorometer
    building, 229–30
    measuring Sun's wattage with, 231–32
    relating color to temperature with, 284–86
    using, 230–31
Parallax, 147–48, 155
Parallax method, 217–19, 223
Partial solar eclipse, 154
Pathfinder mission, 367
Patterns, human hair and height, 275–76
Pavo, 311
Pegasus, 311, 312
Pendulums
    as model of planet behavior, 194–95
    period of, 194–95, 202, 203, 207–9
Period-wattage relationship, 295–96, 303
    applications of, 297–300
    discovery of, 296–97
Perseus, 310, 312
Phenomenon, definition of, 3
Phobos, 186, 188, 206, 367, 368
Photography, photons and, 96–97
Photometer, paraffin block, 108
    building, 229–30
    examining filters with, 265–69
    measuring Sun's wattage with, 231–32
    using, 229–30
Photons, 96–102, 106
    absorption of, 99–100
    bending of, 199
    color and energy of, 247–48, 247–48, 250
    color of the sky and, 251
    defined, 96, 106
    Doppler effect and, 219–20
    energy levels of, 215, 219–20, 247–48, 273–74, 279, 280
    filters and, 250
    greenhouse effect and, 249
    infrared, 250, 301
    lenses and, 121–23
    light bulbs, production by, 106, 108
    mirrors and, 118–21, 123
    path of, 98–101, 106
    photography and, 96–97
    photon model of light behavior, 96–102, 106, 247
    pinholes and, 115–18, 123
    radio, 175–77
    reflection of, 98–99, 107
    scattering of, 100–101
    separating with spectrometer, 279
    size of, 100
    temperature of, 251
    ultraviolet, 250
    X-ray, 250
Pinhole camera, 124
Pinhole tubes, 124
    building and using, 131–33
    estimation of Sun's diameter with, 134–35